AGING AND HEALTH CARE
A SOCIAL PERSPECTIVE

AGING AND HEALTH CARE

A SOCIAL PERSPECTIVE

Neena L. Chappell, Ph.D.
Director
Laurel A. Strain, M.N.R.M.
Assistant to the Director
Audrey A. Blandford, B.A.
Research Co-ordinator

Centre on Aging
University of Manitoba

Holt, Rinehart and Winston of Canada, Limited

Canadian Cataloguing in Publication Data

Chappell, Neena L.
Aging and health care

Bibliography: p.
Includes index.
ISBN 0-03-921840-6

1. Aged - Social conditions. 2. Aged - Medical care.
3. Gerontology. I. Strain, Laurel A.
II. Blandford, Audrey A. III. Title.

HV1451.C48 1985   362.6'042   C85-098758-X

PUBLISHER: Anthony Luengo
MANAGING EDITOR: Mary Lynn Mulroney
COPY EDITORS: Lawrence Haskett, David Friend
COVER DESIGN: Pronk & Associates
INTERIOR DESIGN: Pronk & Associates
TYPESETTING AND ASSEMBLY: Cundari Group Ltd.

Printed in Canada

1 2 3 4 5 90 89 88 87 86

▪ PREFACE ▪

The Focus

This book provides a discussion of the social context of aging and health care. It has a major focus on health status, on informal care from family and friends, and on an assessment of the formal care system for meeting the needs of an aging society. The intent is to draw a realistic picture of the experience of aging in society without undue attention to the frail minority nor to those at the positive extreme. A central question addressed is: "What is aging like for most people and what are the variations encountered?" An answer to this query is followed by the question, "How adequate is the formal care system in meeting the needs of persons in old age?" As such, the book focuses on the circumstances related to the quality of life of elderly people but does not focus on quality of life per se.

Quality of life is a catchword in several areas of study. It symbolizes a concern with more than monetary circumstance and more than health. It symbolizes a broader interest which encompasses the various segments of our lives. Together these parts coalesce into an overall picture. The concept, quality of life, purposely goes beyond quantity to subjective and judgmental areas.

Concern with the concept has been evident in gerontology as inother areas of research. Much attention in the gerontological literature has focused on studies of life satisfaction, morale and happiness. Several measurement instruments have been devised, tested, retested and correlated with demographic, psychological, social and health factors in the lives of old people (see for example the literature reviews by Larson, 1978, and Kozma and Stones, 1978). Accummulated research has informed us that socioeconomic status, various social support variables, health, and other subjective or attudinal variables, such as perceived health, are related to life satisfaction. By and large, this body of literature has not given us an intimate understanding of the quality of life of elderly people in society.

This book seeks a greater understanding of the circumstances that affect quality of life during old age through an examination of our knowledge of the social, health and health care aspects of that period of our lives. This is *not* a review of the life satisfaction studies or a summary of that literature. Rather, the book casts a wider net, examining the social context of elderly people's lives and their health experiences. The place of two core societal institutions is also examined: the family and other members of the informal network and the formal health care system.

The book is also centrally related to the issue of continuity of care, where that phrase refers to the spectrum of options that permit the individual (and the aging population) to maintain autonomy and dignity as much as possible and to the extent preferred within various constraints. This book includes a discussion of the sources of care: self-care, informal support and the formal care system as representing sources of care. It discusses the extent of health problems as we age, the utilization of the formal system and the complementarity between the systems of informal support and of formal care. Used in this way, the phrase continuum of care is different from its popular usage within the health professions to refer to the extent of medical care provided within various formal services, or to the totality of care within such services.

Scientific Inquiry and Practical Issues

In its examination of aging and health care from a social perspective, this book focuses in particular on policy relevant issues. For example, care provided from family and friends, support for the caregiver and the appropriateness of the formal health care system for an aging population, all receive attention. However, the book brings an academic research perspective to practical questions. It is the wedding of the principles of scientific inquiry and the saliency of practical issues, which is too often neglected.

Despite the importance of rigorous research for examining practical issues, far too often there is a lack of communication between the researcher, especially the academic researcher, and the practitioner. One of the reasons for this lack of communication is a perceived gap between the two, discussed by Havens (1980), in terms of the criticisms lodged against researchers by administrators, decisionmakers and service providers:

> The ivory-towered academic does not tell us what we need to know, is not aware of the real constraints under which the delivery systems function. The first call on money is the provision of services, the lowest priority is likely to be research. Although policy-makers require options or alternative strategies; administrators require program evaluations; both require information on which to allocate resources; and service providers require needs assessments, all of these were essential yesterday. Service providers cannot wait six months for a study design and another year or three before the information is collated and analyzed and even longer for the results to be disseminated and used, if they are not completely stale or out-of-date by then. In any case you cannot understand the language and what they are saying.[1]

[1] B. Havens, "The Relevance of Social Science Research in Aging. Presented at *Towards a Mature Society,* Conference on Research in Gerontology in the Social Sciences, Winnipeg, Manitoba, 1980. Reprinted by permission of the author.

On the other hand, researchers have been known to complain about the lack of standardized measures among practitioners, if they record their information at all. Practitioners do not convey their concerns and impressions to the researcher. They do not tell the researcher what information exists in their files so the researcher can decide what could be analyzed, nor do they inform researchers of questions relevant to their work (and have been known to rationalize these omissions in terms of being too busy "doing" to report findings). Often practitioners do not believe researchers know anything about real people. Practitioners who do have an appreciation, or sympathy, for research think it can all be done overnight and that it will provide the answers to all of the questions all of the time (Chappell, 1982a).

An academic, scholarly approach to applied aspects of aging and health care are addressed by this book. The book is a step in attempting to utilize such an approach, seeking to maintain both standards of scientific inquiry as well as saliency of practical issues. In doing so, we do not claim to know, or say, all there is to say; nor do we pretend to be the last word on this subject. On the contrary, we see this book as a beginning to greater efforts to integrate research rigor and applied importance.

The Intended Audience

The book is intended for two different audiences. One consists of current and future administrators, policy makers and practitioners. This includes students of professional and paraprofessional schools such as medicine, nursing, social work, medical rehabilitation, family studies and so on. For applied disciplines the book contains basic information relevant to issues of primary importance, while also pointing to the limits of this knowledge. It seeks to demonstrate the importance of research for understanding and, at least, answer partially questions of vital importance to their work.

The book is also intended for researchers and students in academic disciplines, such as sociology, philosophy, anthropology, psychology and so on. For the academic student, it provides basic information and extensive literature reviews relevant to applied issues in aging and health care. It also illustrates the viability of studying applied questions with research rigor. Finally, it seeks to demonstrate the potential contribution of such investigations to the body of knowledge in aging at both the factual and conceptual levels.

In other words, the book attempts to bring an academic perspective to applied questions in a way that is understandable to both applied and academic audiences. An attempt has been made to delete much academic jargon. Where specialized terms are introduced, they are defined. However, not all specialized language has been removed. Part of the integration of an academic research focus with practical issues is the learning of some of the language from each world.

Not all will approve of the marriage. In trying to bridge the gap, one runs the risk of pleasing neither audience. No doubt some practitioners will find the book too academic, and some academics will find the book too applied. Our hope is that sufficient numbers from each audience will find the book informative and useful.

Theoretical Underpinnings

This is not a theory book. Nevertheless, the chapters in this book have theoretical underpinnings whether discussed explicitly or not. The first author is a sociologist and the underlying perspective of the book is sociological. For those familiar with the discipline, the perspective is unmistakably symbolic interactionism. It is, though, a symbolic interactionism learned through the actual writings of George Herbert Mead (see Chappell and Orbach, 1985) rather than the secondary sources, which abound.

This perspective assumes the social is at least as important as the biological and physical aspects of life. Indeed, the extent of social influence is considered pervasive, defining the very meaning and fabric of life. Within the social context, the individual is viewed as an active, interacting part of the environment, not a passive recipient of social norms and values. The individual helps shape his or her environment, as the environment influences the individual. This interaction between the individual and his or her environment is ongoing. However, gradual or subtle, life is dynamic not static.

This perspective is largely social-psychological, dealing primarily at the level of the individual. This, however, is not contradictory to and does not exclude the study of societal institutions. Mead defines an institution as a common response, or set of responses, in the community in which we live. The individual is always a member of a larger social community, a more extensive social group than that in which one immediately finds oneself. Institutions include the family, the educational system, religion and the health care system. Mead would include the study of individuals, groups and larger social institutions within his perspective. This book includes discussions of various groups, such as social networks, as well as some societal institutions, such as the family and the formal health care system.

The discussion of social institutions, notably of the formal care system, is not inconsistent with other sociological perspectives, such as a political economy perspective found in macrosociology. The book, as a whole, however, has more of a social-psychological focus, examining primarily the experience of old age for the individuals involved. While a political economy perspective has much to contribute, the concern here is at a more individual level. The influence of larger societal forces, however, is recognized and does receive some attention.

Comparative and Historical Perspectives

The book is written within a comparative perspective, highlighting similarities and differences primarily between Canada and the United States. The authors are Canadian and have made an effort to utilize Canadian references and data. However, so much of existing gerontological research is conducted in the United States that Canadian data can be put in perspective only through a comparative approach. Other countries, primarily the United Kingdom, are discussed, but to a lesser extent. The U.K. is used primarily to highlight similarities and differences within the North American context. The United Kingdom was chosen because of her historical relationships with both Canada and the United States. In addition, her more socialist health care system is frequently contrasted with the system in the United States, which offers less universal coverage and more for-profit opportunities.

An historical perspective is also used, although this is not primarily an historical account of aging through time. Rather, some historical background is provided when it is necessary for an adequate understanding of the current situation.

Contents and Organization of the Book

The book is organized to provide students with some of the social context of aging and sociodemographic trends as a critical background to learning about health care issues as we age. This background leads to a discussion of two primary factors concomitant with aging and the main reasons why aging has tended to be viewed from a problem approach: deteriorating health and role exits, that is, no meaningful place in society for elderly persons. Accumulated knowledge suggests neither problem is as bleak, as is sometimes believed. The next major discussion therefore turns to social interaction and the everyday lives of elderly persons. If their lives are not as bad as frequently portrayed, how do they cope and what is the substance of their lives?

Informal relations are an important aspect of people's lives, throughout their lives, including old age. Indeed, most elderly people cope well through their own efforts and those of their families and friends. This leads to the question of the role of the formal health care system. It is from the perspective of aging for most people, not aging for only the frail and vulnerable, that the discussion of the formal system flows.

The chapters on the formal system deal with its adequacy in meeting the needs of an aging society and its facilitation of self-sufficiency and the maintenance of informal relations. The conclusion is relatively critical, suggesting there is much room for improvement in the system. It is here that issues concerning community and social services, especially in times of fiscal constraint, and debates on their complementarity to or substitutability for more traditional medical services arise.

The approach utilized in the book combines research rigor and the saliency of practical issues and has grown out of a commitment to collaborative research among university researchers and practitioners and policy makers. A chapter is therefore included, which emphasizes the importance of joint efforts among academic researchers and practitioners/administrators in the advancement of knowledge concerning issues relevant to aging and health care. More such cooperative efforts are needed, especially in applied areas, such as gerontology, to develop theoretical models appropriate to the real world and for obtaining adequate information for policy development.

▪ ACKNOWLEDGMENTS ▪

Ideas and convictions develop over the years through contact with numerous individuals and within different situations. While particular individuals are too numerous to mention, both our academic colleagues and other individuals dealing with issues relevant to aging have had critical influence on our ideas. Colleagues, most notably from the discipline of sociology and from several disciplines in the substantive area of aging, have been intellectually stimulating and personally supportive. Nonacademic individuals have included elderly persons, practitioners, administrators and policy makers. These people have been invaluable for informing us when our ideas are too abstract, which issues are salient to them and of the urgent importance of more applied research.

All of those at the Centre on Aging, University of Manitoba, demonstrate in their day-to-day work the feasibility and value of applied research. Their support during the writing of this book has not gone unnoticed. In particular, Marilyn Shantz is witness to the adage that a good secretary is worth her weight in gold. She not only input the entire manuscript and all revisions into the word processor but did so while continuing with other duties at the Centre and effectively keeping others at bay so work on the book could proceed.

We also wish to acknowledge the very helpful comments of the anonymous reviewers and of the editors at Holt, Rinehart and Winston of Canada, Limited.

Finally, we thank our families for their continued support and encouragement in our research endeavours.

▪ CONTENTS ▪

CHAPTER 1

THE SOCIETAL CONTEXT

We all age. In spite of the fact that this process is universal, it is only recently that old age has become a concern to most individuals in industrial societies. This is not to say that individuals have been unaware of aging in the past. Today, however, demographic trends are resulting in larger proportions of populations that are elderly, to an extent unprecedented in history. This proportion will peak when the baby boom generation reaches old age. At the current time, it is the parents of the baby boom generation who are entering the latter part of their lives.

Many useful and informative writings are becoming available on aging, specifically on those persons who are 65 and older. Many of these works debunk past and current myths about elderly persons (Lopata, 1979; Marshall, 1980a; Hendricks and Hendricks, 1977; 1981). The beliefs that most older people live in isolation, have serious health problems, are emotionally distraught due to psychological trauma of the so-called empty nest years (if they are female) or retirement (if they are male), are sexually inactive and not interested in sexual activity are not supported by evidence. While some, or all, of these characteristics apply to some elderly individuals, they are also present among persons of other ages (Wershow, 1981).

Another notion common in present-day industrial society is that old age is synonymous with total dependence on others and eventual entry into long-term institutional care. In fact, less than 10 percent of those age 65 and over are in long-term institutions at any one time in Canada, the United States or most European countries. Furthermore, the proportion of elderly persons who choose to live alone has been increasing in a number of countries for several

1

years (Myers and Manton, 1983). Finally, estimates for the United States and Canada suggest the majority of care provided to elderly persons comes from family and friends (Brody, 1980; Chappell and Havens, 1985), not from the formal care system.

With the growing awareness that old age does not necessarily mean total dependency, there is increasing recognition that old age is not synonymous with disease. A view that emphasizes the pathology of aging can over-emphasize the negative aspects and portray a misleading picture of all elderly individuals as requiring extensive care. By examining broader social and health aspects of aging, a more positive picture emerges revealing that frailty and severe disability are experienced only by a minority of elderly persons.

The elderly population is heterogeneous for both social and health care characteristics. Some are self-sufficient, some receive minimal assistance from family and friends, some receive a mixture of both formal and informal care in their own homes and some receive total care within an institutional setting.

In order to understand health and health care issues involved in aging, it is imperative that the societal context within which these issues have arisen is understood. The following sections provide some of this social background as a prelude to a discussion of the issues themselves.

| EVOLUTION TO LONGER LIFE |

One of the first things one notices when investigating aging in past societies, is the paucity of research on the subject and the lack of numerical or quantitative data describing such societies. We lack reliable historical data on either numbers of or the role of elderly persons. In western industrial countries, census-taking and other recording activities similar to those of today generally did not begin until after the seventeenth century. Conclusions rely primarily on the written word, without information on actual behavior. Furthermore, the information available is frequently biased, providing data on the upper class or the "successes" of the society. Data on all economic classes tend not to exist (Harlan, 1968; Hendricks and Hendricks, 1977; 1981).

Despite these problems, and with a cognizance of the care that must be taken when drawing conclusions, there are some areas about which most investigators agree. The evidence seems fairly straightforward, for example, concerning changes in life expectancy. In earlier historical periods, few people lived to very advanced age.

Earlier periods in history experienced higher birth rates and higher death rates, with comparatively short life expectancies. Lerner (1970) estimate that prehistorically a normal length of life was approximately 18 years. Even in later primitive tribes (characterized as preliterate, hunting and gathering and nomadic), Simmons (1960) concludes after comparing 71 nations that persons 65 and over rarely comprised more than one to three percent of the population.

The shorter life expectancy and higher death rates meant that death came earlier in primitive and agrarian economies. Death came to children, youths and young adults more frequently than to the old. It also tended to come abruptly, through hardships of climate, shortage of food, accidents, diseases and wars. This contrasts with the prevalence of chronic illness and disabling physical impairments, which tend to accompany old age today (Hauser, 1976).

By the thirteenth century, male life expectancy at birth in England was still relatively low; estimates range from 33 to 35 years. It was not until the rise of science during the fifteenth and sixteenth centuries that a greater emphasis on record-keeping brought a close scrutiny of life expectancy. It was, furthermore, after the mid-seventeenth century that populations multiplied at a significant rate.

Since that time, assured food supply, changes in food production, better housing conditions and more progressive medical and sanitation facilities have contributed to population growth, declining mortality rates and substantial increases in longevity. By the turn of the twentieth century (well after the transition to modernization which Fischer (1978) claims began around the 1850s), careful recording of vital statistics revealed 10 or more years were added to general life expectancy. The gradual increments finally culminated in a dramatic rise in life expectancy during the first 60 years of the twentieth century in western industrialized countries. People born in 1960 could expect to live fully 20 years longer than those born in 1900. The rate of increase in life expectancy appears now to have slowed, or stabilized, and future predictions suggest this will remain the case for some time.

‖ CHANGING ROLES ‖ FOR OLDER PEOPLE

Although fewer people survived to old age in the past, there seems to be consensus that the transition to "old" was less abrupt than is true today. At the same time, old age was attributed at an earlier chronological date. A primitive tribe transmitted the wisdom of experience from one generation to the next through the memory of its elders. This meant people had a functional role to play as they aged. Primitive societies also provided opportunities for civil and political participation of their elderly. Simmons (1945; 1960) tells us about the roles of chiefs, priests, medicine men and magicians often held by elderly persons of these societies.

This ease of transition into old age is perhaps best illustrated in societies with sedentary occupations, most notably agricultural economies, which are attributed as coming into existence less than 7,500–10,000 years ago (Hendricks and Hendricks, 1977). The most prominent view suggests that the transformation of primitive societies to stable agricultural economies created a situation for providing optimal prestige to elderly individuals. They now possessed not only wisdom and skills but also property rights (Myles, 1980; Quadagno, 1982).

It was in these societies that many of the social rights and roles of elderly people, which had been emerging earlier, became firmly rooted. With the gradual establishment of permanent residence, a stable food supply, the rise of herding and the cultivation of the soil, an increase in influence and security for the old resulted. Elderly people could continue performing simple and routine manual work, withdrawing gradually as physical powers declined. It is usually accepted that family structures, backed by social and cultural sanctions, also entrenched the "power rights of parents." It was, however, the system of landholding and inheritance that assured the power of elderly individuals. Critical for the maintenance of this power was the timing of the transfer of productive property between generations. Transmission at death provided the most secure basis for the authority of aged persons (Fischer, 1978; Myles, 1980).

It was with industrial society and increased life expectancy that mandatory retirement emerged. The decline of agriculture and the rise of modern economic technology, with its rapidly changing knowledge and skills, made the older workers' skills obsolete. In a society that still values occupational participation, older people have no such role.

In addition to the consensus concerning changing life expectancy and transforming roles for old age, there also appears to be agreement that most societies have distinguished between old age and the stage beyond, that is, the period often referred to today as senility. This stage has been called numerous names: the over-aged, the sleeping period, the age of the already dead, the age grade of the dying and the useless stage. It is this distinction that sometimes accounts for whether or not elderly people are treated with much, or with little, status since some societies treat them with much status until they become over-aged. Authors have maintained that elderly people in past societies held higher status. They relinquish this claim for the obviously powerless and incompetent. Past societies, as our societies today, distinguished between the old-aged and the over-aged.

It is at this point that one sometimes encounters examples of seeming brutality towards the aged. However, actual neglect, or even abandonment, of the helpless old was not necessarily disrespectful. Some cultures moved on and left their aged behind to cope for themselves. This may seem brutal but it was, perhaps, the most humane method of dealing with an inescapable necessity. Or, as Carpenter (1954) and Guemple (1980) tell the story of the Inuit, the final passage of life is met with a casualness, which might be viewed as cruel by some who did not understand the belief that death was simply a different form of continued living. All societies have apparently differentiated between old age and this final plight. It must be remembered, though, that until modern civilizations, this over-aged period has not been very significant, since few reached it and they did not live long once in it.

There are, then, some historical changes in relation to elderly individuals, which can be referred to with some confidence. Through the ages, life expectancy has increased to such an extent that a larger number and a greater proportion of people now live to what is considered old age. As a consequence, however, there is a greater prevalence of chronic illness and disabling physical impairment during this time. So, too, has the role of the elderly in society changed. While there is more or less agreement that the place of older people in society has changed, there is less consensus concerning the reasons for the changes or even the meaning of those changes. This becomes evident in the next section on some of the attempts to understand the changing status of old age in society.

‖ UNDERSTANDING ‖ CHANGING STATUS

There are several areas about which there is less consensus concerning the aged in society, and a lack of reliable historical data has proved problematic. A conceptual framework for understanding the changing place of elderly individuals in society is an example of one of these areas. Generally speaking, it is not uncommon for researchers to conceptualize societies as falling into one of three main types: primitive (preliterate) societies, agrarian economies and industrial societies. The distinctiveness of certain oriental civilizations, such as China, India and Japan is sometimes noted.

The classification of societies as primitive, agrarian or industrial distinguishes them by type rather than chronology of existence. Primitive generally refers to preliterate, hunting and gathering, nomadic societies in which technological and social change take place slowly. While most primitive societies existed prior to industrial societies and are frequently referred to as preindustrial, some societies that exist today are characterized in this way.

Agrarian societies are characterized by the establishment of permanent residence, the achievement of a stable food supply and the maintenance of herds. They are generally considered to have occurred later than, and to have evolved from, primitive societies. They are generally classified, with primitive societies, as preindustrial. Industrial society is used as a classification for technologically advanced societies. It is usually assumed to have evolved between the mid-1800s to the mid-1900s. Industrialization is usually characterized by rapidly changing technologies, urbanization, residential mobility and so on. Some authorities further distinguish today's postindustrial society to refer to the stabilization of those industrial processes.

As previously noted, the most prominent view of the status accorded elderly people in various primitive societies, maintains they are held in high esteem, especially when those primitive societies are contrasted with industrial societies such as our own. Simmons (1960) is an adherent of this position, arguing that those who survived to old age in primitive societies played a more significant role than is true today. His argument includes the fact that elderly individuals in the past had a distinct advantage in experience, knowledge and wisdom. Without written records, old people were repositories of valuable information and in favored positions to make good judgments. Seers, magicians, medicine men and priests were frequently old people.

Less popular is the view that elderly people in non-industrial societies were not as esteemed. Harlan (1968), for example, examines the role of the aged in three Indian villages (Burail, Rattan Gahr and Shamirpet), all preindustrial agricultural communities. He reports the status of aged persons was not high in any of them. They experienced status difficulties arising from various circumstances: personal illness, death of spouse, intra-family conflicts, demands of younger persons and economic adversity. Such experiences, he argues, were inherent in traditional family and village life. Similarly, Keith (1982) argues that in past societies old people were respected more in ritual than in everyday life.

The evidence on the social value of elderly persons through the ages is ambivalent, and the debate remains largely unresolved. The difficulty is exemplified by Figner (1984) and Benson (1984), when examining data on the role of elderly persons in medieval Europe. Figner notes that while the European Jewish community viewed growing old, physically and mentally, negatively and did not look forward to the prospect, there is no evidence that elderly people were treated poorly. In a similar vein, Benson notes that medieval thinkers drew upon and accepted two contrary traditions going back to ancient Rome. The philosophical tradition presented an idealized vision of a happy old age. The poetic tradition presented a negative vision of decline. As this author notes, even in our own language, with words such as senior citizen and personal care homes, it is difficult to know how elderly people are actually treated.

It is a debate, which, according to Fischer (1978) is expressed by Adam Smith, Emile Durkheim and Max Weber as a comparison between primitive and civilized societies, and which has become translated in the twentieth century as a dichotomy between pre-industrial and modern, or post-industrial, society. At the same time, the causal factors related to the changing status of old age have shifted in emphasis from values, or norms, to material conditions, or in-dustrialization, and urbanization. The changes that at one time were interpreted as progress—that is, progress from primitive to civilized societies—have now become interpreted as a threat to freedom and a nostalgia for the past.

The Concept of Modernization

The debate concerning the status of elderly individuals in society has centered largely around the concept of modernization. Cowgill and Holmes (1972) and Cowgill (1974) argue that modernization causes the progressive decline in the status and social integration of aged persons. From their study of 14 different societies, including preliterate to modern, they find support for much of this theory. The four most salient aspects of modernization, which decrease the status of aged people, are: the introduction of modern health technology, modern economic technology, urbanization and rising levels of education. In western industrial societies, all operate in a climate incorporating the work ethic and a cult of youth, resulting in no role of consequence for elderly people.

Similar arguments were put forward both before and after these writings, although generally they are not formulated in as much detail, nor do they rest on the empirical examinations of Cowgill and Holmes. An early example is Parsons (1942) who argues that by comparison with other societies, the United States assumes an extreme position in the isolation of elderly individuals. He specifies two primary structural reasons for this: the isolation of the individual conjugal family, which he claims is primarily preferred by children, and the occupational structure, which severs work ties but also loosens ties to the community, resulting in the isolation of elderly persons into segregated communities.

A recent explanation of societal evolution related to the role of elderly people is found in Lopata's (1979) writings. She argues that change in the basic family unit has been a result of industrialization, urbanization, mobility and social complexity. The evolution of capital and the concomitant decrease in the importance of land as a source of status, rapidly changing technology, the development of the family and the removal of educational functions from the family to formal, structural sectors of the society are all part of this process.

The Marxian view is consistent with this position in its *conclusion* concerning the low status of elderly people in modern society. This view asserts that culture and social structure are determined by the economic system and that an individual's status is determined by his of her relationship to the means of production. In this transformation, an industrialized society evolved from one composed primarily of independent farmers, fishermen, craftsmen and small-businessmen to a society consisting of wage and salary workers, most of whom own no productive capacity. Familial resources tend to be transmitted through differential access to education and social skills, which enable or hinder the individual when competing in the labor market. Since, in capitalist industrialized societies, most elderly persons retire and therefore have no relationship to means of production, their status is low.

Thus, the question posed by Myles (1980) as to the structural origins of the problem of aging: when the majority depend on the labor market as their primary source of income, how are those who are excluded to survive? The answer, he tells us, is that most become state dependents, relying on government transfer payments for their income.

The Debate Continues

The issue, however, of the status of elderly people in society both today and historically is far from resolved. Some works report that old age in the pre-Christian and early Christian era (circa 3,000 B.C. – 1,300 A.D.) was viewed as negative and was contrasted to youth (Hendricks and Hendricks, 1977). Contrary evidence is also found in reports of modern societies where elderly people are held in high esteem. Palmore (1975) and Rhoads (1984) argue that the tradition of respect for elderly people in Japan has prevented a major decline in their status and integration despite industrialization. Similarly, Cowgill and Holmes (1972) note that Ireland is a modern-day exception to their theory, with elderly people there retaining property and, therefore, power and control

Some, like Dowd (1980), argue that despite the exceptions, modernization theory is valid. One of the consequences of the shift from agricultural to industrial society, from traditional to modern, is the decline in the power of old people relative to other age groups. The exceptions, he argues, appear to contradict the theory because the explanatory or organizing principles have been insufficiently general. There are two main propositions, consistent with modernization theory, which he claims account for the changes and include the exceptions.

One is the influence of power resources on social ranking (privilege). The second is the advent of recent structural changes, particularly the transition from competitive capitalism (a system of relatively small and numerous firms) to monopoly capitalism (a system dominated by a few larger corporations) in which it has become difficult for the individual to influence the social structure and affect structural change. The first proposition, he argues, is important because aging people in modern society have to exchange more in terms of prestige and status (which is related to available resources, such as intelligence, land, strength or control over machinery) to achieve similar levels of status than did aged people in non-modern societies. The second proposition is important because it means that with monopoly capitalism, social structure and societal institutions have become farther removed from individual influence.

Cowgill (1974) responds to the criticisms of modernization by suggesting that "...while modernization is detrimental to the status and interests of the aged in its early states, this trend may 'bottom out' in later stages of modernization, and from then on there is more comparative improvement in the status and condition of older people." This is a substantial change from the original statement of the modernization theory.

Incorporating Cowgill's revision, but more convincing, is the argument presented by Fischer (1978) in his historical account of growing old in America from the sixteenth century to 1970 and beyond. Fischer reviews studies relevant to the modernization theory in terms of the historical periods with which they deal and finds that:

> ...every recent study of aging in the *early modern era* has taken issue with the modernization model in one way or another. ...when we turn to the subject of old age in what historians call the *modern era* (c.1780–1940), we find another pattern. Almost every essay on old age in that period supports the modernization model in a general way.[1]
>
> ...In historical usage, the "modern era" increasingly refers to a period which has an end as well as a beginning. It is increasingly followed by a *"postmodern,"* or *"contemporary"*

[1] Fischer, *Growing Old in America* (New York, New York: Oxford University Press, 1978) p.255. Reprinted by permission of the publisher.

period which, by convention, runs from 1945 to the present. A great deal of historical research has recently been done on old age in the contemporary world by scholars who are not themselves historians.

...The modernization model, which was generally rejected by "early modernists" and accepted by "modern historians", has been applied in reverse by scholars who study aging in the "post-modern" world (italics added)[2]

Examples of the modernization theory "in reverse" include the substantial improvement in the economic status of the aged from 1940 to the present. Even though income levels still remain very low, they are higher than they used to be (Schulz, 1976). Another example is Hauser's (1976) argument that the adverse effects of industrial society have been somewhat offset by technological advances, which have eased the burden of hard physical labor, and, through increased productivity, raised standards of living for much of the population, including elderly individuals. In addition, unions have helped form seniority rules, which have to some extent protected older workers. He does warn, however, that the economic hazards of old age have, nevertheless, increased and have not been eliminated.

The conclusion seems clear. A theory, such as the modernization theory, does not apply to the types of multiple changes that have occurred over such a long history. It, nevertheless, seems to be applicable for a segment of history and for some aspects of the changes that took place in relation to elderly people. Many factors contribute to the changes, which have and which are taking place. We are only beginning to understand some of the underlying factors at work. This is not to deny the importance of theories, such as the modernization theory, for helping to clarify our thinking.

One of the difficulties in studying social roles is the fact that the meaning of things is always evolving. This is as true of the meaning of old age as it is of other things. The next section discusses the meaning of old age at the turn of the twentieth century and some of the changes that have taken place since that time.

‖ LIFE AT THE TURN ‖ OF THE CENTURY

Because meanings are socially defined within the interaction taking place at various levels in society, those meanings evolve, however slowly, through time. Furthermore, as Riley and associates (1972a) point out, each society consists of successive groups of individuals characterized by their own size, composition and life-course patterns. Society and the individuals constituting it are always undergoing change. Those of us who

[2] Ibid., p.264.

will be elderly tomorrow will differ from those who are elderly today because our histories and our biographies differ. Finally, those who are 65 and over at any one time, are themselves a heterogeneous, not a homogeneous, group.

By examining society at the turn of the century, it is apparent just how much the nature of society, and socially defined meanings, change. Those who are elderly today were young at this period of time. It is those individuals who were born in the 1880s and 1890s who have been the focus of much existing gerontological research. Many of the elderly individuals now living on the North American continent were born elsewhere and immigrated to Canada or the United States. They tended to come from rural backgrounds with little formal education beyond elementary school. They grew up in a climate that placed high value on work, and had few vacations or few opportunities to engage in any form of leisure in their late adolescent or early adult years (McPherson and Kozlik, 1980).

Generally speaking, those who are elderly today started paid labor at an early age and worked an average of 50 or more hours per week. Female participation in paid labor was remarkably lower than today. Men's participation began at a younger age and usually ended later. Individuals married after their economic roles had stabilized and engaged in childrearing for more years of their lives than people do today. At the turn of the twentieth century, most women died before or shortly after their last child left home. They, therefore, did not experience much of the empty nest transition that women experience today. Men retired later and died relatively soon after retirement, if not before. In addition, these people experienced major world events such as two world wars and the Depression (Denton and Spencer, 1980; Riley et al., 1972b).

In comparison to those North Americans who were young at the turn of the century are those who were born later, for example, the baby boom generation. These people were probably not immigrants, were probably born in the city and lived the major portion of their lives there. Their formal education is compressed largely into the early years of life and is dramatically lengthened. They spend fewer years having offspring, they have fewer offspring, and their offspring are more closely spaced in age. Retirement will probably come abruptly at age 65. Few men over 65 will likely be engaged in paid labor (60 percent in Canada in 1921 compared with 14 percent in 1981; 56 percent in the United States compared with 19 percent in 1980) (Bryden, 1974).

Given dramatic increases in longevity, couples in the baby boom generation can expect to live together without the presence of children for 15 years or so before one of them dies, and women can expect to live 10 years or so after that as widows (Marshall, 1980; Riley and Foner, 1968). In addition, when the baby boom generation is elderly, they can be assured of receiving various income security payments and supplements if their income is sufficiently low. Depending on which country these people live in, they may be eligible for universal medical care or medical care based on need.

In summary, those who are elderly today have to a large extent lived through complex social changes. Those who were 65 and over in 1980 could have been born anywhere from 1880 to 1915 or indeed, earlier. During their lifetime, society has gone from an era of the horse and buggy, to an era of the hydrogen bomb, a man landing on the moon, and recently the threat of nuclear warfare. They are the generation that has settled the cities and that has urbanized the country. It is this generation that brought us the technological advances which we take for granted today.

However, the elderly today are not all the same; they are not a homogeneous group. As elderly individuals of tomorrow will differ from those of today, so too do the elderly of today differ from one another.

The Concept of Cohort

The foregoing highlights the fact that groups of individuals share societal experiences as they age. For example, those elderly today have experienced two world wars and the Depression. Individuals could be further divided, say into those who were children during World War I and those who were adults during that time. This division would be warranted on the grounds that being a child during the war constitutes a distinct experience from being an adult during that time. The concept of cohort refers to a group of individuals who have experienced historical events and their consequences together (Bengston and Cutler, 1976).

Riley (1976) defines a cohort as a group of individuals born in the same time interval, who age together. In discussing cohorts in relation to the elderly, we can, for example, examine groups born in 1901, or those born between 1900 and 1909. While there can be much variation among members of a cohort, the concept captures the ideas that different age groups have been affected by, and share with one another, the historical events they have experienced. As such, it can be noted that the concept of cohort can be applied to a group that has entered a particular system, such as a hospital or a community of scientists — that is, a cohort of patients or a cohort of scientists.

There has been a fair amount of effort directed towards distinguishing cohort and other related terms, including generation and age strata. Some authors, such as Marshall (1983), argue that cohort is strictly a methodological term, and it is generation that denotes qualitative differences between groups. This differs from Riley's usage of the term, which treats cohort as the concept and any methodological operationalization of the term, such as a single year or 5-year birth period, as an imperfect empirical representation, as are most operationalizations of social science concepts. Both agree age strata refer to partitions of the population by age, which denote socially significant aspects of people and roles (such as childhood, youth, adulthood, and old age).

No doubt the debate over terminology and precise definition will continue. In the meantime, it is critical to recognize the importance of the underlying concept despite the difficulty of measurement. Interest in empirically measuring cohorts is the same as studying age or year of birth for the broader concept of which it is an imperfect measure but which it clearly denotes.

The societal experience of individuals and cohorts is not restricted to interaction with others and major societal events such as world wars and depressions. It includes, as well, participation in social institutions, which are part of the social structure of society. Educational, economic and political institutions touch the lives of us all.

The family is a core social institution within industrialized society. Gerontological writings inform us about the importance of the nuclear family of today. We know that aging members of those families tend *not* to be dismissed and "dumped" into long-term care institutions. Rather, people today prefer intimacy at a distance (Rosenmayr and Kockeis, 1963), where aging members maintain their own separate living quarters for as long as possible, but where exchanges of gift giving, aid and emotional support are maintained. Within the social institution of the family, there are bonds of both affectivity and obligation. We know further that assistance to aging members is provided through feelings of obligation, even when affection may not be present (Horowitz and Shindelman, 1981).

It is important to note that institutional structures refer not only to formal structures, such as the formal health care delivery system, but also include social arrangements, such as the family, friendship networks and subcultural ethnic groups. This book deals with social institutions such as the family and the informal network, as well as the formal health care system. Without denying the indisputable relevance of other social structures, such as the economic structure of society and the organization of its political institutions, the primary focus of this book lies with the informal and formal care systems as the providers of direct assistance to elderly members of society.

The foregoing has presented some of the societal background within which issues related to aging have emerged. It is this background that provides the context for understanding the experience of aging, for understanding the circumstances which affect the quality of our lives and for understanding issues related to health and health care.

The next section turns to a discussion of some of the salient issues within the area of aging and health care from a social perspective before concluding this introductory chapter.

SALIENT ISSUES IN AGING AND HEALTH CARE

Theories concerned with the status accorded elderly people in society are of extreme importance. It is people's status and position that summarize their relations with others (both individuals and institutions), as well as the rewards or lack thereof that accrue to them. A way of further understanding the place of elderly people in society is to examine the salient practical issues touching the lives of elderly people. Of concern here are those issues directly related to aging and health care from a social perspective.

Of primary interest is a realistic portrayal of aging. While this may seem obvious, there has been and continues to be much debate about the experience of aging. How likely is one's health to deteriorate in old age? Which aspects of health are more likely to deteriorate: physical, functional, psychological? Is adjustment to retirement, to the empty nest, to widowhood as traumatic as many argued in the 1950s, 1960s and 1970s? How do elderly people spend their lives? Contrary to much popular belief, most elderly people cope themselves, with the help of family and friends, and most report satisfaction with their lives. Only about 20 percent of the care provided to aging members of society comes from the formal care system. The remainder comes from family and friends.

Given an understanding of the aging experience for most people and the source of most care, an important issue becomes the intersection of the provision of care to elderly people from informal sources, such as family and friends, and from formal health and social service agencies. Given a desire to maintain aging individuals in the community, the role of family and friends in the provision of care has arisen as a question of major concern. Some argue that the provision of formal care is little more than a substitute for the provision of informal care and, indeed, can lead to a "shirking of responsibilities" by family members (Biaggi, 1980; Schmidt, 1981).

In other words, some believe that the family will not provide assistance if formal services are available to perform these functions. However, others note that families tend to turn to the formal system only as a last resort (Brody, 1980). Family members, by and large, make every effort to look after their aging relatives, until they are no longer capable of doing so. Because these caregivers are often elderly individuals themselves, many authorities argue that, if a substantial amount of respite care is not available for the caregiver, it will cost the system more in the long run. Not only will the original care recipient require assistance but so will the original caregiver.

A related issue is the question of type of care and the adequacy of the formal care system. Many argue that the present system of formal health care delivery, with its medical practitioners and acute care hospitals, is ill-suited to an aging society. A greater emphasis on community and social services, especially in the provision of chronic care, has been suggested to better meet the needs of aging persons. Included in this concern is the debate related to the delivery of services; that is, whether health services should be provided in a system separate from or integrated with one providing community and social services.

Access to and utilization of services is a related area. Research abounds informing us that it is not necessarily need that determines access to and utilization of services (Snider, 1980; George, 1981). Frequently, services are available for but not accessible to elderly individuals. Factors, such as gender, knowledge of the system, having an advocate who knows the system and health beliefs may be more important to an individual's utilization of the system than the health needs of that individual. Related to the question of access and utilization is the question of service coordination and information dissemination, especially given the proliferation of the formal service system at the present time.

The increasing proportion of elderly people in society points to another issue, long-term institutional care of those people. There is currently stabilization of the trend towards long-term institutional care of our aging members and a sympathy towards the opportunity for elderly individuals to remain in the community. One of the myths about aging is that most elderly individuals are in long-term institutional care. At any one time, approximately 6.7 percent of elderly persons in Canada (Statistics Canada, 1983) and about 5.3 percent of those aged 65 and over in the United States (U.S. Department of Commerce, Bureau of the Census, 1980) are in such institutions. The Canadian figure includes nursing homes, personal care homes with and without nursing care and auxiliary hospitals, while the United States figure includes only nursing care facilities. The sentiment favoring elderly individuals to live in the community appears to be consistent with the preferences of elderly individuals themselves. It has, however, coincided with a period of economic constraint in both countries (Chappell and Penning, 1979).

A final issue refers to the need for more collaborative research between researchers and practitioners to gain adequate data bases for decision-making and policy-planning. This question is intertwined with all the issues identified previously and emerges throughout the book. It is also presented separately in a chapter because of its importance and its complexity. Of relevance is the collaborative process itself and different types of research, which can be translated and utilized in policy planning and implementation.

‖ CONCLUSIONS ‖

This introductory chapter has sketched a social context of aging, past and present. Life expectancies have changed over time so that more and more individuals are living to old age. Not only are more individuals living to old age, the social meaning of being old in society is constantly changing. This is true both of past centuries and within the current century, even though the significance of these changes is not fully known. Much debate has centered around the status of elderly people in society, a debate that is still inconclusive. This background has been provided to emphasize the importance of a social perspective for studying health care and aging. A second aim has been to set the context so as to include all, or most, elderly people rather than highlighting only the sick or frail in order to discuss health care issues.

The next chapter focuses on the demographic trends which have contributed to an increasing interest in issues of aging. The main intent of Chapter 2 is to set the stage for an adequate discussion of aging and health care. It examines briefly the changing population structure of society, a topic which is dealt with in many other sources. Of greater concern here is a comparative discussion of Canada, the United States and the United Kingdom in terms of population aging. The chapter highlights demographic trends relevant to aging and health care and brings them together from the numerous existing demographic sources documenting the changing age structure of society.

■ CHAPTER 2 ■

DEMOGRAPHIC TRENDS
A PROFILE
OF CHANGE

Demographic profiles include statistical descriptions and analyses of populations to ascertain the numbers and distributions of people in a country or region. They can include changes in composition over time. We turn early to demographic trends because the age structure is less amenable in many ways to voluntary or policy change than some of the other areas to be discussed. In addition, knowledge about the age structure aids in an understanding of elderly people's living situations, economic situations, health experiences and social circumstances, generally. Indeed, Kalbach and McVey (1979) claim that problems of public health, education and old age can neither be identified nor solved without this type of information. Such data are relevant for the formulation of government policy and effective administration.

An overall statistical description of the current situation world wide and then, specifically, in Canada, the United States and the United Kingdom is presented. The world wide situation is important because it is a comparative context that helps us understand whether or not trends in North America are distinctive. More detail is provided on Canada and the United States as the two countries of primary interest in this book. Fairly extensive data are also presented on the United Kingdom in this statistical chapter, which draws primarily on census data, for which comparable figures are relatively easy to obtain. The U.K. is included to provide a further comparative base from which to better understand the North American context. While many countries could have been chosen for this purpose, the United Kingdom has a unique historical relationship to both Canada and the United States, albeit a different one with each country.

The intent of this chapter is briefly to reiterate facts about the increasing numbers and proportions of elderly persons in society. Sufficient detail is given to orient the reader and to provide an overall picture; but more time is spent comparing Canada, the United States and the United Kingdom and reviewing demographic trends for the aging and health care questions that are less frequently discussed in other sources.

‖ AGING WORLD WIDE ‖

The twentieth century is an era relatively abundant in statistical description. This section presents a demographic profile from the turn of the century to the present day. In an examination of these figures it is important to remember that those who are elderly today experienced firsthand some of the historical changes discussed previously.

International comparisons serve several purposes. They can function as a benchmark against which the degree of social change can be measured. They also provide examples of similar or dissimilar trends that help in the analysis, interpretation and forecasting of events (Michalos and Fortey, 1980). As Kalbach and McVey (1979) point out, the irony of the twentieth-century population "problem" is that it is the direct result of overcoming the hazards of an environment that ensured relative stability in the population for thousands of years. Almost since the beginning of time, maximum reproduction has been required to overcome the natural and man-made hazards of life that, until recently, resulted in at least half of all babies dying before reaching maturity.

Dramatic increases in population growth rates were experienced first by the one-fourth of the world's population in the economically advanced nations of Europe and of European settlement (Hauser, 1976). The European countries have now largely completed their transition to low levels of birth and death rates and have achieved considerably lower growth rates. In 1977 Europe was estimated to have an annual growth rate of 0.4 percent, with some countries showing a zero growth rate and a few with actual net losses.

A second phase of the population explosion has resulted from a rapid diffusion of the means of reducing the major causes of mortality. The result is that the less-developed, or developing, countries have reduced infant and childhood mortality without the levels of economic and social development that first made the rising standards of living and concomitant decrease in mortality among Europeans possible. The three-quarters of the world population living in the developing nations in Asia, Latin America and Africa did not experience this population explosion until after World War II.

The contrast between the so-called developed and developing countries is revealed in a comparison of their indices of aging (the ratio of the population 60 and over to the population less than 15 years x 100). A century ago the typical developed countries had an index of aging of about the same level as those of the developing countries in 1960 (Sheldon, 1960).

In addition, the less developed nations have a higher growth rate (see Table 2-1 for statistics and definition of terms), which means they will double their population in about 30 years, whereas the more developed nations will do so in about 70 years. The more developed nations have a lower birth rate, which means a faster aging population. They also have a lower death rate, which means a greater extension of life. Life expectancy at birth world wide for the 1975-1980 period was 57.9 years, with developed nations showing higher figures (71.9) than the developing nations (55.0).

‖ TABLE 2-1 ‖

SELECTED DEMOGRAPHIC INDICATORS: MORE-DEVELOPED VS. LESS-DEVELOPED COUNTRIES

	More-developed	Less-developed
Death rate (1983)	9	11-12
Birth rate (1983)	15-16	31-34
Growth rate (1983)	0.6	2.1
Life expectancy at birth (1975-1980)	71.9	55.0

Birth rate — The average annual number of births during a specific period of time per 1,000 persons (based on midperiod population). Also called crude birth rate.

Death rate — The average annual number of deaths during a specific period of time per 1,000 persons (based on midperiod population). Also called crude death rate.

Growth rate — The average annual percent change in population, resulting from a surplus (or deficit) of births over deaths and the balance of migrants entering and leaving the country.

Life expectancy at birth — The average number of years to be lived by a birth cohort, if mortality at each age remains constant in the future.

SOURCE: U.S. Bureau of the Census, *World Population 1983 — Recent Demographic Estimates for the Countries and Regions of the World*, Washington, D.C.: U.S. Government Printing Office, 1983; World Health Organization, *World Health Statistics Quarterly*, 1982, 35(3/4).

The proportion of populations aged 65 and over is also changing in the developing nations relative to the developed nations. In 1980, approximately 259.5 million (5.9 percent) of the total 4,432.1 million people in the world are age 65 or over. Of those 65 or over, approximately 55 percent live in the more-developed countries (in both 1970 and 1980), even though these countries account for less than 30 percent of the world's total population. It is estimated from the higher growth rates and lower death rates in less-developed countries that by 1990 the less-developed countries will house more elderly than the more-developed countries. By the century's end, when 6.1 percent of the world's population is projected to be 65 or over, the less-developed countries will have 58 percent of the world's aged and anywhere from 76 percent to 82 percent of the world's population (Siegel, 1981; World Health Organization, 1982).

The United Nations defines populations as "aged" if over 7 percent of a nation's population is 65 or over, "mature" if the percentage is between four or seven, and "young" if that percentage is under four. Of 81 countries examined between 1972 and 1981, 35 nations are reported as aged, 14 as mature and 32 as young (*U.N. Demographic Yearbook,* 1981). Currently, between 14 percent and 16 percent of the populations of the oldest nations is aged. Nevertheless, many of those nations expect dramatic increases in the first 30 years after the turn of the century, as their baby boom generations age. This is expected to be followed by a decrease resulting from the baby bust of the 1960s and 1970s.

Among the elderly population there is an excess of women over men in both the less- and more-developed countries, although the gap between the genders is wider in the more-developed countries. In 1975, the sex ratios (number of males per 100 females aged 65 and over) were 88 for the less-developed countries and 64 for the more-developed countries. The sex ratios for all ages were 102 and 94, respectively. By the year 2000, it is estimated that the sex ratios among elderly populations will decline somewhat among the less-developed countries and increase somewhat among the more-developed countries to decrease the differences between the two sets of nations (Siegel, 1981).

The world wide view of the changing age structure illustrates the similarity of developing countries today. Canada and the United States share much in common with the United Kingdom and other European countries by virtue of their similar levels of development. Nevertheless, the European countries are experiencing greater proportions of elderly persons earlier than Canada and the United States. In some ways, they show glimpses of the future for North America. More importantly, they demonstrate concrete examples of countries already having proportions of elderly people that will not be experienced in North America until the turn of the century.

CANADA, THE U.S. AND THE U.K.: TRADITIONAL DEMOGRAPHIC INDICATORS

We turn now to a comparison of the demographic profiles of Canada, the United States and the United Kingdom. The United States shares the continent with Canada but is economically and politically dominant. The United Kingdom is a "motherland" to Canada and, as a long-established country, offers a different point of comparison than does the United States. As will become evident later, the countries also represent different types of formal health care systems. In other words, three countries can serve as useful comparisons with one another.

This section examines some basic statistical indicators since the turn of the century. Although the statistics used are not always drawn from strictly comparable definitions, they are sufficiently similar to draw conclusions concerning trends. It would, however, be hazardous to attempt exact or short-term comparisons.

Numbers and
Proportions of Elderly
People

It is clear from Table 2-2 that both the United States and the United Kingdom have had and continue to have larger numbers of people aged 65 and over. This is not surprising given their larger overall populations. The proportion of elderly people, however, was approximately equal in the United Kingdom and Canada at the turn of the century (4.9 percent and 5.0 percent, respectively). The proportion at that time in the United States was slightly less (4.1 percent). During the past century, the proportions in the United States and the United Kingdom surpassed those in Canada, most noticeably in the United Kingdom (14.9 percent in the United Kingdom, 11.3 percent in the United States and 9.7 percent in Canada, 1980-1 figures). In all three countries this increase has been gradual and steady.

‖ **TABLE 2-2** ‖

NUMBER AND PERCENTAGE OF POPULATION
65+ IN CANADA, THE UNITED STATES AND
THE UNITED KINGDOM, 1890-1981

	Canada		United States		United Kingdom	
	N	%	N	%	N	%
1890-1*	218,790	4.5	2,392,013	3.8	1,876,000	5.0
1901	271,201	5.0	3,115,777	4.1	2,018,700	4.9
1911	335,315	4.7	3,954,807	4.3	2,577,900	5.7
1921	420,244	4.8	4,968,399	4.7	2,956,300	6.3
1931**	576,076	5.6	6,629,852	5.4	3,316,500	7.4
1941	767,815	6.7	9,085,179	6.9	(figures not available)	
1951	1,086,237	7.8	12,206,486	8.1	5,782,200	10.9
1961***	1,391,154	7.6	16,497,731	9.2	6,504,200	11.7
1971	1,744,405	8.1	20,120,293	9.9	7,307,600	13.2
1981	2,360,975	9.7	25,545,000	11.3	8,328,000	14.9

*Census-taking occurs in the U.S. in the decade years and one year later in Canada and the United Kingdom, except for the last figure shown, which refers to 1980 figures for the U.K.

* *Figures for Ireland not available for this year only in the United Kingdom.

* * *Alaska and Hawaii now included in United States.

SOURCES: Minister of Trade and Commerce, 1897; Dominion Bureau of Statistics, 1962; Statistics Canada 1973; 1978; 1982. U.S. Bureau of the Census, 1975; 1982. Mitchell, 1962; Mitchell and Jones, 1971; Central Statistical Office, 1980; 1982.

Similarly, the proportion of old elderly (here defined as 75 years of age or older) has been increasing in all three countries (Table 2-3). The proportions, furthermore, are roughly comparable. In 1980-81, 37.9 percent, 37.8 percent and 37.4 percent of the people 65 or older in the U.S., U.K. and Canada, respectively, were old elderly.

TABLE 2-3

PERCENTAGE OF POPULATION 65+ BY AGE IN CANADA, THE UNITED STATES AND THE UNITED KINGDOM, 1890-1981

	1890-1	1900-1	1910-1	1920-1	1930-1*	1940-1	1950-1	1960-1**	1970-1	1980-1
Canada										
65-69	38.8	39.2	39.3	41.0	40.1	40.1	39.9	35.0	35.0	35.8
70-74	28.7	28.4	28.2	28.0	29.8	28.3	29.0	28.9	26.2	26.8
75+	32.5	32.4	32.5	31.0	30.0	31.7	31.0	36.1	38.2	37.4
Total	100.0	100.0	100.0	100.0	99.9	100.1	99.9	100.0	99.4	100.0
United States										
65-69	41.8	42.3	42.5	41.9	41.8	42.2	41.0	37.8	34.8	35.3
70-74	29.0	28.7	28.2	28.3	29.4	28.5	28.0	28.6	26.8	26.8
75+	29.2	29.0	29.3	29.8	28.8	29.3	31.0	33.6	38.4	37.9
Total	100.0	100.0	100.0	100.0	100.0	100.0	100.0	100.0	100.0	100.0
United Kingdom										
65-69	70.4	70.2	72.1	42.3	42.8	figures	37.6	36.0	37.0	33.9
70-74				28.9	29.5	not	29.7	28.1	27.4	28.3
75+	29.6	29.8	27.9	28.8	27.7	available	32.7	35.9	35.5	37.8
Total	100.0	100.0	100.0	100.0	100.0		100.0	100.0	99.9	100.0

*Figures for Ireland not available for this year only.
**Alaska and Hawaii now included in the United States.

SOURCES: Minister of Trade and Commerce, 1925; Dominion Bureau of Statistics, 1935; Statistics of Canada, 1973; 1978; 1982. Mitchell, 1962; U.S. Bureau of the Census, 1950; 1970; 1980. Mitchell and Jones, 1971; Central Statistical Office, 1980; 1982.

Birth and Death Rates

The aging of the population, referred to here as a larger proportion of old persons in the population, results from a decline in the birth rate, which decreases the number of young and therefore increases the proportion of old. It is the decline in fertility, which is the main factor in the aging of a population (Clark and Collishaw, 1975; Hauser, 1976). All three countries have experienced a decline in birth rate, and all three have comparable birth rates at the present time: 15.5 per 1,000 population in Canada, 15.8 per 1,000 in the United States, 13.5 per 1,000 in the United Kingdom in 1980 (*U.N. Demographic Yearbook,* 1981).

A decline in the death rate can, however, have differential impacts on the age structure. For example, if the decrease is the same at all ages, the age structure remains the same. If the death rate decreases mainly among the young, the proportion of young will immediately increase, but over the long run the proportion of elderly persons will increase. If the death rate decreases among the elderly population, there will be an immediate increase in the proportion of older persons. The population will remain aged and grow even older if the death rates at older ages continue to go down.

In all three countries, the death rate has been declining in the population as a whole since the turn of the century. This decrease has been attributed primarily to a decrease in the death rates of the young, including infants. Factors, such as improved sanitation, have had a major impact on infant mortality and morbidity.

A distinction should be made here between two concepts, lifespan and expectation of life. Lifespan is the theoretical length of time the human organism can survive under the best of conditions, or the genetically determined life of the species. Expectation of life is the average number of years remaining for a person at a specified age (Hauser, 1976). The decline in the death rate has resulted in increases in the expectation of life, although not in the span of life. Thus, extension of the expectation of life is possible even if a population grows younger as measured by decline in average or median age. For example, with the post-World War II baby boom, the average age of the population declined, but the expectation of life continued to rise.

The death rate tends to be slightly lower in Canada (7.2 per 1,000 population in 1980) and in the United States (8.9 per 1,000 in 1980) than in the United Kingdom (11.8 per 1,000 in 1980) (*U.N. Demographic Yearbook,* 1981). For all three countries, this has been a considerable drop since the turn of the century. Interestingly, at that time the relative position of the three countries was the same as it is today. Canada had the lowest crude death rate and the United Kingdom had the highest (15.2 per 1,000 for Canada, 17.2 per 1,000 for the United States and 18.2 per 1,000 for the United Kingdom).

Life expectancy at birth is comparable among all three countries. In all instances, women can expect to live longer than men (men: 71.5 years in Canada, 70.3 years in the United States and 70.7 years in the United Kingdom; women: 78.7 years in Canada, 77.9 years in the United States and 76.8 years in the United Kingdom, — 1980-81 figures). Life expectancy at age 65 is also similar among the countries, although women in Canada can expect to live slightly longer than women in the United Kingdom (men: 14.7 years in Canada, 14.3 years in the United States and 12.6 years in the United Kingdom; women: 18.9 years in Canada, 18.7 years in the United States and 16.7 years in the United Kingdom, in 1980-81). In all three countries, life expectancy is longer for women than for men at birth and at age 65.

Gender Differences

Looking at the gender distribution among the elderly population, Table 2-4 shows the statistics since the latter part of the nineteenth century. While there were almost equal proportions of each gender in the elderly populations of all three countries at the turn of the century, Canada and the United States show slightly more men than women, while the United Kingdom shows slightly more women than men. In all three countries, however, there has been an increasing proportion of women in the elderly populations since that time. Today, all three reveal more female than male elderly persons. The United Kingdom, which began with a greater proportion at the turn of the century, today still has proportionately more than the two North American countries (60.9 percent women in the U.K., 57.2 percent in Canada and 54.7 percent in the U.S., all 1980-1 figures). Of equal interest is the fact that women are increasing as a proportion of the old elderly.

Given that the life expectancy for females is higher than for males, it is not surprising to find increasing proportions of females among older age groups of elderly persons. Similarly, it is to be expected that there would be more widows among this age group. Table 2-5 shows distributions for marital status, Table 2-6 shows distributions for females only and Table 2-7 for males only. Looking first at general trends in marital status, without taking gender differences into account, it is evident that elderly persons in the United States and Canada are more likely to be married than single, widowed or divorced. This has been true since the turn of the century. The next largest category for both countries is widowed.

Among the elderly population in the United Kingdom, however, the largest category is the widowed, until 1971, when the married elderly become the largest. The next largest category in the United Kingdom, until 1971, is married. There also appear to be slightly more singles among the elderly population in the United Kingdom than in the other two countries. Because of the lack of consistency in the definition of the divorce category (see note at end of Table 2-5), comparisons between countries cannot be made.

A striking feature of these data is the distribution of marital status in the United Kingdom. With increasingly more females than males, one would expect a larger widowhood category for this country than the other two. In addition, as just noted, the proportion of females is increasing in the country, so that one would not expect the reversal appearing in the 1971 census. However, the distributions by gender (see Tables 2-6 and 2-7) reveal the proportion of widowed women has been decreasing only slightly over time. There

TABLE 2-4

PERCENTAGE OF POPULATION 65+ BY GENDER IN CANADA, THE UNITED STATES AND THE UNITED KINGDOM, 1890-1981

	Canada		United States		United Kingdom	
	Male	Female	Male	Female	Male	Female
1890-1	52.3	47.7	51.0	49.0	44.5	55.5
1900-1	51.2	48.2	50.5	49.5	44.2	55.9
1910-1	50.9	49.1	50.3	49.7	43.5	56.6
1920-1	51.2	48.8	50.3	49.7	43.2	56.8
1930-1*	51.1	48.9	50.1	49.9	43.0	57.0
1940-1	50.9	49.1	48.9	51.2	figures not available	
1950-1	50.8	49.2	47.3	52.8	41.5	58.5
1960-1**	48.5	51.5	45.3	54.7	38.9	61.1
1970-1	44.8	55.2	41.9	58.1	38.4	61.6
1980-1	42.8	57.2	45.3	54.7	39.1	60.9

* Figures for Ireland not available for this year, only in the United Kingdom.
** Alaska and Hawaii now included in the United States.

SOURCES: Minister of Trade and Commerce, 1873; 1925; Dominion Bureau of Statistics, 1962; Statistics Canada, 1973; 1982. U.S. Bureau of the Census, 1975; 1980. Mitchell, 1962; Mitchell and Jones, 1971; Central Statistical Office, 1980; 1982.

TABLE 2-5

PERCENTAGE OF POPULATION 65+ BY MARITAL STATUS IN CANADA, THE UNITED STATES AND THE UNITED KINGDOM, 1890-1981

Marital Status	1890-1*	1900-1**	1910-1	1920-1	1930-1	1940-1	1950-1	1960-1	1970-1	1980-1
Canada										
Total 65+: Single	—	—	—	9.4	10.7	11.1	11.1	10.5	10.6	9.1
Married	55.7	—	—	53.9	53.0	52.9	53.8	54.5	53.8	53.3
Widowed	37.1	—	—	36.5	36.2	35.4	34.9	34.8	34.7	34.1
Divorced	—	—	—	.1	.1	.1	.2	.3	.8	1.6
Unknown***	7.2	—	—	.0	.0	.0	.0	.0	.0	1.9
Totals	100.0	—	—	99.9	100.0	99.9	100.0	100.1	99.9	100.0
United States†										
Total 65+: Single	5.6	5.9	6.2	7.2	8.3	9.6	8.7	8.1	7.9	5.2
Married	53.0	50.7	50.3	49.4	49.2	48.7	49.7	49.5	51.5	55.8
Widowed	40.9	42.9	42.6	42.5	41.5	40.7	40.1	40.3	37.5	35.5
Divorced	.4	.4	.5	.6	.8	1.0	1.5	2.0	3.1	3.5
Totals	99.9	99.9	99.6	99.7	99.8	100.0	100.0	99.9	100.0	100.0
United Kingdom††										
Total 65+: Single	11.9	12.1	12.5	12.7	13.7	—	14.4	14.5	12.2	10.5
Married	35.2	33.7	33.5	34.6	35.3	—	38.2	40.2	49.2	51.3
Widowed	52.9	54.2	54.0	52.6	50.9	—	47.2	45.2	38.6	36.4
Divorced	—	—	—	.0	.1	—	.1	.2	.0	1.7
Totals	100.0	100.0	100.0	99.9	100.0	—	99.9	100.1	100.0	99.9

*Figures collected for only those married and widowed in Canada. Divorce figures were not separately enumerated for the United Kingdom until after 1921.

**Figures not available for 1901 and 1911 for Canada.

***The unknown figure includes those in Canada separated in 1981.

According to the 1950 census definition, people who were separated, common law or other were included in the married category. The 1960 and 1970 data in this table also considers these groups married, even though the spouse may be absent.

†Figures for 1980-1 are for Great Britain only. Adapted from the 1981 Census of Great Britain, Table 1, Usually Resident Population of Pensionable Age: Marital Status by Age by Sex. By permission of the Office of Population Censuses and Surveys, England.

SOURCES: Minister of Trade and Commerce, 1925; Dominion Bureau of Statistics, 1946; 1953; 1966; Statistics Canada, 1973; 1982; U.S. Bureau of the Census, 1950; 1982; U.S. Department of Commerce, 1960; 1970; Mitchell and Jones, 1971; Central Statistical Office, 1973.

TABLE 2-6

PERCENTAGE OF FEMALE POPULATION 65+ BY MARITAL STATUS IN CANADA, THE UNITED STATES AND THE UNITED KINGDOM, 1890-1981

Marital Status		1890-1	1900-1*	1910-1**	1920-1	1930-1	1940-1	1950-1	1960-1	1970-1	1980-1
Canada Females 65+:	Single	—	—	—	10.2	10.9	11.2	10.4	10.2	11.1	9.5
	Married	40.6	—	—	39.8	40.2	41.0	41.6	41.2	36.5	38.4
	Widowed	5.3	—	—	49.9	48.9	47.7	47.9	48.4	51.6	49.0
	Divorced	—	—	—	.1	.1	.1	.1	.2	.8	1.5
	Unknown***	8.1	—	—	.0	.0	.0	.0	.0	.1	1.5
	Totals	100.0	—	—	100.0	100.1	100.0	100.0	100.0	100.1	99.9
United States Females 65+:	Single	5.6	6.0	6.3	7.1	8.1	9.3	8.9	8.5	8.6	5.9
	Married	35.4	34.2	35.0	33.9	34.7	34.3	35.7	37.3	29.6	39.5
	Widowed	58.6	59.3	58.1	58.4	56.5	55.6	54.3	52.1	59.0	51.2
	Divorced	.3	.3	.4	.4	.5	.7	1.1	2.0	2.8	3.4
	Totals	99.9	99.8	99.8	99.8	99.8	99.9	100.0	99.9	100.0	100.0
United Kingdom Females 65+:	Single	15.3	15.6	16.2	16.5	18.1	—	19.1	19.2	15.0	12.1
	Married	21.3	20.1	20.5	21.6	22.6	—	24.7	24.3	34.9	37.2
	Widowed	63.4	64.4	63.4	61.9	59.2	—	56.1	56.2	50.1	48.9
	Divorced	—	—	—	.0	.0	—	.1	.3	.0	1.8
	Totals	100.0	100.1	100.1	100.0	99.9	—	100.0	100.0	100.0	100.0

*Figures collected for only those married and widowed in Canada. Divorce figures were not separately enumerated for the United Kingdom until after 1921.
**Figures not available for 1901 and 1911 for Canada.
***The unknown figure includes those in Canada separated in 1981.
†According to the 1950 census definition, people who were separated, common law or other were included in the married category. The 1960 and 1970 data in this table also considers these groups married, even though the spouse may be absent.
††Figures for 1980-1 are for Great Britain only. Adapted from the 1981 Census of Great Britain, Table 1, Usually Resident Population of Pensionable Age: Marital Status by Sex. By permission of the Office of Population Censuses and Surveys, England.

SOURCES: Minister of Trade and Commerce, 1925; Dominion Bureau of Statistics, 1946; 1953; 1966; Statistics Canada, 1973; 1982. U.S. Bureau of the Census, 1950; 1982; U.S. Department of Commerce, 1960; 1970. Mitchell and Jones, 1971; Central Statistical Office, 1973.

TABLE 2-7

PERCENTAGE OF MALE POPULATION 65+ BY MARITAL STATUS IN CANADA, THE UNITED STATES AND THE UNITED KINGDOM, 1890-1981

Marital Status	1890-1	1900-1*	1910-1**	1920-1	1930-1	1940-1	1950-1	1960-1	1970-1	1980-1
Canada Males 65+:										
Single	—	—	—	8.7	10.5	11.8	11.8	10.8	10.6	8.5
Married	69.5	—	—	67.4	65.2	64.5	65.7	68.5	71.7	73.2
Widowed	24.1	—	—	23.7	24.1	23.6	22.3	20.4	16.7	14.1
Divorced	—	—	—	.2	.1	.2	.2	.4	.9	1.8
Unknown***	6.4	—	—	.0	.1	.0	.0	.0	.0	2.3
Totals	100.0	—	—	100.0	100.0	100.1	100.0	100.1	99.9	99.9
United States Males 65+:										
Single	5.6	5.7	6.2	7.3	8.4	7.0	8.4	7.6	8.0	4.9
Married	70.5	67.1	65.6	64.7	63.7	63.7	65.7	61.8	65.3	78.0
Widowed	23.3	26.4	27.1	26.9	26.6	28.3	24.1	28.5	23.8	13.5
Divorced	.4	.5	.7	.7	1.1	1.0	1.8	2.1	2.3	3.6
Totals	99.8	99.7	99.6	99.6	99.8	100.0	100.0	100.0	99.4	100.0
United Kingdom Males 65+:										
Single	8.5	8.6	8.9	9.0	9.4	—	9.7	9.7	7.7	8.0
Married	49.1	47.4	46.6	47.6	48.0	—	51.8	56.0	72.1	72.9
Widowed	42.4	44.0	44.5	43.4	42.6	—	38.3	34.2	20.1	17.4
Divorced	—	—	—	.1	.1	—	.1	.2	.0	1.6
Totals	100.0	100.0	100.0	100.1	100.1	—	99.9	100.1	99.9	99.9

*Figures collected for only those married and widowed in Canada. Divorce figures were not separately enumerated for the United Kingdom until after 1921.

**Figures not available for 1901 and 1911 for Canada.

***The unknown figure includes those in Canada separated in 1981.

†According to the 1950 census definition, people who were separated, common law or other were included in the married category. The 1960 and 1970 data in this table also considers these groups married, even though the spouse may be absent.

† ††Figures for 1980-1 are for Great Britain only. Adapted from the 1981 Census of Great Britain, Table 1, Usually Resident Population of Pensionable Age: Marital Status by Age by Sex. By permission of the Office of Population Censuses and Surveys, England.

SOURCES: Minister of Trade and Commerce, 1925; Dominion Bureau of Statistics, 1946; 1953; 1966; Statistics Canada, 1973; 1982. U.S. Bureau of the Census, 1950; 1982. U.S. Department of Commerce, 1960; 1970. Mitchell and Jones, 1971; Central Statistical Office, 1973.

has been a dramatic increase in the proportion of elderly men who are married (49.1 percent in 1891, 56.0 percent in 1961 and 72.1 percent in 1971); that is, while both men and women are increasingly likely to be married, the dramatic rise is occurring among men. Corresponding decreases in the widowhood category are evident.

In both Canada and the United States, there is a more stable trend throughout time in marital status among females. There is more change taking place for men, more so in the United States than in Canada. Both countries, like the United Kingdom, reveal more men in the married category over time and fewer of them in the widowed category. These trends are not particularly pronounced in Canada. They are fairly pronounced in the United States but less so than in the United Kingdom.

All three countries show relative stability in their proportion of singles throughout time, confirming the report of others (Myers and Manton, 1983) that marriage is still the preferred state in society.

The numbers and proportions of elderly persons, those aged 65 and over, in Canada, the United States and the United Kingdom have been increasing since the turn of the century and continue to do so. In all three countries, the proportion of females among elderly persons is also increasing, as is the proportion of old-old. Elderly men are more likely to be married, while elderly women are more likely to be widowed.

The increasing proportions of elderly persons is one reason for the increasing awareness of, and concern for, this age group, which is evident in current publications, media attention and so on. The fact that there is a greater increase in the old-old points to the importance of more attention to the needs and, particularly, the needs for care among this age group; that is, despite arguments that those entering old age are healthier, more economically advantaged, and have more formal education than was true of earlier cohorts (Neugarten, 1979), the fact that there are increasingly more old-old among this age group means that issues of care are still important. More will be said about the implications of this age distribution among elderly persons in the next chapters.

The fact that there are increasing proportions of women among the elderly population and that these elderly women are more likely to be widowed than married also has implications for health care. The fact that women tend to have a longer life expectancy than men and that they still tend to marry men a few years older than themselves, generally means they are available to a large extent to provide care to their husbands in their last days. However, they themselves are most likely to spend their last years without a spouse and without a household member to provide care. They are also likely to be in a situation of decreased economic circumstance, given the traditional role of women in society, particularly among cohorts who are elderly today.

Among the three countries examined, the United Kingdom emerges as somewhat distinctive, with the United States and Canada more similar to one another. In particular, while the United States has more elderly individuals in terms of numbers than do the other two countries, the United Kingdom has a larger proportion of its population who are elderly than does the United States or Canada. While the age distribution among the elderly population is similar in all three countries, the United Kingdom has a greater proportion of elderly women and a greater proportion of elderly persons who are widowed.

CANADA, THE U.S. AND THE U.K.: SOCIAL INDICATORS

There are several other descriptors that are relevant for the provision of care to those who are elderly, but for which historical data are largely unavailable or difficult to obtain. For many of them, however, current data are available, and it is important given the discussion in the remainder of the book to have some understanding of the present situation. This section, therefore, discusses some of these additional factors but does so only for the latest data available, referring to the 1980-81 decennial census, where possible.

Paid Labor

One area of debate is mandatory retirement, flexibility in work and retirement patterns and the general exclusion of elderly persons from paid labour. The occupational, or paid labor, role is still considered a major function in society, which provides one with a sense of usefulness and identity, so that exclusion from this activity may result in feelings of uselessness, or meaninglessness. Furthermore, irrespective of government transfer payments, pensions are tied to paid labor, excluding most women, particularly those who are elderly today. Even among those who work for pay, women tend to participate in the low paying, part-time and intermittent occupations and therefore receive minimal pensions, if any. Women still, by and large, are responsible for childrearing and are judged as desirable, to a large extent, for their youth. That is, women's participation in society does not tend to be rewarded monetarily as they grow older.

Current statistics support the popular belief that those who are elderly today are, by and large, outside of the paid labor force. Because of the dramatic gender differences in labor force participation, it is relevant here to examine the genders separately. In 1981, only 14.3 percent of elderly men in Canada are working at any paid labor — that is, part-time, intermittent or full-time employment (Statistics Canada, 1982). The figure for the United States is 18.5 percent (U.S. Bureau of the Census, 1982) and for Great Britain, 13.8 percent[1] in 1981 (Office of Population Censuses and Surveys, 1981a). As expected, the figures are even

---

[1] Adapted from 1981 Census of Great Britain, *Table 12: Usually Resident Population Aged 16 and Over: Economic Position by age by marital status by sex.* By permission of the Office of Population Censuses and Surveys, London, England.

lower for elderly women: 7.8 percent in Canada, 7.9 percent for the United States and a low 4.2 percent for Great Britain. Retirement, or the lack of involvement in paid labor, can free these individuals for the provision of informal care and assistance. This is discussed in more detail in chapter five.

Formal Education

Figures for formal education of those who are currently elderly are particularly hazardous to interpret, especially when comparing data across countries. Translating one formal educational system into the terms of another is extremely difficult. This difficulty does not diminish the potential importance of formal education within an elderly population. While elderly individuals today tend to have less formal education than younger adults, the elderly population of tomorrow will have more formal education than it does today. The consequences of this fact for the provision of care are not yet known, but its importance could be great.

Those with more formal education could enter old age with greater expectations of the formal system, with more flexible attitudes towards living arrangements and with more confidence and ease in managing massive government bureaucracies. An important unknown factor, however, is the extent to which there will be major qualitative changes within society and within the health care system by the time these individuals become elderly. Few who are elderly today would have predicted the major societal changes that have taken place during their lifetime.

Subcultures

Similarly, subcultures (ethnic, minority and racial) can have implications for the provision of care among an elderly population. However, simple categories accurately describing a subculture are difficult to find, especially within national census data. All three countries examined have national data on nativity. For 1980-81, Great Britain shows the greatest proportion of its elderly population as native born (95.5 percent, Office of Population Censuses and Surveys, 1981b), while Canada has the smallest proportion (70.1 percent, Statistics Canada, 1982). The United States falls in the middle with 76.5 percent of its elderly native born (U.S. Bureau of the Census, 1970).

The figure for the United States refers to the white population only. A nativity breakdown is not available for nonwhites, who constitute 7.9 percent of the elderly population. However, given that they constitute a small proportion of the elderly population overall, the figures for the white population are representative of the majority of elderly persons in that country.

The age structure of the foreign born population reflects past trends in immigration, as the age structure of the native population reflects past trends in births. The differences between these countries in the proportion of elderly people who are foreign born therefore reflect differences in past trends in immigration. The United Kingdom's larger proportion of native born elderly reflects the fact that this country was settled long before the North American continent was being inhabited by its immigrants. The differences demonstrated between Canada and the United States suggest that mass immigration to the United States occurred earlier than to Canada, and that many of those people have now died and/or the immigrants to the United States were older and have now died (Sheldon, 1960).

Future cohorts of elderly persons, especially in Canada, may show increased proportions of foreign born. The increase could result as waves of recent (during the 1970s) immigrants' age, assuming the aging of the immigrants is not offset by some other factor, such as early death, or mass immigration of younger persons in the decades to come.

The relevance of subculture for the elderly population and, in particular, for the provision of care is an underresearched area in gerontology. Even though conceptually and theoretically it has been argued that subcultural cohesiveness is likely to result in more social support for its elderly members, this has not been established empirically. Some recent analyses (Chappell and Penning, 1984) suggest a lack of confirmation of this popular belief. The question, however, is just beginning to be studied in relation to old age.

Rural-urban Differences

The extent to which rural-urban differences are relevant for the provision of care to elderly individuals is another continuing debate. Some argue that the concentration and accessibility of medical services in the city mean health care needs of elderly persons will be better served in urban areas (Taietz and Milton, 1979). Others argue that the informal resources available to elderly residents of rural areas lead to a collective sense of responsibility, which results in better health care (Gardner, 1981). However, the assumptions regarding stronger supports for rural elderly residents are unproven (Copp, 1980). The underlying question of whether or not fundamental changes have taken place in industrial society, which have made rural life different from or similar to urban life, is unresolved.

Data on place of residence for Canada, the United States and the United Kingdom are available, although census definitions are not strictly comparable. For example, in Canada rural areas are defined as those with less than 1,000 inhabitants, and a population density of less than 400 per square kilometer, while in the United States they are defined as areas with less than 2,500 inhabitants. Rural in the United Kingdom is not defined in terms of size but instead as an area not classified for government purposes, that is, not administrative county boroughs, municipal boroughs or urban districts. Canada reports 21.9 percent of its elderly population living in rural areas, while comparable figures for the United States are 23.9 percent and for the United Kingdom 21.5 percent (Statistics Canada, 1982; U.S. Bureau of the Census, 1982; *U.N. Demographic Yearbook,* 1979).

It is clear that in all three countries the majority, at least three-quarters, lives in more-populated areas. These statistics, however, tell us nothing about proximity of these rural areas to larger centers. It should also be noted that these definitions of rural refer to such small areas that numerous small towns are classed as urban. When rural is so defined, it masks small town and large city differences.

For example, Sheldon (1960) tells us that the village component of the rural nonfarm population contains a high concentration of older persons in the United States. Similarly, Shulman (1980) informs us there is some evidence that elderly persons in Canada are slightly over-represented in small towns (defined in this instance as centers between 1,000 and 10,000 in population). This is not particularly surprising in light of the out-migration of the young to the cities, of older farmers retiring off the farm to rural nonfarm communities and of the location of rural nursing and personal care homes in nonfarm areas.

Furthermore, it should be noted that those elderly who are living in large urban areas today are mainly rural in their derivation; that is, most elderly individuals living in cities today moved from rural areas to the city during their adult lifetime. It is they primarily who settled our cities; it is they who have lived through the so-called rural-urban transition.

A statistical profile of the elderly population, relevant to health care, should necessarily include health statistics. Because it is such an important area for this topic, the entire next chapter is devoted to a discussion of health and aging. National statistics are presented there.

This section has examined the current social situation of elderly persons in Canada, the United States and the United Kingdom in relation to several variables. Perhaps most importantly, these statistics highlight the lack of knowledge and in-depth understanding of the relevance of many of these factors for the quality of life and the care of elderly people. While much concern has been expressed that elderly persons do not have a meaningful role through which to contribute to society, due largely to their forced retirement from paid labor, we do not know how this lack affects the quality of their lives and how their role may change in the future. There is some speculation that healthy elderly people will be a reserve force of volunteers to care for elderly people who are ailing. Similarly, it is unclear how educational levels affect life-styles, or how the increasing formal education being gained by younger cohorts today will affect their lives when they themselves are older.

All of the variables discussed, however, do point to the relevance of social factors in the lives of elderly people. Finally, while the statistics in these areas are not as detailed nor as comparable as the ones discussed in the previous section, the three countries do emerge as relatively similar to one another.

‖ CONCLUSIONS ‖

This chapter has reviewed changing demographic statistics in relation to age, specifically for Canada, the United States and the United Kingdom. There is a striking similarity among developed countries in this regard. Canada and the United States, like the United Kingdom and other European countries, are experiencing an aging of their populations. This is so, even though both Canada and the United States are comparatively younger countries. Canada and the United States also differ from the United Kingdom in that the increase in the proportion of their elderly population has happened more recently. To this extent, the United Kingdom provides a concrete example of a country with higher proportions of elderly persons, proportions that will be experienced in North America at the turn of the next century.

When Canada, the United States and the United Kingdom are compared on selected demographic characteristics from the turn of the century through to the present day, Canada and the United States once again emerge similar to one another, while the United Kingdom appears somewhat distinctive. The United Kingdom not only has a greater proportion of its population who are elderly, it also has a greater proportion of its elderly who are women and who are widowed.

When examining these three countries on social characteristics, the three countries are more similar. In all three countries, a large proportion of their elderly persons is external to the paid labor force, have relatively low formal educational levels and tend to live in urban areas. These data suggest the potential importance of various social factors to the lives of elderly people, while pointing to the lack of knowledge in this area.

This chapter has provided data on the sociodemographic structure, which is part of the context within which elderly persons live. Knowing the sociodemographic characteristics of these individuals tells us something, but it is clearly an incomplete picture. Among other things, it fails to capture the processes that are involved in our daily lives.

The relevance of these factors for health care and aging become clear throughout the remainder of the book. We turn attention next to a discussion of health in an aging population.

■ CHAPTER 3 ■

HEALTH STATUS AND AGING

The historical trends and descriptive statistics discussed in chapter 2 are directly relevant to health and health care issues in aging. Societies are now faced with increasing proportions of elderly people. With increasing age comes deteriorating health in many forms and, by and large, increasing distance from major societal roles (i.e., retirement from paid labor, completion of childrearing tasks, widowhood). While the proportion of elderly persons is growing, society has not yet recognized useful and contributing roles to replace those that people have left. Rather, many are forced to maintain themselves economically through government transfer payments. This is particularly true for women who have not participated to the same extent as men in paid labor throughout their lives, yet who constitute the majority of elderly persons and, increasingly, the greatest proportion of the old elderly. These factors have led to increased concern that there will be escalating demands on society to meet the needs of this growing segment of the population.

This chapter explores the extent to which major changes in health status take place during old age. Chapter 4 examines meaningful social involvement. Then the relevance of the demographic trends for health care will be more evident.

∥ HEALTH AND OLD AGE ∥

One of the major concerns about old age for both the individual and the society is a decline in health. It is, to a large extent, deteriorating health that is associated with increasing individual dependence, or lack of self-sufficiency. This is also of concern societally. Demands on the formal health care system by increasing numbers of elderly people have led to an awareness of the changing demographic situation on the part of policy makers, politicians and government officials.

The health status of elderly persons has been interpreted primarily in terms of either the presence or absence of disease, or the degree of functional capacity or disability. However, the World Health Organization (1958) defines *health* as "a state of complete physical, mental, and social well-being and not just the absence of disease and infirmity," that is, health has physical, mental, social and subjective aspects.

In this section, various aspects of health are examined. More specifically, attention is given to physical health in terms of chronic conditions and the degree of functional disability; to mental health, primarily in terms of dementia and depression; to subjective health in terms of self-perceptions of personal health and satisfaction with life. Wherever possible, criteria for the measurement of these aspects of health are provided, followed by figures on elderly persons and figures that compare elderly with non-elderly persons. These data focus on Canada and the United States.

Physical Health

Measures of physical health frequently refer to chronic conditions, such as heart and circulation problems, stroke, arthritis or rheumatism, palsy, eye trouble not relieved by glasses, ear trouble, dental problems, stomach troubles and diabetes. Two such measures are the summative index, such as the H.I.S. instrument used in the United States Health Insurance Study (U.S. National Center for Health Statistics, 1957), and the International Classification of Diseases (World Health Organization, 1977). Individuals can be read a list of conditions and asked if they have had any of them within the last year, or are still having effects from earlier episodes. Alternatively, the conditions can be diagnosed by a physician.

Diagnoses by physicians and self-reports may be highly correlated. These are similar to one another when individuals are asked about actual behavior rather than global questions about their health (Shanas and Maddox, 1976). One of the major difficulties in the measurement of chronic conditions and disease is that categories are listed by parts of the body rather than severity or consequence of the illness (Greenlick et al., 1968).

Most elderly persons report some physical health problems (see Table 3-1). The 1978-79 Canada Health Survey (Health and Welfare Canada and Statistics Canada, 1981) indicates only 14.4 percent of those aged 65 and over living in the community report no problems at the time of the interview, including both acute and chronic conditions. Fully 85.6 percent report at least one health problem. The 1979 United States National Health Interview Survey also reveals over 80 percent of the 65+ interviewees had one or more chronic conditions (U.S. Bureau of the Census, 1983).

‖ TABLE 3-1 ‖

CHRONIC CONDITIONS AND FUNCTIONAL ABILITY

	≤ 64 Canada	U.S.*	65+ Canada	U.S.
A) *Chronic Conditions*				
No problems	48.7%	N/A	14.4%	20%
At least one problem	51.3%	N/A	85.6%	80%
B) *Functional Ability*				
No limitation	91.0%	86.5%	61.8%	54.8%
Some limitation	2.1%	3.1%	3.2%	6.7%
Major activity limited	5.4%	6.8%	26.2%	21.8%
Cannot do major activity	1.5%	3.6%	8.7%	16.7%

* These data are not for the population less than 65 years of age but for the total population. Figures for those less than 65 years old were unavailable for the United States.

SOURCES: Health and Welfare Canada and Statistics Canada, *Canada Health Survey*, Ottawa, Ont.: Minister of Supply and Services, 1981, and Wolinsky, F.D. "Health care policy and the elderly: Short-term cures and long-term catastrophes." Paper presented at the annual meeting of the *Society for the Study of Social Problems*, Detroit, Michigan, 1983.

Not only do most elderly persons report having chronic health problems but most also tend to have more chronic conditions than do younger adults. Among those less than 65 years of age in the Canada Health Survey, 48.7 percent report no chronic conditions, 51.3 percent report one or more.

Comparable figures from the United States are not available, since these data tend to be reported in terms of limitation of activity due to chronic conditions rather than chronic conditions irrespective of their effect on functioning. Limitation of activity is a measure of functioning and is discussed below.

Before turning to that discussion, we look at disease specific crude mortality (death) rates for those 65 and over, shown in Table 3-2. In both Canada and the United States, heart disease is the leading cause of death among old people. Cancer is second, and cerebrovascular disease is third. Although these three disease categories are listed as the leading causes of death, factors that may lead to reductions in mortality are not necessarily the same factors that lead to reductions in diseases.

While elderly persons tend to suffer more from chronic than acute illness, they tend to suffer from chronic illnesses that are not necessarily the cause of their death. The most frequent chronic conditions are heart disease, arthritis and chronic rheumatism, then hypertension (Neugarten, 1982a); that is, the illnesses of old age are not necessarily the causes of mortality.

‖ TABLE 3-2 ‖

COMPARISON OF DISEASE SPECIFIC CRUDE MORTALITY RATES FOR THOSE 65+

Rates Per 100,000	Canada 1978	United States 1979
Ischaemic heart disease	1787	1708
Cancer	1061*	986
Cerebrovascular diseases (strokes)	604	577

* Includes benign neoplasms.

SOURCES: Barker, R.A.J., Dewdney, M.G. Kovar, C. Schwenger, B. Stocking, and B.A. Schroeder. "Health care for the elderly in five english speaking countries: Basic data set." Paper presented at the *Commonwealth Fund Forum*, London, England, 1983, Table 6, and U.S. Bureau of the Census *America in Transition: An Aging Society*, Current Population Report Series P-23, No. 128. Washington, D.C.: U.S. Government Printing Office, 1983.

Future advances in combating diseases will have an unknown effect on mortality. They could lead to healthier elderly cohorts who, nevertheless, have the same life expectancy as those today. On the other hand, new diseases could develop, or existing diseases could become more prevalent. Some (U.S. Bureau of the Census, 1983) speculate that, if life expectancy increases beyond the age of 85, we could see a delay in the onset of these illnesses but without a shortening of the period of illness. Others (Fries, 1984) talk about a society in which elderly persons would be relatively healthy with a short period of severe illness just prior to death. This concept is referred to as the compression of morbidity.

Chronic conditions need not translate to limitations on activity or functional disability. Measures of functioning are popular because they provide a social definition of health and permit measurement in terms of departures from normal role functioning, rather than from primarily medical or biological criteria (Stewart et al., 1977; Reynolds et al., 1974).

There is general consensus on the definition of functional disability. It refers to functional limitations on the performance of normal daily role activities as a result of illness or injury. The activities chosen for assessing functional ability usually include activities of daily living (Katz et al., 1963; Sullivan, 1971) or general questions asking about restricted activity.

Studies vary considerably in the specific items used to measure activities of daily living, making it difficult to generalize. Nevertheless, Wolinsky (1983) reports from the 1978 United States National Health Interview Survey that 54.8 percent of those persons aged 65 and over indicate no limitations to their activity. The figure from the Canada Health Survey is only slightly higher (61.8 percent). (See Table 3-1.)

Some, such as Lawton and Brody (1969), and, more recently, Branch and Jette (1981), distinguish between basic activities, such as eating, dressing, personal mobility and going to the toilet and those that are more instrumental, such as housekeeping, transportation, food preparation, grocery shopping and personal business affairs. Branch and Jette report that over 80 percent are able to take care of their own basic activities but less than 20 percent are assistance-free when it comes to instrumental activities. In other words, although many individuals do not require assistance and are self-sufficient in activities such as dressing and eating, many do require assistance and are dependent on others for activities such as housekeeping and transportation.

The finding that a small proportion of elderly persons has severe disabilities is supported with data from the United States on the housebound. Kutza and Zweibel (1982) report from the 1976-77 Health Interview Survey that about 17 percent cannot carry out a major normal activity, 7 percent are housebound and 3 percent are bedridden at home.

Nevertheless, functioning does decline with age. The Canada Health Survey reveals fully 91 percent of those aged less than 65 to be disability free compared with 61.8 percent of those 65+. Similiarly, the 1981 United States National Health Interview Survey reports 90 percent of those less than 65 having no limitation on activities due to chronic conditions compared with 54.8 percent of those 65+.

In sum, both the number of chronic conditions and the extent of functional disability tend to increase with age. However, chronic conditions do not necessarily translate into functional disability. Furthermore, while most elderly persons have some functional difficulty, only a minority appear to have functioning problems with basic activities of daily living, such as eating, personal mobility and toileting. That is, while over three-quarters of elderly persons have at least one chronic condition, only about half experience some functional disability. Even fewer, about one-fifth, require assistance with basic activities.

While none of these measures refers specifically to pain and discomfort, it is assumed that severe pain results in functional disability. It is then measured to the extent that it interferes with activities of daily living.

Mental Health

Changes in mental health as we age are less straightforward. Mental health encompasses numerous aspects, including cognitive, psychological and emotional functioning. It is known to be related to both physiological conditions and social environments.

Physiologically, evidence appears more or less conclusive that there is loss in both the visual and auditory senses as we age, with some minor losses of sensitivity as well in taste, balance, touch and the perception of pain (Horn, 1978; Gutman, 1983). Such losses can affect psychological well-being and can lead to a misdiagnosis of mental confusion. Changes in behavior, especially lack of response and a tendency to walk into things, are sometimes assumed to be mental in origin, when in fact they are due to declines in auditory and visual senses.

In terms of cognition, or intelligence, it would appear that groups of older people do less well than groups of younger people, regardless of the test used, and especially when speed of completion is held constant. However, individuals who are followed over time into old age show little or no intellectual loss. That is, the differences between younger and older groups are accounted for, to a large extent, in terms of cohort differences, especially differences in levels of formal education (Cattel, 1971; Horn, 1978). While much research is being conducted on various aspects of cognitive structuring, memory and learning, few conclusive generalizations can be made at this time. There is no conclusive evidence of dramatic declines in intellectual functioning or memory due to age. There is a higher risk of diseases that can affect memory.

Concern surrounding the loss of intellectual function is long-standing. It is the area commonly referred to as senility, or dementia. The two most common causes of dementia are Alzheimer's disease, affecting more than 50 percent of all people with dementia, and vascular or multi-infarct dementia, accounting for another 20 percent. The remaining causes of dementia are Pick's disease, alcoholism, multiple sclerosis, Huntington's and others. Multi-infarct dementia (as a result of strokes) should become less frequent in the future with reduction in the risk factors for strokes. In contrast, there is no known prevention or cure for Alzheimer's disease. It is a dementia with a progressive course of four to twelve years and is fatal. One of the difficulties is that there is no conclusive diagnostic test other than autopsy (McLachlin, 1983; Eisdorfer and Cohen, 1982).

Recently, concern has been expressed over the apparent increase in dementia, generally, and Alzheimer's disease, specifically. But in fact only 5 percent to 6 percent of elderly people are estimated to have dementia (Roth, 1978; Bergmann, 1980). That is, the current concern over increases in dementia is not due to greater proportions of elderly people suffering from dementia, rather it is a reflection of greater numbers of elderly people and therefore greater numbers with these problems. Nevertheless, one should not lose sight of the fact that it is a very small percentage of the total. It is, however, true that the likelihood of dementia increases as one ages (Pitt, 1982).

Increasing attention is being paid to depression during old age. A major difficulty in this area is proper diagnosis. Depression can vary from mild to severe and a variety of somatic symptoms may be present. Difficulties stem from the fact that nearly everyone experiences decreased mood levels sometimes and that more severe forms of depression have additional symptoms. These can include poor appetite, loss of weight, sleep disturbance, poor concentration, difficulty in remembering things and feelings of hopelessness. Standard measurement instruments ask people to respond to various statements about their energy level, feelings of helplessness and so on. (See, for example, the Geriatric Depression Scale, Yesavage et al., 1983, and the CES-D Scale, Radloff, 1977.) Clinical diagnoses are also used. Differing symptoms, together with the belief that confusion accompanies old age, may lead to incorrect diagnoses of senile dementia. Estimates of the prevalence and incidence of depression are considered unreliable for these reasons. Nevertheless, it is particularly important to recognize depression because, in most instances, it is responsive to treatment.

Despite the difficulties of classification, there is evidence to suggest that depression is a problem among a significant minority of elderly persons. Studies of community-living elderly cite between 13-15 percent with symptoms of depression (Blazer and Williams, 1980; Gurland et al., 1983). Both infirm homebound elderly persons and institutionalized elderly persons have been identified as having higher rates of depression than others living in the community.

Whether or not depression is more prevalent among older people than among younger age groups is much debated. One view Davison and Neale (1982) argue that the prevalence is higher among elderly persons. In a review of cross-sectional and clinical studies on depression, Hirshfeld and Cross (1982) conclude that depression is more prevalent in young adulthood. This is confirmed in a recent Canadian study (Barnes and Chappell, 1982), showing a negative correlation between age and depression.

Thus while senile dementia is still a major concern of old age, it is a small proportion that suffers from the illness at any one time. This does not obviate the effect on those who do have it, or on their family and friends. In terms of numbers, depression affects more elderly individuals than does dementia. Because it is usually reversible, it is a critical area for accurate diagnosis. Unlike chronic conditions, functional disability and dementia, and contrary to much popular belief, the likelihood of depression does not appear to increase during old age.

Subjective Health

Self-perceptions of health have received attention in relation to overall well-being, as well as to objective measures of health status. The literature reports a rather consistent general relationship between physical and mental incapacity. However, numerous surveys now exist that indicate a better subjective rating of health than would be assumed from the more objective measures of disease and disability.

Surveys reveal that most elderly people perceive their health to be good or excellent. Wolinsky (1983) reports that 30.2 percent of those aged 65 and over in the United States Health Interview Survey (which is representative of the non-institutionalized population) report poor or fair health, 41.1 percent good health and 28.3 percent excellent health. Comparable national figures could not be located for Canada. Local studies reveal comparable figures (Chappell, 1983a; Government of Manitoba, 1973).

Comparable figures are difficult to find for either country for those aged less than 65. Wolinsky (1983) reports only 12.3 percent of the entire U.S. population (those younger and older than age 65) rate their health as fair or poor. This is substantially less than the 30 percent of those aged 65 and over. While sufficient data are lacking, it would appear that more individuals rate their health as being worse when they are older, but not to the extent one would expect, based on the figures for chronic conditions, or even for functional disability. Subjective health ratings are, however, consistent with figures for those functionally disabled in basic activities of daily living, that is, those considered severely disabled.

A considerable amount of attention has also been devoted to the concept of life satisfaction, morale or general well-being in the gerontological literature. This focus reflects a concern with the quality of life of older persons, as well as a recognition that measures of specific aspects of health do not necessarily inform us how individuals experience the effects of health nor of the social circumstances of their lives.

Life satisfaction, the individual's appraisal of life past and present, has been measured using numerous instruments, most notably the Life Satisfaction Index – A and the Life Satisfaction Index – Z (Neugarten et al., 1961; Adams, 1969) and global questions used as single indicators. Marshall and Tindale (1978-9) argue that this emphasis on studying life satisfaction and morale has resulted from a focus on individuals rather than on the social context. It is no doubt also a reflection of current methodologies, which permit easier measurement of such concepts than of more macrosocietal ones.

Global indicators of happiness, such as "Taking all things together, how would you say things are these days? Would you say that you are very happy, happy, so-so, or not too happy?", tend to indicate very few respond with "not too happy." Drawing on 1972 and 1973 national probability samples in the United States, Sprietzer and Snyder (1974) report only 19 percent of those aged 65 and over fall in the negative category. One-third (33 percent) report being very happy. A 1978 U.S. National Survey similarly reports about one-third (31 percent) of those aged 60 and over as very happy. These data suggest only about 8 percent are in the not-very-happy group (Campbell, 1981). See Table 3-3.

National data from the Canada Health Survey, which used Bradburn's Affect Balance Scale (Bradburn, 1969) rather than a single indicator, reveal few Canadian elderly people on the negative end of the scale (7.1 percent) and more in the positive category (53.3 percent). Despite variation between studies, it would appear that some, again a small percent, of elderly people have low life satisfaction.

The 1978 U.S. National data (Campbell, 1981) reveal no differences in life satisfaction between those over and those under 65. The data from the Canada Health Survey reveal virtually no differences (53.3 percent of those aged 65 and over report positively versus 50.0 percent for those less than 65). That is, life dissatisfaction, like depression, does not appear to increase with age. It is noteworthy that it is the more attitudinal, or psychological, measures that do not reflect general declines as we age, or during old age.

In summary, there are declines in health with age: in physical health, mental health and functional ability. Nevertheless, at any one time, it is a minority of elderly persons who suffer from severe, and incapacitating, physical and mental health conditions. In addition, morale and perceptions of health among those who are elderly tend not to be at all bad. There are a minority who

TABLE 3-3

SUBJECTIVE WELL-BEING

1) Psychological well-being of those 65 and over, Canada, 1978-79

Bradburn's Affect Balance Scale	% 65+
Positive	53.3
Mixed	39.6
Negative	7.1
	100.0

2) Perceived happiness of those 60 and over, United States, 1976 and 1978

1976	% 65+
Very happy	28
Not too happy	14

1978	
Very happy	31
Not too happy	8

SOURCES: Health and Welfare Canada and Statistics Canada *Canada Health Survey* Ottawa, Ont.: Minister of Supply and Services, 1981, Table 68, p. 133 and Campbell, A. *The Sense of Well-Being in America* New York, N.Y.: McGraw-Hill Book Company, 1981, Appendix Table 9, p. 245.

have low morale and who perceive their health to be poor. In other words, the declines that accompany aging are not necessarily predictive of incapacity either in functioning or general well-being.

This is not to be interpreted as an argument that health status in old age is always enjoyable or that improvements are neither necessary nor desirable. Rather, it is intended only as an effort to draw a realistic image of health status, broadly defined, with aging. Such a realistic portrayal is considered essential for an adequate understanding of both the experience of aging and health care needs of an aging population. It is equally important to ascertain whether, and what types of, improvements are required and desired.

The increasing proportions of elderly persons then does mean increasing numbers and proportions of people with declining health, but not necessarily incapacitating illness. There are, furthermore, important age and gender differences among elderly persons. These are discussed in the next section, before we turn to a discussion of dependency and interdependency.

AGE AND GENDER DIFFERENCES IN HEALTH

Age Differences

Because of important age differences among those 65 and over, many geron-
tologists refer to the young-old and the old-old. Frequently age 75 is used
as the age of demarcation and less frequently age 70 or 80 (Neugarten, 1975).
It is becoming increasingly common to distinguish three groups: young-old,
middle-old and old-old, following an awareness that the dichotomy (young-
old and old-old) still masks important differences.

Indeed, some existing research (Chappell and Havens, 1980) suggests that
while the use of age 75 to dichotomize the groups can be appropriate, it is
not always so. For women, these findings suggest a trichotomy of less than
75, 75 to 84, and 85 and over would reveal important differences. For elderly
men, age 80 rather than age 75 may be a more appropriate marker for a
dichotomy. This was true, for example, for perceived well-being, perceived
health, frequency of contact with friends and proximity of nearest relative.
This was not always the case, though. For mental health status and perceived
economic security, for example, similar results emerge irrespective of the age
breakdown utilized.

Given the heterogeneity of elderly persons, many of the stereotypes of
decline that are applied to those aged 65 and over are more appropriate for
the old-old rather than for those who are younger. However, as noted in the
previous chapter, not only is the proportion of elderly persons increasing, but
the proportion of old elderly is also increasing and will continue to do so for
some time.

Not surprisingly, health continues to decline among elderly persons as they
age. Among those 65 and over, with increasing age comes deterioration in
health in the form of chronic illness, physical health problems and mental
health problems. Unfortunately, most national statistics do not provide detailed
breakdowns by age for those 65 and over. Data from the Canada Health Survey
(Health and Welfare Canada and Statistics Canada, 1978-79) show that 20.2
percent of those between the ages of 65 and 69 compared with 16.5 percent
of those age 70 and over, report no chronic conditions. The figures for those
with one or two chronic conditions are 50.5 percent and 48.7 percent respectively. The figures for those with three or more chronic conditions are 29.3
percent and 34.8 percent respectively. No doubt statistics comparing those
less than and greater than age 75 or 80 would reveal greater differences.

Similarly, functional disability increases as we age. Data from the United
States reveal that it is not until they are aged 85 or over that about half the
population report being unable to carry on a major activity. Further distinc-

tions can be made in terms of the areas of assistance. For example, 18 percent of those 85 and over need help bathing compared with 4 percent of those 64 to 84 years old. Similarly, 11 percent of those over 85 need help dressing compared with 3 percent of the elderly less than 85 (U.S. Bureau of the Census, 1983). Data from the Canada Health Survey show that 65.2 percent of Canadians aged 65 to 69 compared with 59.7 percent of those aged 70 and over have no limitation to their activity. The figures for limitation to a major activity are 22.8 percent and 28.6 percent respectively.

Similarly, the old-old are more likely to suffer from senile dementia than the young elderly. Estimates hover around 2 – 3 percent for those aged 65 to 74, 4 – 6 percent for those between the ages of 75 to 79, and around 20 percent for those aged 80 and over (Roth, 1978; Pitt, 1982). These figures are only estimates, but they indicate increased likelihood of dementia as the old themselves age.

The same declines, however, are not evident in attitudinal and subjective measures of health. Declines in physical health, functioning and mental status are not translated to the subjective level to the extent one might expect. An adjustment to changing situations and an acceptance, or accommodation, of the inevitable are suggested by these data.

As Ferraro (1980) notes, elderly persons seem to rate their own health with regard to their age and expectations. When assessing their health, elderly persons compare themselves to a reference group of other persons of similar age. Such an interpretation is further supported by the finding that self-ratings of health have been found to be *inversely* related to age. Even though the old-old (75+) report more health problems, they tend to be more positive in rating their health (Riley and Foner, 1968).

Although some, such as Maddox and Douglas (1973), argue that global questions, such as self-perceptions of health, may be influenced by optimism, such reasoning does not account for the apparent greater "optimism" among the old-old compared with the young-old. It would appear to be related to an acceptance of their declining health, given their age, as well as the fact that most of these changes take place gradually, so the individual has time to adjust to them. With increasing age, decline in health status is accompanied by attitudinal, or subjective, acceptance of this fact.

These expectations may change with future cohorts. Easterlin (1978) argues that the expectations of today's elderly persons developed through comparisons with their own early life experiences and the experiences of their parents. Given old age security payments, a universal health care system and a generally higher standard of living, elderly people today have a low level of perceived relative deprivation. In addition, in contrast with others their age who have died, they are the survivors. The extent to which expectations will change is, however, still unknown.

The increase in the old-old suggests that attention should be directed to their health and health care concerns to a greater extent than seems appropriate from examining those 65 and over without distinguishing among age groups. This point also demonstrates the need to ensure the collection and analysis of adequate data, and it indicates the necessity of going beyond personal experience and common stereotypes for planning and policy purposes.

Gender Differences

Similarly, there are important gender differences evident in the health of elderly individuals. As noted earlier, women tend to live longer than men. However, they tend to have more days per year of restricted activity, more days of bed disability, more doctor's visits, higher expenditures for health care and higher rates of institutionalization than men (Clark and Collishaw, 1975; Health and Welfare Canada and Statistics Canada, 1981; Atchley, 1976a).

These gender differences tend to be as true among elderly persons as among those who are younger. In the Canada Health Survey, for example, elderly women are less likely to report no chronic conditions (15.3 versus 21.0 percent) or to report one or two chronic conditions (48 versus 51.2 percent) but are more likely to report three or more chronic conditions (36.8 versus 27.6 percent) than are men.

Functional disability is less clear cut, partly because of the gender bias within the measures themselves, although this is less true in more recent research. Some of these data report limitations in major activity, interpreted as paid labour for men and housework for women. Such wording can bias "disability" towards men. Many of the disability indices measure actual assistance with various activities of daily living rather than ability to perform the activity. The extent to which women prepare meals and clean the house as part of their roles, while men do not, will also bias the instrument so that men emerge as more disabled. Given these difficulties with the measurement instruments, it is not surprising to see few studies reporting gender differences or men appearing to be more disabled.

However, even among studies avoiding these difficulties, the findings are not consistent. According to the Canada Health Survey, among elderly persons, men are as likely as women to report no limitation of activities (59.2 percent versus 63.8 percent) or limitation to major activity (24.8 percent versus 27.9 percent). The 1981 United States National Health Interview Survey data indicate that elderly men are more likely to experience limitations in major activity compared to elderly women (45 percent versus 35 percent). The data further indicate that elderly women (57 percent) are more likely to be disability free than elderly men (50 percent).

Senile dementia appears to be more common among women than men, when looking at Alzheimer's disease. Multi-infarct dementia is more common in men (Pitt, 1982; Roth, 1978).

Both Ferraro (1980) and Fillenbaum (1979) report better perceptions of health among elderly women than men, despite more disability and illness among women. Harris (1978) and the Canada Health Survey report that elderly women are no more likely than elderly men to perceive their health as fair, or poor, or report general unhappiness.

The tendency of women to report poorer health than men has led to much discussion about the meaning of these differences. Whether these differences between men and women are real or artificial is unknown. Men may be more likely to deny health problems because of sociocultural factors and not because of "real" limitations. Marcus and Siegel (1982), for example, hypothesize that gender differences may be due to the fixed-role effect; that is, women may report a greater use of health services because they have fewer work and time constraints, making it easier for them to visit the doctor. Among elderly people one would expect such role differences to be less striking between the genders, although one could argue that a lifetime of such differences continues into old age. This explanation, however, has not been adequately tested to establish that such an effect operates independently of the need for care.

Other explanations of reported gender differences include a greater willingness on the part of women to report illness, a greater ability on the part of women to adopt sick-role behavior and a real difference in health (Cleary et al., 1982; Coulton and Frost, 1982). Some observers suggest that men experience higher mortality, and women experience higher morbidity (Gove and Hughes, 1979). While women tend to report more symptoms of ill health and use services more than do men, whether or not these indicate differences in health is not known.

While findings are not always consistent and measures sometimes biased, it would appear that elderly women report more symptoms and disability than men. This seems most certain in relation to chronic conditions. Findings for functional ability are less conclusive. The objective conditions do not necessarily translate to the subjective level. The *interpretation* of the above differences is even less definite.

The gender differences revealed here, in conjunction with the age differences discussed immediately beforehand, are especially relevant in light of the increasing proportions of old people in society, the increasing proportions of old-old and the predominance of women among the elderly population, especially among the old elderly. Increasing attention on women, especially upon old-old women, is warranted, given the changing demographic structure and the age and gender differences just highlighted.

It must be emphasized once again that among elderly men and women, and even among old-elderly men and women, most cope. Most are not totally disabled. The myths that all, or even most, elderly people lose their capacity for self-sufficiency and have damage to the brain as a result of aging are simply not true.

Importantly, knowing the elderly population's health status does not necessarily tell us the prevalence of dependence, or requirement for care, among that population. While the concept of independence/dependence is a central reason for concern over health, its definition and measurement remain elusive. The following section examines the concept.

INDEPENDENCE/
INTERDEPENDENCE/
DEPENDENCE

The dictionary defines *dependence* as "relying on another for support" and *independence* as "not requiring or relying on something else or on someone else" (Merriam-Webster Dictionary, 1974). These definitions are not sufficient for our understanding of the term, since the meaning of "relying on another for support" is no less vague than the term *dependence* itself.

Kalish (1977) understands the inherent complexity of defining the term when he writes, "No one is independent; although many people work very hard at being 'dependent on no one'." An individual may appear to be totally independent of others in some aspects of her or his life, but that same individual may be totally dependent in other ways. For example, one may be able to dress and undress oneself without assistance and therefore be considered independent in this task. At the same time, one may rely on others for going up and down the stairs and be considered dependent in this task.

The complexity of the concept is obvious from the different types of dependency that are discussed. Van den Heuvel (1976) suggests that dependency can take any of numerous forms: physical, mental, emotional, cognitive, social, economic and environmental. He then reclassifies these into three broad groupings: practical/physical helplessness, interpersonal or social powerlessness and psychological need. Clark (1972) describes the concept in terms of six types: socioeconomic, developmental or transitional, neurotic, dependency of crisis, dependency of nonreciprocal roles and as a culturally-conditioned character trait. Blenkner (1977) argues that dependencies may be divided into four categories: economic, physical, mutual and social.

As these authors note, dependencies are intermixed and interacting, occurring simultaneously as well as at different times and with different impacts. For example, the individual who requires assistance going up and down stairs is dependent physically but also environmentally, since an environment free of stairs would remove the need for assistance. Similarly, one's impairment may be emotional, but this may lead to the need for assistance in the social, physical and economic areas.

Physical Dependency

Despite the complexity of the concept and the endless areas in which one may be dependent, a major focus in the gerontological literature has been on physical dependency. Physical dependency is frequently discussed and measured in terms of activities of daily living. It is these types of needs that tend to be assessed for the receipt of health and social services.

Even for these physical activities, a precise scientific definition eludes the investigator. As Kane and Kane (1981) point out, independence in the task of bathing might be defined as the ability to lather and rinse the whole body, including the back and all extremities. Yet few people, irrespective of age, reach their backs without the help of a long-handled scrub brush. The point is that imposing an overly rigid definition of ability for independent functioning defeats the purpose.

While a large number of instruments exist to measure this concept, the Katz Index of ADL is one of the best known and most widely used (Table 3-4). This index is an evaluation of functional independence or dependence, defined in terms of whether or not the individual performs the task without supervision, direction or active personal assistance (with some exceptions, as noted in the accompanying table). It is based on performance rather than the ability of the individual. In other words, a person who refused to perform a function would be considered as not performing that function, even though he or she may have the ability to do so (Katz et al., 1963). It might be noted that this measure, like similar ones, incorporates a continuum of assistance, reflecting the meaning the concept has in general usage.

Variations occur in the measures for functional disability. Some, such as the Index of Living Skills (ILS) (Shanas et al., 1968), are not unidimensional. Earlier research shows the ILS measures two basic underlying constructs, one referring to more arduous or heavier tasks and the other to lighter tasks. However, Shanas' Index of Disability has been found to be internally consistent and reliable, measuring only relatively light tasks (Chappell, 1981).

Another distinction within various activities of daily living measures mentioned earlier in this chapter is that between basic, or hands on, care and instrumental or less basic types of assistance. Branch and Jette (1981) and Danis and Silverstone (1981) make this distinction. The distinction between basic and instrumental activities is potentially of importance. This is a relatively unresearched area at the present time, but one that is receiving increased attention.

Other Types of Dependencies

Physical dependency is not the only type of dependency that result in need for care. Mental disorders, or psychological/emotional dependencies, while characteristic of only a minority of elderly persons, can lead to total care if impairment is extreme. While assessments of mental capacity are made frequently by clinicians and by specialists, such as psychiatrists, there exists a plethora of quick-answer instruments that can be used by nonexperts. A longtime favorite is the Mental Status Questionnaire (Kahn et al., 1961), where the individual is asked to answer a series of factual questions, such as "What is your mailing address?" and "What is the year?". A more recent modification of that instrument is the Short Mental Status Questionnaire developed by Robertson et al. (1982). (See Table 3-5.)

TABLE 3-4

KATZ INDEX OF ADL

Activity	Independent	Dependent
Bathing (sponge, shower, tub)	Assistance only in bathing a single part (as back or disabled extremity) or bathes self completely.	Assistance in bathing more than one part of the body; assistance in getting in and out of tub or does not bathe self.
Dressing	Gets clothes from closets and drawers; puts on clothes, outer garments, braces; manages fasteners; act of tying shoes is excluded.	Does not dress self or remains party undressed.
Going to toilet	Gets to toilet; gets on and off toilet; arranges clothes; cleans organs of excretion (may manage own bed-pan used at night only and may not be using mechanical supports).	Uses bedpan or commode or receives assistance in getting to and using toilet.
Transfers	Moves in and out of bed independently and moves in and out of chair in-dependently (may or may not be using mechanical supports).	Assistance in moving in or out of bed and/or chair; does not perform one or more transfers.
Continence	Urination and defecation entirely self-controlled.	Partial or total incontinence in urination or defecation; partial or total control by enemas, catheters or reg-ulated use of urinals and/or bedpans.
Feeding	Gets food from plate or its equivalent into mouth; (precutting of meat and preparation of food, as buttering bread, are ex-cluded from evaluation).	Assistance in act of feeding (see independent state); does not eat at all or parenteral feeding.

SOURCE: Katz, S., A.B. Ford, R.W. Moskowitz, B.A. Jackson and M.W. Jaffee "Studies of illness in the aged, the index of ADL: A standardized measure of biological and psycho-social function." *Journal of the American Medical Association*, Vol. 185, 1963, p. 94. Reprinted by permission.

‖   TABLE 3-5   ‖

SHORT MENTAL STATUS QUESTIONNAIRE

1 What is your full name?	Correct forename and surname
2. What is your address?	Correct street address and municipality
3. What year is this?	Correct year
4. What month is this?	Correct month
5. What day of the week is this?	Correct day of week (not date)
6. How old are you?	Correct age; verify by another person, or from date of birth
7. What is the name of the Prime Minister of Canada (or President of the United States)?	Correct answer to include surname of current Prime Minister or President
8. When did World War I start?	Year 1914
9. Remember these three items. I will ask you to recall them in a few minutes...bed, chair, window. Have subject repeat items correctly before proceeding.	
10. Count backwards from 20 to 1. (If necessary like this, 20, 19 and so on)	No error. Any uncorrected error = 0
11. Repeat the three items I asked you to remember.	All items correct = 1 Any uncorrected error = 0

SOURCE: Adapted from Robertson, D., K. Rockwood and P. Stolee "A short mental status questionnaire." *Canadian Journal on Aging*, Vol. 1, No. 1 and 2, 1982, p. 16-20. Reprinted by permission.

As physical and mental impairments can relate to and interact with one another, so too economic factors can be confounded with the others. It is now well-known that living in disadvantaged economic situations is related to poorer physical health, various types of diseases, lowered survivorship and poorer nutritional status. Frequently, the economic situation of elderly people is an extension of that experienced at younger ages or a worsening of their earlier situation. The extent to which the effects are cumulative is unknown, although there is some evidence to suggest they could be (Kozma and Stones, 1978; Larson, 1978).

While actual monthly or yearly income is a relatively easy measurement of economic circumstances, the concept is much more complex than gathering such a dollar figure. There are, for example, those who maintain that quality of life among elderly persons is not as low as income figures would lead one to believe (Cheal, 1983). These persons argue that elderly people can maintain a comparable standard of living on less money than is required for a younger individual who is working.

In addition, dollar values of government transfer payments and private pension plans for elderly people may or may not be included, depending on the study. Noncash transfers are difficult to put a dollar value on, since they come in the form of services rather than money. Further, subjective perception of one's economic situation is not necessarily related to dollar income. There can be two individuals, each with the same amount of objective income but, depending on life-styles, expectations, the life-styles of friends and so on, one individual may feel relatively poor, while the other may feel much more comfortable, financially.

Social Dependency

While there are a multitude of different dependencies and interdependencies, the last one we shall discuss here is social dependence. The social category is perhaps the most inherently related to the concept of interdependency, while at the same time the most elusive to objectify and define. It is also perhaps the best for pointing to the social component of the terms dependency, interdependency or independency, as its very meaning is socially derived.

Recently there has been a surge of gerontological literature on social aspects of the lives of elderly persons under the rubric of social support, social networks and social interaction. A clear consensus on the meanings of these terms has not arisen. Despite the variety of terminology, there seems to be general consensus that the social aspect includes a subjective dimension, which may be referred to as the quality of interaction. Social interaction within the informal network involves, or at least is assumed to involve, a quality of interaction that is not expected from a formal relationship. It is this quality of interaction, this human element, that Schmidt (1981) uses to distinguish informal from formal care.

It is this quality of the interaction that also tends to elude research and study. It is now well accepted that the actual numbers of people with whom we interact, the frequency with which we interact with them and other such quantitative measures of interaction are not of primary importance for the meaning of that interaction in our lives. It is the qualitative dimension that needs to be studied (Strain and Chappell, 1982; Conner et al., 1979).

Since everyone engages in interactions of varying kinds and degrees virtually every day, it is particularly difficult to know when such interaction indicates social dependency. Indeed, even though the term interdependency has, by and large, not been popular in the gerontological literature, it is a more apt description than the term dependency or independency. While some may speak of social dependency as less equal, or less balanced, relationships (see, for example, Van den Heuval, 1976), it is clear that what some people would interpret as a dependent social relationship, others would not.

Similarly, what would be considered a life of relative social isolation by some is considered the optimal living situation by others. For example, when a mother does shopping for a daughter who is busy in paid labour, or busy at home with small children, this could be considered a form of assistance. It is unlikely, however, that this would be interpreted as a care situation or that the daughter would be considered dependent on the mother in the sense the term is being used here.

The term is further confounded by its use at the societal, as well as at the individual, level. Social dependency in the former use refers to the relationships and situations created for the individual by the structure of the society. The fact that elderly persons are excluded from paid labour and therefore tend to be disadvantaged economically, the fact that poor people have worse health, the fact that the built environment tends to be most accessible to younger adults with good mobility, and not to older people who are less agile and mobile, are all forms of social dependency in the larger sense.

It is, nevertheless, true that there is an accepted commonsensical understanding of the term within everyday society at the individual level. It is equally true that the term eludes precise scientific definition, unless it becomes so narrow as to lose its general applicability. What is of primary importance is that the term refers to the complexity of interaction between the different spheres of dependency and that the process by which a particular individual becomes defined as dependent in any of its aspects is itself a social definition.

It is equally important to become aware of and understand the concept used and the exact measure implemented when reading the literature and research in this area. For most research purposes, the term measured will be a specific type of activity, such as assistance actually received in certain activities of daily living. It may not include other activities of daily living, may not include the person's actual ability to perform these tasks, and, in all likelihood, it will not take into account interaction with other spheres, such as the economic and the environmental. Such literature can still be important and useful, provided the reader recognizes the specific areas to which the data apply.

Finally, a large component of the concept necessarily includes subjective perceptions of the situation. For example, if some elderly individuals believe that they are coping well without specific types of assistance from either friends or formal agencies, this may lead them to refuse offers of assistance should they arise, and could well prevent them from seeking such assistance. Similarly, others could perceive themselves as requiring assistance, while the informal network of family and friends and/or a particular formal agency could consider them capable of fulfilling these functions for themselves.

‖ CONCLUSIONS ‖

This chapter has examined health status as people age. Cumulative knowledge supports the notion that most aspects of health tend to decrease as we grow older. It does not, however, portray a picture of old age that is all bleak. Not all chronic conditions translate into disability, and dementia strikes only a minority of elderly individuals. Attitudes and perceptions and dimensions of subjective well-being tend not to reflect these physical declines. Indeed, there is some suggestion of a negative relationship between objective health indicators and subjective well-being, especially among the old elderly.

These findings tend to be explained in terms of expectations for one's age, reference groups of others one's own age (including those who have not survived as long, as well as those with worse health), the tendency for the onset of conditions to be gradual, allowing time for adaptation, and cohort beliefs about adequate standards of living. This discrepancy between the physiological reality of aging and the subjective perceptions of quality of life, however, requires greater in-depth study. It is an important issue in aging. It suggests the adaptability of the human species, but it is not well understood.

The relevance of health status in the lives of elderly persons is confounded further with the fact that health status does not necessarily translate readily into dependency or independency. The need for a broad definition of health becomes clear in an examination of this term. It also clarifies the necessity for studying health care within a context that includes, but is not exclusive to, physiological health.

The next two chapters extend this thinking through an examination of social involvements as we age. Chapters 6 and 7 then deal explicitly with the formal health care system.

■ CHAPTER 4 ■

ROLE TRANSITIONS

During the 1950s, and 1960s, much was written about the "roleless" role of elderly persons (Burgess, 1960; Parsons, 1954; Tibbitts, 1954). It was said that they had no function in society. Men had been involved in paid labour and upon retirement lost their major life role. Women, upon the death of their spouses, were said to lose their major role, that of wife. Women, because they had a greater life expectancy and often lived in households geographically separate from their children, were believed to experience an empty nest syndrome. Role exits (completion of childrearing tasks, retirement and widowhood) led some to the conclusion that elderly people had no place in society, resulting in detrimental effects on these individuals.

This chapter examines these three role exits and existing knowledge about adjustment to them. It becomes evident that most elderly people do adjust to these transitions in their lives and that, retirement, children's departure and widowhood are not as negative and traumatic as once believed, especially after the events are past. The extent to which volunteering replaces these roles is examined briefly. Prior to looking at the effects of retirement, however, we shall look at some brief historical background on the development of social security programs as they relate to retirement. Some background on the development of the legislation which has resulted in the social definition of retirement at age 65 is informative.

‖ RETIREMENT ‖

The Development of
Social Security
Legislation

A clear-cut chronological age arose as the start of old age due to the advent of social security in the income area. It was not until well into the 1900's that either the American or Canadian governments entered this area in a significant way, although social security activity was evident a century earlier. In Canada, for example, Workmen's Compensation laws were generally adopted in various provinces between 1851 and 1928. In the United States, around 1875, the American Railway Express Co. was one of the first companies to offer old age pensions (Schlabach, 1969). Workmen's Compensation was started in practically all states between 1911 and 1915 (Witte, 1962).

After World War I, during the 1920's, old age pensions became an important political issue (Cassidy, 1943; Bryden, 1974). During this time, federal governments provided extensive services to war veterans. There were declining birth rates, slowing of immigration, increases in life expectancy, and injury incurred to many able-bodied in the war, who were no longer able to care for aging family members. Nevertheless, during the 1920's, old age relief, like other forms of relief, fell first to private charity, then to municipalities and states or provinces and, finally to the federal government (Schlabach, 1969).

For both the United States and Canada, the Depression demonstrated the social nature of human need (Irving, 1980). According to Bryden (1974), poverty among the aged was so widespread during the 1920's that it simply could not be ignored. It was becoming evident that many people could not save systematically, and that unemployment was another type of industrial hazard whose whole cost the victim should not have to bear alone. Why should industry exploit labor for profit but share none of the burden of unemployment and old age? The drain on municipal and provincial or state coffers was too high.

In addition, other countries were establishing old age pensions. For example, a non-contributory Old Age Pensions Act was passed in the United Kingdom in 1908, effective in 1909. The Act gave pensions scaled to income to those who were 70 years of age and over; who were residents of Britain; who were not in prison; who were not receiving poor relief except medical poor relief; and who had been habitually employed. That is, pensions were subject to a moral (i.e. for those morally deserving aged poor) and a means test. Contributory schemes were rejected because they would not help those most in need (Gilbert, 1966). The Act represented Britain's entrance into the area of social welfare legislation. (In 1940, pensions were given to men aged 65 and women aged 60 regardless of means.)

The federal government in Canada entered the area of income security a decade later than the United Kingdom; the federal government in the United

States did so a decade later than Canada. Old age pensions were passed in Canada in 1927, with a national, non-contributory, means-tested pension plan at age 70. The passage of the Old Age Pensions Act of 1927 established the principle of public responsibility for ensuring that an aged person received a basic subsistence allowance and represented the first major federal intervention in the social welfare field. It did so while establishing the principles of federal-provincial cost sharing, national program standards and provincial administration of old age pensions (Wilson, 1982; Chappell, 1980a). These principles reflect the federal provincial divisions of authority and decentralized government system in Canada, which contrasts with the centralized system of, for example, Britain.

Once Canada entered the welfare field, legislation evolved fairly regularly. In 1930, the federal share of old age pensions increased to 75 percent because some of the poorer provinces could not pay (Bryden, 1974). In 1951, an amendment to the British North America Act of 1867 (as it was then named) resulted in old age security payments to all persons aged 70 and over, irrespective of means and the old age assistance act provided means-tested assistance starting at age 65. In 1970, the old age security payments were given to everyone aged 65 and over, irrespective of means, and the Guaranteed Income Supplement provided means-tested assistance to those between the ages of 60 and 65.

The 1920's in the United States saw increased interest in the pension issue, with eight states passing optional old-age pension laws. However, legislation at the national level was not passed until eight years later than it was in Canada. It was not until 1934 that a Cabinet committee on economic security was appointed to formulate a comprehensive program. Benefits were introduced in the 1935 U.S. Social Security Act, giving the United States a national, contributory (that is, based on earnings at age 65) old age insurance scheme (Ashford et al., 1978). At the same time, a program of means-tested old age assistance for those 65 years and older was created. Amendments in 1939 extended benefits to survivors and dependents. Amendments in 1950 extended coverage to those who had not paid into the system. In 1970 the Supplementary Security Income program replaced Old Age Assistance to guarantee income to the aged, the blind, and the permanently and totally disabled, subject to an income test and an asset test. None of these amendments changed the central principle of the 1935 Social Security Act, of supporting itself through payroll taxes (Leman, 1977).

Retirement and a social definition of old age at age 65, evolved with national income security legislation which became the benchmark for private pension schemes and mandatory retirement. Although original legislation developed in reaction to widespread poverty and destitution, with increasing life expectancy and mandatory retirement from industrial labor, the lack of paid labor after age 65 has now become a normal life stage.

Without entering into the current debate regarding mandatory versus flexible retirement options, we can say that retirement has become normal. Whether or not mandatory retirement will change with the Charter of Rights and Freedoms and the Constitution Act, 1982, in Canada is unknown. Legislation, which had initially been established as a benefit, became an obligation. Today the majority of elderly people does not have the option of work for pay, despite several years remaining with reasonably good health, and regardless of their preference for paid labor. In many instances this exit from paid labour is abrupt.

The abruptness of this experience, at least in North America, where gradual retirement has not yet become widespread, is in contrast with some of the physiological aspects of aging. Signs of the aging human body appear long before retirement and increase gradually. For most, graying of the hair, deterioration in eyesight and menopause begin long before they reach their sixties. How people react to and experience retirement is the topic of the next section. As it becomes clear, cumulative evidence suggests it is not a particularly devastating experience for most.

The Experience of Retirement

The lack of involvement in paid labor, particularly for men, together with the belief that occupational life provides one of the major contributory roles in society has resulted in one of the major concerns in gerontology. In the 1950s and 1960s the phrase roleless role was used to describe the role exits that were believed to lead to a greater likelihood of isolation (Burgess, 1960; Havighurst, 1952; Tibbitts, 1954). This concern continued into the 1970s, when old age was characterized by gradual pauperization, illness and social isolation (Myles, 1978; Lopata, 1973; Rosow, 1974). Concern over the exclusion of elderly persons from major roles and the concomitant concern that no role replacement is readily available to provide meaningful participation in society is prevalent in gerontological literature. It is well expressed by Blau (1973):

> . . . In the present era, vastly increased numbers of people survive middle age and face the prospect of living for a long time in a society that as yet has found no way to use the qualities, talents, and skills of its aging citizens. . . I question the wisdom of a society that allocates considerable resources and talent to prolonging human life but fails to provide meaningful social roles for older people. That I submit is the critical problem of aging in modern society.

This description of the plight of elderly people in society conjures up images of destitute, lonely individuals with nothing to do, nowhere to go and no useful activity in which to engage. This view assumes relinquishing the occupational role results in loss of prestige, inability to perform and loss of a major source of identity. Miller (1965) argues that, with the loss of occupational identity, an individual finds it extremely difficult to maintain other roles such as head of the household (also see, for example, Cumming and Henry, 1961).

More recently, there has been greater popularity for the view that occupational identity is not the central role for many workers (Atchley, 1976b; Palmore, 1981). Work is only one of many roles. Palmore et al. (1984) argue that retirement is accepted and can be desired. Indeed, it is viewed by some as an opportunity for continuation of other roles and development of new ones. Without denying that elderly individuals could contribute much to paid labor if permitted to do so, research suggests their lives are not as negative and hopeless as presented by some authors.

Much literature indicates leaving paid labor is not as traumatic as once thought. Rather, retirement is increasingly viewed as an expected life event (Friedmann and Orbach, 1974). Recent research on attributes toward, and the consequences of, retirement tend to support these views. Goudy et al. (1980), analyzing data from a panel study of older Iowa males, report an acceptance of retirement as a legitimate stage in the life cycle. At the same time, substantial numbers of the men express preferences for a delay in their own age of retirement, had it been possible. The researchers argue that these findings indicate the need for freedom of choice in the timing of retirement.

A different approach to studying the effects of retirement is used by Martin Matthews and associates (1982) in their study of retired men and women in southwestern Ontario. Respondents were asked to indicate the relative impact of a series of selected life events. The findings indicate that retirement is not as disruptive and critical as one might anticipate when compared with other life events, such as the death of a spouse, the birth of a child or marriage.

Longitudinal data on the effects of retirement confirm this view. Streib and Schneider (1971), using the Cornell Study of Retirement initiated in 1952-53 and spanning seven years, report a sharp reduction in income, as one would anticipate. This decrease, however, is not accompanied by increases in worry about money in the year immediately following retirement. Furthermore, the findings indicate no significant changes in health, feelings of usefulness or satisfaction with life after retirement. Parnes (1981) reports similar findings. Satisfaction with retirement is expressed by a majority, despite reduced levels of income. At least three-fourths report they would retire at the same age, or earlier, if they had it to do over again.

Palmore et al. (1984) examine the effects of retirement, while controlling for a number of preretirement characteristics, using six longitudinal data sets. In other words, they take into account differences that existed prior to retirement in their comparisons of working and retired individuals. Their results indicate that at least half of the difference in income, not surprisingly, is caused by retirement. However, few, if any, of the health differences are caused by this event. In addition, retirement has little effect on social activity, life satisfaction or happiness. When preretirement characteristics are taken into account, leaving paid labor has few effects other than reduced income.

Low income levels during old age, relative to the younger adult years, are well established. The figures for men and women for Canada and the United States appear in Table 4-1. They refer to incomes for all individuals, whether working in paid labor or not. Lower incomes for women, compared with men, are evident throughout all age groupings. Those less than 25 and those over 64 years of age also tend to have low incomes. Women experience less of a proportionate decrease than men as they age, but they start with less.

TABLE 4-1

AVERAGE YEARLY INCOME OF INDIVIDUALS BY AGE AND GENDER, CANADA AND THE UNITED STATES

Age	Canada 1982		United States 1980	
	Male	Female	Male	Female
≤ 19	$ 3,893	$ 3,636	$ 2,728	$ 2,190
20-24	11,902	9,298	8,984	5,918
25-34	21,135	12,582	16,320	7,913
35-44	26,958	12,999	21,485	8,117
45-54	26,998	12,329	21,965	8,012
55-64	23,354	10,139	19,090	7,199
65+	14,221	8,678	10,208	5,798

SOURCES: Statistics Canada, *Income Distribution by Size in Canada, 1982.* Ottawa, Ont.: Minister of Supply and Services, 1984, Catalogue 13-207, Table 55 and U.S. Bureau of the Census, *Statistical Abstract of the United States: 1982-83.* (103rd Edition) Washington, D.C.: U.S. Government Printing Office, 1982, Table 724, p. 438.

Furthermore, a person's feelings of economic security vary somewhat from his or her objective economic situation. In fact, perceptions of economic security emerge as an important predictor of life satisfaction, independent of actual dollar income (Elwell and Maltbie-Crannell, 1981). Atchley (1979) notes that while the amount of income may change from pre- and post- retirement, so too might expenditures and access to other transfer payments. This is the argument that, as people age, their life-styles change.

The view that the relatively little economic deprivation perceived by elderly persons is due to a downward adjustment of needs is disputed by Liang and Fairchild (1979). These authors argue that the concept of relative deprivation is central to an understanding of elderly people's perceptions of their financial situation. The concept assumes that people evaluate themselves and orient their behavior by reference to values, or standards, of other individuals and groups. If elderly people have relatively low incomes but think they are better off than many others in their reference group, they are likely to view their situation as better than can be expected and be relatively satisfied. Similarly, those with more income may be dissatisfied because of a feeling of being worse off than their peers.

Liang and Fairchild argue that an older person's perception of the adequacy of income depends both on current financial situation and disparities in financial status. They derive two central hypotheses: that financial adequacy is not only a function of income but also of feelings of relative deprivation, in reference to others' financial circumstances and to their own previous situations; and that feelings of relative deprivation are in turn related to social status, labor force participation and annual income. Examining data from six studies, they conclude overall support for their hypotheses. Liang and Fairchild note that intrapersonal comparisons (comparisons with one's state at other times) appear to have more impact on financial satisfaction than relative deprivation.

Women and Retirement

One note of caution must be sounded. Much of the available research focuses on the effects of retirement on males, largely because it is males who have tended to be in paid labor. There is a paucity of research on the effects of retirement on women. Szinovacz (1982) points out that research specifically concerned with female retirement was practically unheard of until 1975. Even prior to 1981, when such research started becoming available, it was limited to small, nonrepresentative samples. Not until 1981 did an increased interest in the retirement of females become evident.

Much of the early work on women's adaptation to retirement examines their adaptation to their spouse's retirement, rather than to their own if they were involved in paid labor. Studies that do explore adjustment to retirement were often based on the assumption that the primary role of women is in the home. Adjustment to retirement was therefore supposed to be relatively easy. Retirement was believed to be a more demoralizing experience for men than for women (Blau, 1973).

Later work opposed this view, arguing that women had strong commitment to work and that retirement had the same negative consequences for women as it did for men. Atchley and Corbett (1977) suggest that women may experience greater adjustment if they start their career late and have not reached their career goals at the time of retirement. Some (Atchley, 1976b) report greater adjustment problems for women. Gratton and Haug (1983), however, argue that many of these findings, based on unrepresentative samples, reflect the assumption of retirement as a negative consequence, which has not been upheld by empirical testing. Skoglund's (1979) research suggests that women, like men, adjust to retirement. In other words, retirement is a life event experienced satisfactorily by both genders.

Further research requires larger samples with data on both the retiree and the spouse, longitudinal designs and careful collection of health and attitudinal data. Connidis (1982), focusing specifically on the retirement of females, suggests that the interaction between work and familial careers must be considered, as well as the meanings attached to them. Women's work histories, rather than mere participation/nonparticipation, need to be explored, as well as the decision-making process of women regarding the choices and coordination of careers. Comparisons of women in different circumstances, working full-time outside the home through to not working outside the home, are required. Comparisons with men are also needed.

Although in the past, females in the labor force were proportionately few, this is not the case today. Changes in life-style are evident. The trend towards greater participation in paid labor on the part of women is due, in large part, to the return of middle-aged women to the work force. This, combined with increasing divorce rates, suggests changes in the life-styles of women in generations to come. Research suggests greater diversity in the life-styles of women, especially in the younger cohorts. The older patter of sequential involvement — first as students or employees and then in family roles — (with optional return to a job in middle age) that characterizes older women of today is disappearing as a model life course among younger women (Kuhn, 1980).

Brody (1980) reports from a study of three generations that all generations, the youngest most emphatically, believe that women should have careers and educational opportunities equal to those of men and that men should share child care, household and parental responsibilities. Nonetheless, study by Bell and Schwede (1979) suggests that, while many laws regarding the activities of women outside the home are changing, younger women are still socialized primarily to be wives and mothers. In an empirical study, they find that women across four generations are more egalitarian on legal-political and economic issues than on domestic and family issues. The extent of these changes and their effects on retirement are still unknown.

In sum, there is reason to believe that new styles of living in retirement for men and women are likely to evolve. As younger cohorts with different histories enter old age, they are likely to bring with them different expectations and preferences for these years. It is also important to recognize that for most of those who are elderly today, retirement is not the devastating experience it was once thought to be.

Most people seem to adjust to retirement, although research has focused primarily on men and not on women. However, even though retirement is increasingly viewed as a normal life event, all people do not view it positively. Martin Matthews and associates (1982) argue that those who report retirement has affected them in a negative manner are more likely to be those who did not prefer it at the time. Those individuals who accept retirement as another stage in life do not appear to suffer the negative consequences early writers describe.

‖ THE EMPTY NEST ‖

Since most children leave the homes of their parents, the empty nest, or postparental, stage is an expected event. Many people will experience it when they are middle-aged and will have twenty years or more living as a couple. Axelson (1960) defines the empty nest stage as the "interval in the family life cycle when the children are no longer regular physical members of the parent's home, but the parents have not yet entered the period of 'old age.'"

The empty nest has been thought of as traumatic, particularly for women. On the other hand, it is recognized that it may allow parents the freedom to experience new activities, or activities neglected during childrearing. Deutscher (1968) reports that almost half of his respondents indicate the post parental stage is better than previous stages, and an additional third feel it is equally as good. Freedom is an important element and includes freedom from financial responsibility, restricted mobility, housework and other chores as well as freedom to do as one pleases.

Although relatively little research has been conducted in this area, most authorities suggest that the empty nest is not as traumatic as previously thought. The few empirical investigations that do exist suggest the effects of children leaving the home include both improvement in the marital relationship (Lowenthal et al., 1975) and a magnification of dissatisfactions (Atchley and Miller, 1980).

As Borland (1982) points out, consideration needs to be given to the cohorts who experience empty nest. With the increasing number of women in the work place, some discussion of the meaningfulness of, and commitment to, the work role vis-à-vis the parenting role appears necessary. Parents today expect their children to leave home, and it may be when those children do *not* leave home, it is more traumatic. Also, with economic constraints and the high divorce rate, there may be a trend to return to the nest. As yet, there is no evidence that indicates the prevalence of such a return or its effects. Given that elderly persons tend to prefer intimacy at a distance with their children, it is not surprising that the empty nest does not appear particularly disruptive. It is, however, an area in which little research is available. (Contact and involvement with children and grandchildren is discussed in detail in the next chapter, on informal networks.)

WIDOWHOOD

Another major role transition characterizing old age is that of widowhood, an exit from the marital role. As was shown in Chapter 2, this exit is more likely to be experienced by women than by men, because of the greater life expectancy of women, and because of their tendency to marry men older than themselves. Indeed, widowhood has become a stage of life for women in our society.

Widowhood is reported as more traumatic than retirement (Martin Matthews et al., 1982). The life of a woman at the time of her husband's death is likely to be disorganized and in a state of flux. Her life in partnership with her husband is over. Ties with many people may be broken and friendships with some individuals, particularly those couple-companions, may have to be modified (Lopata, 1979). However, as Ferraro (1984) notes from his review of the literature, the majority of research shows very few, if any, decrements in social participation immediately upon widowhood. After a few years, interaction with friends and neighbors is likely to increase.

As Lopata (1973) writes:

> Widows are expected to be devastated, even years after the death of their husband, and this marital condition is not defined as having any advantage over marriage. Yet, in spite of some tendencies in that direction, most women do not become fatally ill, commit suicide, or become institutionalized in mental hospitals after the death of the husband. Regardless of the amount of shock and grief, the human capacity to adjust and reconstruct reality asserts itself and life continues either in passive acceptance or in assertion of a new life style.

Most women adjust after the immediate bereavement period. Lopata argues that adjustment will depend on a variety of factors, including age at widowhood, the importance placed on the role of wife and the life-style of the couple. The length of the mourning and the adaptation phases varies. Regardless of the adjustment, loneliness is one of the major problems experienced by widows. It may take several forms: being lonely for a partner, or companion, in activities; being lonely for someone to talk to; being lonely for someone to care for; and so on. Other problems can involve financial difficulties, childrearing, decision-making, shortage of time and self-pity.

Many widows have a strong desire to be independent. Many live alone. Most do not want to rely on their own families and even less on their husband's families. They tend not to live with their offspring, preferring intimacy at a distance (Rosenmayr and Kockeis, 1963). The importance of children in the support system of the widow, however, cannot be understated. Daughters tend to be more helpful than sons and are relied upon for emotional closeness and comfort. Sons, on the other hand, are expected to assist in task-oriented duties, such as making arrangements, giving advice and, in some senses, taking over some of the duties of the husband. Financial support is generally not obtained from children. Indeed, many widows report feeling that they are the givers rather than the receivers of economic assistance (Lopata, 1973; 1979).

Other components of the support system, such as siblings, relatives outside the immediate family and non-family members, including co-workers and professionals, tend to be untapped resources. This is not to deny that some widows do rely on some of these individuals.

Friendships are also important. Widowed females are reported as having higher levels of interaction with friends than the married and the never-married (Atchely et al., 1979). Arling (1976) finds that widows who are the least lonely and feel the most useful are those who have a number of neighbors and friends. He reports that it is the availability, and not the amount, of contact that is significantly related to morale, suggesting the importance of feeling that there are caring individuals around. Friends and neighbors can provide companionship and share activities with the elderly widow, while children tend not to fill these roles. Family ties are not voluntary and are sometimes viewed as increasing the dependency of the widow on her offspring.

Adjustments with friends are sometimes required, particularly if the couple tended to have couple-companions. Yet Lopata's study indicates that most widows continue to consider some married friends as close to them, and few limit their contacts only to women of the same marital status. In terms of social activities, 43 percent of the widows report no change in their social life. Lopata (1973) suggests that some of these individuals may have been involved in sex-segregated activities prior to the death of their spouse. She concludes further that re-engagement of women in society after the death of their husband can be classified into three types: modern, traditional and social isolates.

The modern widow is able to reexamine her life-style and goals and decide which aspects of the wife role she wants and is able to continue. If she has adult children, she recognizes there are needs on both sides; she modifies friendships to move away from couple-oriented leisure to relationships where greater or different personal intimacy is available.

The traditional widow is able to retain her life much as it was, prior to the death of her spouse. She may be immersed in kin relations, may have a very close peer group or a network of neighbors and may continue her involvements with little or no adjustment after becoming a widow.

The third type of widow, the social isolate, becomes isolated upon the death of her husband. Perhaps she was never involved in kin groups or neighborhoods, or she may be unable to retain those involvements, because of poor finances, mobility or health, after her husband dies. As friends die or move away, the social isolate cannot replace them. She tends to lack the social skills necessary to engage in new social roles or to change some of the older roles.

The relationship of these types to the economic situation of the widow has not been examined. Harvey and Bahr (1974) suggest that the negative impact on morale associated with widowhood may not be the result of the experience per se but rather from socioeconomic circumstance. Availability of economic resources has been identified as one of the principal factors associated with involvement with family, friends, and neighbors and participation in activities (Arling, 1976).

Widowed Men

Most of the research on widowhood has focused on women. Relatively little has been written on men who experience the loss of their spouses — widowers. The attention focused on women is not surprising, given the demographic characteristics mentioned earlier. Table 4-2 shows the greater likelihood of women to be widowed compared with men. This is true for all age groups but especially so in the later years. Factors, such as the different life expectancy, the tendency for women to marry men older than themselves and the greater likelihood of men to remarry are reasons for the focus on women. The tendency within social science to study retirement among men and widowhood among women is also a reflection of the assumed difference in the importance of the work role for men and the spouse role for women.

‖ TABLE 4-2 ‖

PERCENTAGE OF WIDOWED INDIVIDUALS IN SELECTED AGE GROUPS BY GENDER: CANADA AND THE UNITED STATES

Age	Canada 1981 Females	Males	United States 1980 Females	Males
18-19	.0%	.0%	.1%	.0%
20-24	.1	.0	.2	.0
25-29	.3	.1	.3	.1
30-34	.6	.1	1.2	.1
35-44	1.6	.3	2.2	.4
45-54	5.8	1.2	7.0	1.6
55-64	16.7	3.3	18.9	4.0
65-74	37.0	8.4	40.3	8.5
75+	66.9	25.4	67.9	24.0

SOURCES: Statistics Canada *1981 Census of Canada.* Ottawa, Ont.: Minister of Supply and Services, 1982, Catalogue 92-901, Table 5 and U.S. Bureau of the Census *Statistical Abstract of the United States: 1980-81.* (102nd Edition) Washington, D.C.: U.S. Government Printing Office, 1981, Table 49, p. 38.

Some researchers have examined the differences between widowed males and females and report widowed females in their 60s tend to have higher social participation than their male counterparts. However, in the 70 and over age group, this gender difference disappears. Blau (1961) and Elwell and Maltbie-Crannell (1981) speculate that, after the initial bereavement period, the adverse effect on social participation occurs only when it places the individual in a position different from that of his or her age and sex peers. In other words, women in their 60s are likely to have female friends who are also widows, while men are not.

Elwell and Maltbie-Crannell also suggest that loss is less devastating for women than for men and that financial security may be a more important coping resource for men. Social participation may be more important for mediating stress for women. In a similar vein, Watson and Kivett (1976) argue that widowhood may be much worse for men than women because of a weaker grandparent role, because of an expectation that they will die before their spouse and therefore do not rehearse for widowhood (for example, a lack of anticipatory socialization), because of loss of a companion and because of a decline in kin interaction.

Lowenthal and Robinson (1976) suggest that men's capacity for emotional intimacy is limited to marriage. Men tend to rely on their wives for intimacy and experience great social disruption with the loss of a spouse (Berardo, 1970; Trela and Jackson, 1979), while women have a greater affinity for confidant relationships outside of marriage. This may be a contributing factor to the tendency for widowed males to remarry. No conclusive evidence exists on the role of intimacy and confidant relationships in the lives of either men or women. Much more research is required on the widowhood experience, especially among men, irrespective of whether they remarry.

‖ VOLUNTEER ‖
INVOLVEMENT

Volunteering and involvement with volunteer associations has been suggested as a possible substitute for the loss of other roles during old age (Swartz, 1978). However, such involvement has not been particularly popular among elderly persons. Admittedly this has not been an area of extensive study. Research that does exist sometimes focuses on participation in volunteer associations (Ward, 1979; Babchuk et al., 1979), sometimes on the individual's participation in any volunteer work (Chambre, 1984).

Participation in leisure activities after retirement reflects the pattern of involvement in the middle years (McPherson, 1983; Ward, 1979). A Kansas study (Babchuk et al., 1979) reveals about one-fifth reporting no involvement with volunteer organizations and over one-half (58 percent) belonging to more than one association. Church-related groups are among the most popular. In fact, church, fraternity-sorority and patriotic-veteran associations account for over half of the total involvement among those participating in such organizations.

When asked if they have done any volunteer work, few people respond affirmatively. Chambre (1984) reports only 16 percent of her repondents aged 60 and over have done volunteer work. A national study in Canada reveals 21 percent of all age groups are engaged in volunteer work (Statistics Canada, 1980). In a Canadian urban study (Chappell, 1982c), a comparable 15 percent of those aged 65 and over indicate they do community volunteer work. Among those who do this type of work, almost half (46 percent) indicate they participate once a week or more. Most (85 percent) indicate they would like to maintain their current level of participation.

To have some indication of change in participation, all respondents were asked if there had been any change in the amount since age 60. Fully 81 percent indicate no change. Only 4 percent indicate a great increase and a further 2 percent indicate a slight increase. In total, only 6 percent of this sample increased their participation in community volunteer work after age 60. Furthermore, 4 percent indicate a slight decrease, and 10 percent indicate a great decrease since that time. In other words, there has been virtually no change for the majority of the respondents in this study, supporting the notion that earlier participation patterns are continued in retirement.

‖ CONCLUSIONS ‖

With increasing age, and in particular at age 65 in our society, there tends to be retirement from paid labor. This is true for most men and is increasingly true for women. By this age, children have left the home and have established themselves elsewhere. It is around this age, or not long after, that significant proportions of women find themselves widowed.

These exits from major roles in life have led to much concern that elderly people in society have no useful role, have no meaningful way to contribute and, therefore, do not have a positive identity and self-image. Indeed this idea of the "problem" of aging is a major theme running throughout both gerontological and nongerontological literature.

When adjustment to these role exits is examined, the literature suggests they are not as traumatic in the long run as has been assumed. Most people adjust to retirement, and many enjoy it. The empty nest is not filled with despair. Even widowhood can be coped with after the initial bereavement stage. People make these role transitions in their lives and do so without major negative consequences. These role exits, however, do not appear to be replaced by another major role and certainly not by volunteer activities.

Role exits can be dealt with, partly, because they have become normal and expected in the lives of elderly people. As noted in chapter 2 on demographic trends, elderly men are more likely to be married and to remarry if widowed. Elderly men who do not remarry will experience a life situation they can share with few men. It is this group of elderly widowed men that has been suggested as particularly at risk in terms of declines in health, social participation and integration. This latter point becomes clearer in the next chapter, on informal networks.

If retirement is not as traumatic for most as previously thought and adjustments to widowhood evolve in time, what then is the substance of the lives of elderly individuals? How elderly persons fill their lives is critical to understanding the aging process. The next chapter examines the social world of elderly members of society today, focusing on their informal networks and resources. Their social situation is intimately tied to whether or not they will require care and the types of care they need. For example, long-term institutional care may not be an issue in societal arrangements where individuals age at home within the family context. Trends towards living alone or having fewer children may result in fewer people being available in the informal network to provide care. The issue of the provision of formal care is discussed in chapters 6 and 7.

■ CHAPTER 5 ■

INFORMAL NETWORKS
FAMILY AND FRIENDS

If most elderly people adjust to retirement, to widowhood and to the role transitions that characterize their lives, what is the substance of their day-to-day activity? How do they fill their lives? Is contact with others of central importance?

Nostalgic belief would have us think the extended family was commonplace in preindustrial Europe and North America, in contrast with today. Many still believe that, in times past, an elderly person lived his or her final years withdrawing gradually from the family farm, contributing wisdom and experience to the end. A popular portrayal of today's elderly persons is one of alienation from family, especially from children. Old people are said to be isolated and alone, frequently put in long-term care institutions and forgotten.

These beliefs, however, do not withstand careful scrutiny. The three-generation family living under one roof and providing an integrated role for elderly members was temporary and seldom widespread in Europe. More often it was nonexistent in the United States (Laslett, 1976). Fewer persons lived as long in preindustrial times. Among those who did, not all found themselves in such comfortable circumstances. Most research, however, does suggest that family relationships have traditionally provided, and continue to provide, a major source of interpersonal support, warmth and commitment for people of all ages (Abu-Laban, 1980).

Thus the nuclear family as the dominant family form today does not preclude a spectrum of emotional and instrumental exchanges between family members. Furthermore, friends and neighbors provide many of these exchanges. Interaction with family and friends are a source of much pleasure and satisfaction. These informal sources are often turned to for companionship, assurance and assistance.

Regardless of whether an elderly individual resides in the community or in an institution, she or he will in all likelihood have an informal network of some kind. For some individuals, this system will consist of 50 or 60 people, while others will have small, tightly knit groups of four or five people. Some members will be blood relatives; many will be age peers; some will provide assistance; and some will participate with them in recreational activities.

This chapter begins with a discussion of the concept of informal networks and the importance of recognizing peer-intergenerational and family-nonfamily distinctions. While the importance of family ties has long been recognized, the distinctiveness of relations with people of differing ages has received less attention. This discussion is followed by an examination of living arrangements, the frequency and types of interactions within the network and care provided by members of the network. Although the importance of informal support for the institutionalized elderly is discussed, attention is focused on elderly persons living in the community, who constitute approximately 90 percent of those aged 65 and over in industrialized society.

| INFORMAL NETWORKS |

The area of informal networks has received increased attention over the past decade among all age groups. While it is generally agreed that the topic is important, there is no one definition or measurement of the concept. The area has been addressed in terms of social bonds, social networks, meaningful social contact, availability of confidants, human companionship, social support, social integration, social participation, activity and disengagement.

One aspect shared by these terms is the experience of being supported by others, which is defined as including an affectional content and a psychological function. For example, Cobb (1976) conceptualizes social support as belonging to one or more of the following classes:
• it provides emotional support, that is, the person believes he or she is cared for and loved.
• it provides information, which leads the person to believe she or he is esteemed and valued.
• it leads the person to believe he or she belongs to a network of communication and mutual obligation.

As Lopata (1975) puts it, the informal network is a primary support system involving the "giving and receiving of objects, services, and social and emotional supports defined by the receiver and giver as necessary, or at least helpful in maintaining a style of life." There is general agreement that social support includes a subjective dimension, which refers to the quality of interaction (Lowenthal and Robinson, 1976; Carveth and Gottlieb, 1979).

The exact nature of this qualitative relationship, however, is not agreed upon. For example, Satariano et al. (1981) argue that the common theme among the different definitions of social support is that people receive something from the group. These definitions neglect the process of reciprocity, the degree to which people give as well as seek support from others. Said another way, *social* network tends to be inappropriately equated with only the *support* aspect of the network. There can be demands and stresses tied to social integration as well as to social isolation (Rundall and Evashwick, 1980). Some may find social isolation less stressful than others.

Actual measurement of social support reflects just as many, if not more, inconsistencies, and has tended to focus on those easily measurable aspects such as size, connectedness and density (Mitchell and Trickett, 1980). It is sometimes measured as type of assistance received, availability of network members, rate of interaction with family and friends, presence of a marital relationship or living arrangements.

Still others (such as Liang and Bollen, 1981) distinguish between subjective and objective integration. The former is defined as the individual's assessment of whether she or he is socially isolated or lonely, whether he or she is satisfied with his or her social relationships and the presence of one or more significant others towards whom she or he feels emotionally close. Objective integration is defined as the amount, frequency and intensity of social interaction.

Social support systems are frequently thought of as formally recognized entities, such as the family, neighborhood, church or social organizations. They are also defined as the unique configuration of these entities in the individual's life, which constitute that individual's salient reference group.

Despite this diversity of measurement and indeed, some such as Cobb (1976) argue, because of it, empirical evidence demonstrates the importance of social support:

> We have seen strong and often quite hard evidence repeated over a variety of transitions in the life cycle from birth to death, that social support is protective. The very great diversity of studies in terms of criteria of support, nature of sample and method of data collection is further convincing that we are dealing with a common phenomenon. We have, however, seen enough negative findings to make it clear that social support is not a panacea.

Informal social networks is an area that has seen a burgeoning of research interest in the recent past, together with a recognition of its importance when studying aging. Much of the empirical research still exists in the form of working papers and those presented at professional meetings. Nevertheless, some of the first systematic attempts to study social networks were initiated some 30 years ago by the British, when Barnes (1954) studied a Norwegian fishing village and plotted the interactions individuals had with others.

The informal networks of individuals is the focus of this chapter. To aid in the understanding of this diverse literature, conceptual distinctions will be discussed first.

THE CONCEPT OF THE FAMILY

A clarification of some of the implicit assumptions in the literature helps an understanding of the interactions and exchanges in which elderly individuals are involved. Gerontological literature tends to promote a family, nonfamily distinction. It is argued here that this has resulted in a relative neglect of nonkin peer relationships.

The emphasis has been on parent-child relations with a concomitant paucity of research on other family members. This literature reflects the assumption that the most appropriate conceptual distinction is between familial and nonfamilial support. Furthermore, as Jonas (1979) points out, the literature assumes the primary importance of the family and that friends cannot serve the same functions.

An inverse relationship is also assumed between participation in the two sets of social bonds (family and nonfamily): primacy of time, energy, interest and emotional investment is given to kinship bonds, and this investment in turn detracts from involvement in nonfamily relationships. This assumption is explicit, for example, in Rose's (1962) and Hochschild's (1973) discussions of the development of peer-type bonds among elderly persons. Both authors argue that these bonds arise only when older people are loosened from family ties sufficiently that they are free to develop such a subculture.

It can be argued, however, that involvement with kin is not necessarily competitive with involvement with nonkin. Irrespective of whether the relationships are qualitatively different or similar, one can be equally involved with both (Chappell, 1980b; 1982b). A conceptual distinction between peer and intergenerational relationships is as meaningful as between family and nonfamily relationships. Intergenerational relationships are defined as relationships between elderly people and those who are substantially younger. A peer-intergenerational distinction has special relevance for elderly women. A person's structural ties to family members are important. However, relations with people to whom we are less formally linked, such as friends, can also be important.

There are several reasons why elderly peers (whether family or nonfamily) might constitute a different category than intergenerational relations. For example, Blau (1973) discusses the role exits shared by elderly individuals, as examined in the preceeding chapter. Today a couple can expect to live together without the presence of children (a role exit from childrearing) another 16 years or so before the death of one of the partners. Similarly, retirement and widowhood are two statuses typical of old age and primarily of old age, both designating exits from major social roles.

Rose (1976) notes additional circumstances, which he believes are shared only among elderly persons, such as adjustments to declining health and common interests based on similar generational experiences in a rapidly changing society. Elderly persons also share adjustment to impending death (Marshall, 1975). Potentially, elderly persons share all of these experiences by virtue of being elderly. They share them with other elderly people, whether they be family (spouse, siblings, cousins) or nonfamily (friends, neighbors, strangers). Peers are equals, or similar others, who share the same age, skills and status (Hess, 1972). Ward et al. (1981) argue that the importance of age as a basis of friendships may be greater in old age than at any other time. It is during old age that ties to other age-mixed networks are loosened by virtue of role exits.

Friendships, it is further noted, have a voluntary nature based on similarity and consensus. This is said to have the potential of leading to greater communication and intimacy and has been contrasted with the obligatory nature of kin relations, which may be strained by this obligation and by generational differences in interests and experiences (Wood and Robertson, 1978; Cantor, 1979).

Haas-Hawkings (1978) speculates that the involuntary nature of family ties may involve perceptions of increased dependency on the part of older people whose capacity to reciprocate and maintain equal exchange might be limited. Since friendships rest on mutual choice and mutual need and involve a voluntary exchange of sociability between equals, they sustain a person's sense of usefulness and self-esteem more effectively than familial relationships. Children and parents, by definition, cannot be contemporaries.

It should be noted, however, that the definition and meaning of friend and friendship is culture based (Cohen and Rajkowski, 1982). Not all groups share affectivity and free choice as part of their definition of friendship. For example, the single room occupant's definition of friendship is characterized by material assistance. That is, while friendship is a term frequently arising in the literature, it is a relationship about which little is known and deserving of more detailed, in-depth study.

Support can be found in existing research for the conceptual distinction between peer and intergenerational relations among elderly persons. Hochschild (1973) reports that elderly residents of a subsidized apartment building compare themselves to other old people, not to the young. She also finds much evidence of the "sibling bond," a relationship between elderly individuals, involving reciprocity (implying equality) and similarity (meaning each has the same things to offer and the same needs to fill). In other words, their relationships rest on adult autonomy.

She goes on to elaborate how the peer community immunizes its members against the full force of stigma attached to old ways and to speculate that the taboo on discussing death is lifted in age-segregated company. The old among the old feel free to talk about death. They exchange solutions to problems they have not faced before. Finally, she reports that those most active with children are also most active with nonkin, a finding that suggests the roles do not necessarily compete with one another and can be maintained simultaneously.

Examples of the importance of peer bonds are evident among elderly persons themselves, as illustrated by the following passages (Chappell, 1982c):

An 85-year-old married female
I'm closer to people my own age because they have had more experiences in life than younger people. Education varies. Older women my age went to ladies school and never were career-oriented. Young people have a form of independence difficult to understand. More common experiences with people our own age. I don't understand their [young people's] attitudes and they don't understand us. However, there wouldn't be any change if the young thought the same as we do.

A 70-year-old single female
I would try to listen rather than talk with younger people. With older people there is more freedom. There is more of a bond with people your own age. There is more stability in relationships with older people. I feel more confident that it will last . . . . We might talk about troubles with people our own age, whereas with younger people we talk about the day-to-day events . . . . I enjoy younger people, but they're not as important to me as my friends.

Similarly, Jonas (1979) and Sherman (1975) report that kin and community roles are additive. In their studies of housing project residents, those more involved with kin are also more likely to have friends. Finally, the counterintuitive findings that contact with intergenerational family members, especially children, does little to elevate morale, while friendship/neighboring is related to less loneliness and worry, suggest that age peers have something important to offer (Arling, 1976).

Support for studying relationships with friends, neighbors and other age peers is also present in the argument that it is the quality of the relationship that is important (Conner et al., 1979; Liang et al., 1980). It is a stable, intimate relationship that moderates stress rather than the formal tie to the relationship. Cantor's (1975) study of elderly persons in inner city New York reveals that over half of her respondents have at least one intimate friend, usually someone unrelated. There is, however, less research on the subjective than the objective aspects, and even less on how the two are integrated.

BEYOND THE CONCEPT OF THE FAMILY

The family-nonfamily distinction is also very important and no doubt should be maintained. Current knowledge suggests nonfamily age peers may sometimes, but not always, substitute for family peers. The fact that elderly persons, especially men, most often name their spouse as confidant (Haas-Hawkings, 1978) suggests the interchangeability of these roles.

Lowenthal and Haven (1968) point out that having a confidant is more important than having many friends but no confidant. They also note that those involved in more social roles are more likely to have a confidant. Similarly, Jonas (1979) finds being married means the person is more likely to have close friends, suggesting at least no conflict between the two.

Lopata's (1973) study of Chicago-area widows demonstrates how peer family relations can nevertheless be different from peer nonfamily relations. She reports that siblings are sources of comfort and of more pragmatic help in time of need, more so than friends who are no longer close by. Contrary to the argument made by some concerning the significance of the voluntary aspect of friendships, Lopata finds that the family bond is better able to weather the interruption of contact than is friendship and that crises bring the family together.

The social role of friend does not have strong ideological support for adults in North American society. There is a more explicit recognition of and value attached to family relations than to friendships in our society. Nevertheless, friends are important in the daily lives of many of the widows Lopata studied. Only one-third of the respondents are extremely low in such interaction and negative in attitudes towards such relations. Some, such as Blau (1973) and Depner (1983), explain the social role of friend as different from family because of differentiation in tasks. They suggest aged persons almost never turn to their friends for financial assistance; they look to family. But in times of illness, friends and neighbors constitute viable substitutes for family.

There seems to be consensus that intergenerational relations tend to be confined to family members, children and grandchildren (Bultena, 1968). However, few elderly persons live with their children or grandchildren (Myers, 1982), and a recent study demonstrates that very few participate with them in recreational or leisure activities (Chappell, 1983a). Intergenerational relations seem to revolve around social visits and the provision of assistance, as will become clear later in the chapter.

Drawing conclusions in this area is confounded by the fact that not all researchers draw comparable conceptual distinctions. A common practice groups friends and neighbors and compares them with relatives. Few of these studies contend with the fact that a respondent may define a neighbor, a relative, a fellow worker or a casual acquaintance as a friend (Peters, 1978).

Especially little is known about the interplay between the various relationships and their relative importance in the lives of elderly people. One study by Pihlblad and Adams (1972) reports, in general, that contact with family is more conducive to female satisfaction than to male satisfaction, among elderly persons. Contact with siblings is more conducive to high satisfaction than is contact with children. Furthermore, contact with friends is more strongly associated with satisfaction than is contact with the family. The conclusiveness of these findings will not be known until much more research is conducted.

Recent data (Chappell, 1983a) provide more direct evidence for the arguments that a peer and intergenerational distinction is valid when studying elderly people. Nonfamily age peers, in particular, emerge as important in the lives of elderly persons. These data refer to a representative sample of elderly persons living in the community, not in long-term institutional care and not receiving formal home care services. Most of these elderly persons identify both peer and intergenerational relations within their networks. Nonkin friends, however, tend to be age peers, regardless of whether age peer is defined as someone aged 65 and over, or as someone within 10 years of the age of the respondent.

Contact with individuals outside the household is more frequent with friends (who are primarily age peers) than with relatives or neighbors. Furthermore, more satisfaction is expressed with relationships with friends than with any others outside the household. Specifically in terms of recreational activities, the greatest satisfaction is expressed by those participating with nonfamily members (peer friends).

The data suggest the viability of both the family-nonfamily distinction and the peer-intergenerational distinction. However, the importance of the distinction becomes apparent only as different groups of individuals and different types of interaction are examined. The data point clearly to both family and non-family age peers as important aspects of elderly persons' networks. They confirm the importance of nonfamily age peers, a largely neglected area of research.

The peer-intergenerational distinction highlights the unique social situation of elderly women. The family-nonfamily distinction by itself can over-emphasize the roles of mother and wife. This is not to deny the importance of such roles nor to deny that peer family (spouse, siblings, etc.) can and often do provide friendship roles for many, even most, married persons. It is to recognize that some married people do not have friendship roles with their spouses, that people can have similar relationships even though they are not married, and that marriage and mother roles are not the only roles in which women are involved, nor are they the only roles within which women develop their identities.

As noted in chapter 4, there is reason to believe that these roles may be less important for many women in the future and may not be part of the lives of increasing proportions of them. Some researchers, such as Lee (1979), argue that the trend away from obligatory concern of children for their parents to a more "voluntaristic" model will increase the meaningfulness of intergenerational relationships. Furthermore, with widowhood now a normal life stage for most women, virtually all elderly women can expect to live many years in neither the mother (in the sense of raising children) nor the wife roles.

Current demographic trends suggest it is increasingly important to study informal social networks among the elderly. The trend of the baby boomers to have fewer children may mean fewer people available to provide support when that generation reaches old age. Recall that the cohorts currently entering old age are the parents of the baby boom generation, who have more children available than their children will when the latter reach old age. However, as life expectancy has increased, those who have children are more likely to be members of extended families; that is, the young elderly are likely to have parents who are old elderly. If the trend for women to marry men older than themselves continues, and the life expectancy gap between the genders remain stable or increases, women, particularly widowed women, will continue to constitute a large proportion of the elderly group.

These trends mean fewer family resources to call upon when the baby boom generation reaches old age fewer children, grandchildren, siblings and cousins. Those who are available may be elderly and themselves at risk for care. The decrease in the availability of family members adds greater importance to the area of nonfamily social relations. Relationships with friends and neighbors are an area of potential change; the content, direction and extent of those changes are currently unknown.

The area of friendship and neighboring can involve losses, as well. As elderly persons themselves age, some friends will inevitably die. The concept of friendship, however, is fluid. The possibility of establishing new friendships is always there. Lopata (1975) argues that those who have developed such social skills earlier in life are the ones apt to fare best during old age in this regard.

To summarize, it has been argued that the area of peer relationships is one of potential importance. Peer relationships have been emphasized here, not to contend that they are more important than family relations, but to argue they have potential importance that has been largely neglected. This point is not intended as an argument for age segregation, only for greater recognition and study of age peers in the lives of elderly individuals.

The remainder of this chapter focuses on the totality of the informal network, examining both household members and those outside the household. The assistance provided from these informal sources then receives explicit attention. Wherever possible, distinctions will be made between peer family and nonfamily and intergenerational family and nonfamily. It must be repeated, however, that much of the literature does not use these distinctions. The importance of the family clearly emerges.

‖ HOUSEHOLD ‖
MEMBERS

One important component of the informal network is household composition — whom elderly people live with, if anyone. In Canada in 1981, 26 percent of individuals aged 65 and over in private households live alone, while the remaining number live with at least one other person. The 1981 figure for the United States is similar, with 31 percent living alone. Over half (60 percent) of the Canadian elderly population live with a spouse or with a spouse and others, and only 14 percent live with persons other than a spouse. The figures for the United States are 54 percent and 16 percent, respectively; that is, the vast majority live either alone or with a spouse (Statistics Canada, 1984; U.S. Bureau of the Census, 1982).

Gender differences in living arrangements are also evident (see Table 5-1). Similar trends are experienced in Canada and the United States. Females aged

65 and over are much more likely to live alone than males of the same age. Males, on the other hand, are more likely to live with a spouse. These differences are not surprising, given the greater tendency of women to be widowed.

‖ **TABLE 5-1** ‖

LIVING ARRANGEMENTS OF PERSONS AGED 65+ IN PRIVATE HOUSEHOLDS, CANADA AND THE UNITED STATES, 1981

| | Canada | | United States | |
	Male	Female	Male	Female
Living alone	14.0%	36.1%	14.3%	41.4%
Living with spouse	77.2%	46.7%	77.0%	37.8%
Living with someone else	8.9%	17.2%	8.7%	20.7%
(Total number)	939 thousand	1,202 thousand	10.1 million	13.6 million

SOURCES: Statistics Canada, *The Elderly in Canada*. Ottawa, Ont.: Minister of Supply and Services, 1984, Catalogue 99-932, Table 3 and U.S. Bureau of the Census, *Statistical Abstract of the United States: 1982-83.* (103rd Edition) Washington, D.C.: U.S. Government Printing Office, 1982, Table 35, p. 31.

Canadian Census data provide a more detailed breakdown of the relationship of household members. Table 5-2 provides the figures for those who live with someone. The vast majority live with spouses. About one-quarter live in households composed of a spouse and other individuals, while over half live with a spouse only. Very few live with nonrelatives. When gender differences are examined, the greater tendency of women to be widowed is again evident, with more females residing with relatives in the absence of a spouse than do males. Neither males nor females tend to live with nonrelated individuals, no doubt reflecting the traditional living arrangements of the population and the importance of the marital relationship. Indeed, marriage is generally accepted as the paramount example of an intimate dyadic relationship in adult life.

Though traditional living arrangements continue, there has also been a trend towards living alone among elderly persons. In Canada, 10 percent of males and 15 percent of females aged 65 and over were living alone in 1961, compared with 14 percent of males and 36 percent of females in 1981 (Stone and Fletcher, 1980). A similar trend is evident in the United States, with 13 percent of males and 29 percent of females aged 65 and over living alone in 1965, compared with 14 percent of males and 41 percent of females in 1980.

This trend has persisted for several decades and characterizes many developed countries (Myers and Nathanson, 1982). Factors contributing to the trend include the number of older widowed women, increases in levels of economic independence and better levels of health for this population group. The supply of suitable housing for living alone (apartments and subsidized housing built especially for seniors) has also increased, and living alone appears to be more socially acceptable.

TABLE 5-2

HOUSEHOLD COMPOSITION FOR INDIVIDUALS AGED 65+
WHO LIVE WITH AT LEAST ONE PERSON, CANADA, 1981

Live with:	Total	Male	Female
Spouse only	59.3%	66.1%	52.1%
Spouse and others	22.3%	23.6%	21.0%
Other relatives	14.6%	7.1%	22.5%
Nonrelatives	3.8%	3.2%	4.4%
Total number who live with at least one person: (in thousands)	1,576	808	768

SOURCE: Statistics Canada *The Elderly in Canada.* Ottawa, Ont.: Minister of Supply and Services, 1984, Catalogue 99-932, Table 3.

Whether or not living arrangements in the future will be different is unknown. For example, there could be more elderly women living together for both economic and social reasons. These life-styles could evolve among elderly persons, especially elderly women and old elderly women, because of their numbers and the nonexistence of the nuclear family among those who are widowed. One might expect more living arrangements of the type of which Kuhn (1980) speaks: persons from several different generations, or the same generation, living in a household together as a family bonded through blood ties, but these would be "families of choice." The family will no doubt remain of utmost importance for many individuals in the provision of human needs but, perhaps, less so, in the sense that there may be greater flexibility in our social interactions and social arrangements.

Much more research is needed to understand the importance of living arrangements. Because most elderly people who live with someone live with their spouse, and because the marital relationship involves caring and assistance, it is difficult to know the importance of living arrangements *per se* as distinct from the spouse bond. More is said about this later in the chapter, when specifically discussing informal assistance and the provision of care.

INTERACTION WITH OTHERS OUTSIDE THE HOUSEHOLD

Given that elderly persons tend to live with spouses or alone, their involvement with family and friends tends to be as nonhousehold members. This section explores the interaction of elderly persons with others. Attention is paid to interactions that do not involve assistance, or care, since they are discussed in a separate section later in the chapter.

Elderly people have fairly extensive contact with their children who live outside the household (Shanas, 1979a). The maintenance of close family ties despite geographical separation is aptly described by the phrase intimacy at a distance (Rosenmayr and Kockeis, 1963). Most elderly persons with children live close to at least one child and see at least one often. Canadian data, (Synge et al., 1981) report only one-fifth of children living more than one-and-a-half hour's drive away. Interaction with children depends on proximity. Bultena (1969) and Heltsley and Powers (1975) report lower interaction with children for the rural aged because of the outmigration of children.

Seldom discussed, and even less researched, are the obligations involved in maintaining networks with family, generally, and with children, in particular. Cohler and Lieberman (1980) studied three ethnic groups in the United States and reported that the maintenance of face-to-face relations is a source of strain, especially for women. As Lee (1979) points out, few studies report a correlation with frequency of contact with children and the subjective well-being of elderly persons. He finds a negative correlation between amount of contact and morale.

The interrelationships between parents, siblings, children and friends (i.e., the different normative contexts) is not well understood. Shanas (1979a) maintains that for the childless elderly, a niece or nephew often assumes the responsibilities of a child, on a principle of family substitution. Similarly, she argues that brothers and sisters become especially important for widows and those who have never married. Others have found that elderly people with no children, or only one child, tend to develop closer relationships with cousins, nieces and nephews, but not with siblings. Johnson and Catalano (1981) studied childless individuals, comparing the married and unmarried. They report the childless married have the slimmest kinship resources, relying on one another for support in times of need. The unmarrieds have broader networks of kin and nonkin and report siblings as the most important source of support.

Others, however, postulate both additive relationships and more complex network patterns in lieu of the substitution model (Trela and Jackson, 1979). Atchley and associates (1979) suggest there is a conceptual distinction between patterns of interaction with parents, siblings and children as a category compared with other kin. The idea that we form closer or qualitatively different ties with our parents, brothers, sisters and children than with other kin is intuitively appealing but unproved.

Current evidence consistently points to the belief in the fragmented, nuclear family of today as unwarranted. The family still fulfills the role of social support and what Cantor (1975) refers to as the more idiosyncratic human needs. Overall, the role of family kin is considered supportive.

Despite the emphasis on the family and particularly on relations with children and with spouse, there is some literature available on nonmarrieds. Most of that literature is on widows, rather than widowers, those separated or divorced or the never-marrieds (see Chapter 4 for a discussion of widowhood).

Never-marrieds have been found to be less socially involved, but there is some suggestion they may be well adjusted and happy (Norris, 1980; Braito,

1978). Larson's (1978) review suggests that never-marrieds show the same level of satisfaction as marrieds and that it is the widowed, divorced and separated who have lower life satisfaction. In Canada, in 1981, approximately 9.1 percent of elderly people had never married (Statistics Canada, 1982). The figure for the United States is 5.2 percent (U.S. Bureau of the Census, 1982). It has been argued that the single older person is a unique type, characterized by continuity of life events and relatively minimal social involvement. The argument concerning minimal social involvements overlooks never-marrieds who have had long-term personal involvements with either males or females.

It is not known whether the proportion of never-marrieds will increase among future generations. Singleness is viewed increasingly as a viable and healthy alternative to marriage. Childlessness is not as stigmatized as it used to be. It should be cautioned that never-marrieds constitute a particularly underresearched area, and any conclusions would be hazardous at this time.

As elaborated in the previous section, the extent to which nonfamily friends, neighbors and acquaintances substitute for family relations is unknown. Nevertheless, the data that are available suggest friends tend to be age peers and probably fulfill an important function in the lives of elderly individuals, hitherto not fully recognized. The focus in existing research on the family has told us much about family relations but tended not to take friends into account. Therefore, it has not placed family relations within the total social network of the individual.

Even though there is much to learn about interactions with others in the lives of elderly persons, it is clear that, for many, other people are central to their activities. They are not alienated from family, and prefer intimacy at a distance. There is little doubt that social interaction is important throughout our lives. Such continues to be the case when health begins to decline. Indeed, the majority of care provided to the elderly comes from informal sources. This is the topic of the next section.

INFORMAL NETWORKS AND THE PROVISION OF CARE

Even though research in the area of informal relations is incomplete, Brody (1981) summarizes existing thought well:

> As gerontologists well know, research during the past several decades has systematically disproved the notion that contemporary families are alienated from the aged and do not take care of them as used to be the case in the "good old days". The accumulated evidence documents the strength of intergenerational ties, the continuity of responsible filial behavior, the frequency of contacts between generations, the predominance of families rather than professionals in the

provision of health and social services, the strenuous family efforts to avoid institutional placement of the old, and the central role played by families in caring for the non-institutionalized impaired elderly. On the theoretical level, the concept of the isolated nuclear family has yielded to that of the "modified extended family"...[1]

We do not, however, know under what circumstances what types of assistance are best provided or by whom.

Informal social support is not only of interest in its own right but also in terms of the provision of care to elderly people. Estimates suggest that 80 percent of all care provided to elderly members of society comes from informal sources, such as family and friends (Biaggi, 1980). Recent American estimates suggest that families assume the major caring function for most impaired and disabled individuals who do not require regular medical attention and who are living in home settings. Furthermore, it is estimated that 10 percent of those living in the community are as functionally impaired as those in institutions (Callahan et al., 1980; Brody, 1981).

As is evident from Table 5-3, most elderly persons are not in long-term institutional care. It should be noted that the definitions of the types of institutions, which are included, vary for each country (see note at bottom of the table). Specifically, the figure for the United States does not include personal care homes or domicillary care. The extent to which a smaller proportion of elderly persons are in long-term institutional care in the United States is therefore not known. Nevertheless, at any one time, most elderly persons live in the community.

It is just as true that increasing proportions live in long-term care facilities, as one examines older age groups. This distinction was drawn by Kastenbaum and Candy (1973) some time ago. The percentage jumps to one-fifth or more in both the United States and Canada among those aged at least 85. As Kastenbaum notes, while the proportion in such facilities at any one time is indeed small, nevertheless, approximately one-fifth to one-quarter of elderly persons can expect to spend some time in a long-term care facility before they die.

Recent Canadian data (Chappell, 1985; Chappell and Havens, 1985) directly illuminate the issue of informal assistance. Individuals were asked about their involvement in assistance relationships, referring to helping with grandchildren, helping out with illness, giving advice about personal problems and jobs, financial aid, providing a home for others, household tasks, transportation, emergency aid and other assistance. Assistance could be either provided to, or received from, the respondent. It could also refer to formal or informal relationships.

Over half (58 percent receive assistance of some form. Over half (55 percent also provide some form of assistance to others. Almost half (47 percent)

[1] E.M. Brody, "Women in the Middle and Family Help to Older People," *The Gerontologist* (Vol. 21, 1981), p.471. Reprinted by permission.

‖ TABLE 5-3 ‖‖

PERCENTAGE OF ELDERLY UNDER INSTITUTIONAL CARE, CANADA AND THE UNITED STATES, 1981 (EXCLUDES ACUTE HOSPITAL CARE)

	Canada 1981	United States 1981
Percentage 65+ in institutions	6.7*	5.3**
Percentage 85+ in institutions	33	21

*In Canada, the definition of institutional care includes nursing homes and institutions for the elderly and chronically ill.
**This figure includes nursing homes only. Personal care homes and domicillary care are not included in the definition of nursing homes.

SOURCES: Statistics Canada *The Elderly in Canada.* Ottawa, Ont.: Minister of Supply and Services, 1984, Catalogue 99-932, Table 3 and U.S. Bureau of the Census, *America in Transition: An Aging Society.* Current Population Report Series p-23, No. 128. Washington, D.C.: U.S. Government Printing Office, 1983.

are in a reciprocal relationship; that is, they are either receiving and providing assistance or not receiving and not providing assistance. Over half (55 percent) of the sample receive assistance from informal sources on the particular items examined, and only 15 percent from formal sources.

Those receiving some form of assistance (either formal or informal) were examined further. Fully 94 percent of these individuals receive assistance from informal sources. Among the 15 percent receiving formal care, 80 percent receive care from informal sources at the same time. These data confirm the provision of informal care to the elderly population and the provision of informal care even when formal care is provided. The data are Canadian and substantiate information from the United States, suggesting that most elderly people cope well within the community without an inordinate amount of formal assistance and with the help of their family and friends.

This is true even when they are recipients of formal care, such as that provided by the universal, no-cost-to-recipient-of-service, home care program in the province where the data were collected. It should be pointed out that it is home care program policy in that province that informal assistance received from family be taken into account when determining amount and type of services to be provided by the program. This policy supports complementing informal assistance rather than replacing it. These data could be reflecting the successful implementation of that policy.

Individuals receiving these home care services were compared with those not receiving such services. The data reveal that recipients differ significantly from nonrecipients on several important criteria; most notably, they are in worse health, as measured by several indicators (chronic conditions, functional ability, perceptions of health), and are less active, as indicated by less involvement in recreational activities.

The recipients also show lower satisfaction with their relationships with others, but this finding is accounted for by their worse health and the fact that much of this interaction revolves around assistance. These analyses suggest that the finding, reported by others (and discussed earlier in this chapter), that increased interaction with children is correlated with low morale may well be due to deterioration in health.

Sources of Support

A fair amount of research exists informing us of the content of these informal assistance relationships. This literature reflects the same emphasis on the family as noted earlier in this chapter. Studies of intergenerational exchanges inform us that while the social class of the old person affects the magnitude and direction of parent-child help in old age, old persons in every social class help their children and their children help them (Shanas, 1979a). Similarly, Sussman and Burchinal (1968) report financial aid flowing along generational lines on various occasions, and not just in emergencies. Marshall et al. (1981) report from Canadian data that long-term care, consisting mainly of help with chores and errands, followed by a need for help with personal care, letter writing and medications, is provided in one-third of the cases by a child. A spouse is named one-fifth of the time. That is, taken together, a child or a spouse is named in about half the cases.

Further, elderly people feel assistance within kin structures is appropriate and the interdependency between parents and children is desirable (Cantor, 1975). In Cantor's study, two-thirds receive help from children when ill, and two-thirds receive help in chores of daily living. The amount of help from children is positively related to age and the paucity of income. Children are most frequently identified as the people who could provide assistance when needed (NRTA et al., 1980).

The role played by daughters is well documented as different from that which sons play. Treas (1977) reports that, devoted though sons may be, the major responsibility for the psychological sustenance and physical maintenance of aged persons has fallen traditionally to female members. Daughters provide direct service. Sons play a more substantial role in decision-making or with financial assistance.

Horowitz's (1981) data show that in 88 percent of cases where males provide care, there is no female alternative (the son is the only child, there are no daughters, the sister is geographically distant), suggesting that females still provide such care, and males do so primarily in their absence. Sons also enlist the aid of their spouses more than do daughters.

Concerning stress resulting from the caregiving role, emotional strains are reported as predominant followed by stress from restrictions on time and freedom. Expenditure of financial resources is not uppermost in the minds of children caring for aging parents.

Lipman and Longino (1983) examine differences in the types of support provided by sons and daughters, taking marital status of the mother into consideration. They report that there are no significant differences in the amount of emotional, social or instrumental support given to *married* mothers by their sons or daughters. For the *widowed* mother, the daughter is by far the greatest source of support. This is consistent with Lopata's (1979) finding that daughters provide more support for widows, particularly emotional support, than do sons.

Three factors are said to contribute to this gender difference. Females traditionally assume nurturing tasks, tend to maintain stronger emotional ties with the family of orientation (their parents and siblings) than males, and are more likely to be in the homemaker role and therefore have more time for such care than men, who are in occupational roles. Two demographic trends that question the continuation of the gender difference are the trend to smaller families and the increasing number of females working in paid labor.

A large proportion of the increase in women working for pay can be attributed to the return of middle-aged women to paid labor. These are the women whose parents are entering, or have entered, the old age cohorts (Scharlach, 1983). Current evidence, while still scarce, suggests these women are having increasing demands placed on them without corresponding shrinkages in other areas. They are acquiring roles in paid labor and in the care of aging parents without concomitant reductions in other areas.

It is still too early to know how these changing roles will stabilize, but much concern is being expressed that this group of women is particularly at risk. Because of the new demands on them, they have been referred to as the sandwich generation and the group in the middle (Grans and Fengler, 1981; Brody, 1981).

The spouse, as well as children, is also important as physical health deteriorates. Older couples can maintain considerable independence in the face of infirmities by nursing one another and reallocating housekeeping chores. Because women tend to marry men older than themselves and to have a greater life expectancy, the caregiver role tends to fall to the wife (Fengler and Goodrich, 1979). Brody (1981) claims the phrase "alternatives to institutions" is a euphemism for daughter. We would add it is a euphemism for wife, as well.

The importance of living arrangements for social support and, in particular, for the provision of care requires more attention. Living with someone changes the social context of one's life. If it is a household member who is required for assistance, the number of children may not be so important. Then only those children willing to live in the same household as the parent would be relevant to assistance, a trend which is currently not apparent. It is further important to understand the relevance of the marital (or couple) relationship to the caregiving role. If the marital relationship brings with it a unique obligation for caregiving not found among household members in other relationships, then living together per se becomes less important in this context.

Some note that informal sources other than the family are preferred after the family and before social and government agencies (Cantor, 1983; Weeks and Cuellar, 1981). As O'Brien and Wagner (1980) point out, however, there is normative support in our society for family involvement, but ambiguity surrounds the role of nonfamily assistance in times of need. A study by Wagner (1978) highlights the potential lack of consistency between beliefs and actual behavior. Although it is commonly believed that elderly persons go first to family for aid and that they express greater acceptance of aid from family (Riley and Foner, 1968), Wagner found actual aid split between friends and family.

The Instrumental-Expressive Distinction

Crucial for understanding the provision of care from informal sources and the emphasis on the family reflected in the literature is society's concept of the family and the primary function it is believed to perform. The conceptual distinction between instrumental and expressive interaction is long-standing and important for appreciating this emphasis.

Instrumental exchanges are those used for getting things done. Expressive exchanges are those that meet the need for companionship and caring. Clearly, any relationship can be a source of both types of interaction, but it is instrumental exchange that is thought to characterize formal care and services. Informal interaction, by contrast, is characterized by expressive exchanges. The latter involve people personally in an interaction to which there is a reciprocal quality. It is this human element that is said to be the main feature of informal relations (Schmidt, 1981; Stein et al., 1981).

Kin ties are assumed to contain this affective human element. In addition, they are believed to contain aspects of obligation. Family and kin are said to have at least tacit normative support for becoming involved in the care of aged relatives. The situation for nonrelatives is more ambiguous. The fact that we do speak of close friends becoming just like family, both suggests the possibility of friends as a source of the same types of emotional interaction as family and highlights the fact that this interaction is not necessarily an expected component of such relationships. The current nuclear family form in North American society, with geographical distance between adult children and parents together with their relative economic independence from one another, has led some to argue that the family unit of today is more free than in the past to fulfill the expressive and affective role (Adams, 1968; Lee, 1979).

As noted earlier, informal sources currently provide the majority of care to elderly persons. Within these sources, family and kin are believed to provide the majority of care. It is commonplace gerontological knowledge that the role of primary caregiver is assumed first by spouse, if there is one, a child, if there is no spouse and, in the absence of either, other relatives, such as siblings, nieces or nephews, provide extensive support (Cantor, 1979; Marshall et al., 1981). Family support is followed by that of friends and neighbors.

Despite this popular finding, and as Horowitz and Shindelman (1981) point out, a relationship between emotional closeness and general interaction frequency has not been established. In fact, contact is maintained and is independent of affective feelings between family members. These investigators report that, while most of the respondents in their United States sample state relatively close and enjoyable relations with older relatives, some of those not expressing affective relations still provide care. Furthermore, most caregivers report closer emotional ties with their elderly relatives but enjoy less the time spent together. When asked why they provide care, the most frequent reason is obligation. The second most frequent reason is affection.

Additional evidence demonstrating the complexity of social relations is reported by O'Brien and Wagner (1980). These authors find that elderly persons overwhelmingly assert they would first turn to family for assistance but do so in response to hypothetical questions. When the same population is studied in terms of actual patterns, assistance is divided almost equally between friends and family.

The different approaches to studying the question make it difficult to establish conclusions, even though research in the area is growing and is now fairly extensive. For example, some have discovered differences in where help is sought, depending on marital and motherhood differences. Johnson and Catalano (1981) report older couples, both those with and without children, rely extensively on each other. The childless older couple relies almost completely on one another. Widows, on the other hand, rely extensively on their children, while the childless unmarried have more extensive networks, calling on relatives and friends, as well as formal supports.

Still others (Evans and Northwood, 1979; Cantor, 1979) examine different sources of help by studying the type of assistance from each source. Evans and Northwood report older persons seek assistance first from relatives for financial and medical help and turn to friends and neighbors primarily for concerns such as housing. Cantor, however, reports most turn first to the family for instrumental needs and to friends and neighbors primarily for sociability, and when lonely.

In fact, Cantor argues that social networks are "hierarchical-compensatory," with relatives outside the immediate family, then friends and neighbors, turned to only as children become increasingly removed. This differs from those who view social networks as "task-specific" (as discussed earlier in this chapter), with primary groups differentiated structurally according to the types of tasks they can handle most effectively. Here kin are characterized by permanent membership but differential mobility. While geographic mobility impedes face-to-face contact, modern systems of communication, transportation and monetary exchange are said to allow maintenance of ties.

One of the difficulties is that different studies focus on different questions, tending not to examine the interplay of several factors at one time. There is, nevertheless, a general consensus that informal provision of care is more likely to bring with it a human and qualitative element absent from the formal provision of care. A difficulty arises because formal caregivers treat primarily the physical problems of the person and assess only particular definable aspects (i.e., have a task orientation), which prevents a global approach to the care of the individual. More about the formal care system and the interface between formal and informal care appears in chapters 6, 7 and 8.

The Institutionalized

Much of this chapter has focused on informal support for community living elderly persons. We now turn to a brief discussion of informal support for institutionalized elderly persons. These institutions may include hospitals, psychiatric care facilities and personal care or nursing homes. Attention here centers on those in personal care or nursing homes. This is not to say that the informal supports for individuals in other institutions is unimportant. However, there is more research on elderly persons who reside in personal care homes.

It will be recalled from the beginning of this chapter that only a small proportion of the Canadian and American populations are in long-term institutional care but that one-fifth to one-quarter can expect to spend some time in a long-term care facility before they die. Empirical studies suggest these individuals are not abandoned by their family and friends. There is generally a continuation of the relationship established prior to institutionalization (Smith and Bengtson, 1979). Dobrof and Litwak (1977) studied five long-term care facilities in the United States. They report half of the patients have families who visit at least once a week and 85 percent have families who visit at least once a month. York and Calsyn (1977) record an average number of 12 visits a month by relatives of residents in three nursing homes, noting that those with more contact prior to institutionalization have more contact afterwards.

As with the research on interaction with community-dwelling elderly, the emphasis has been on the quantity rather than the quality of that interaction. Harel (1981) finds that continuing ties with *preferred* members of their informal network are of primary importance to the well-being of the institutionalized elderly. Almost all residents have at least one visitor; almost half also name one or more individuals whom they would like to see but do not (Harel and Noelker, 1982). Informal networks of the long-term institutionalized is another underresearched area.

The Caregiver

Another of the main concerns arising in the area of informal social support now receiving increased attention is burden on the caregiver. Individuals providing care, particularly wives of disabled spouses, constitute a group at risk of deteriorating health, whom Fengler and Goodrich (1979) have referred to as "the hidden victims." Johnson and Catalano (1983) discuss the increased health risk to the spouse caregiver among childless couples even when devoted and exhibiting few signs of stress or ambivalence. With death of the ill spouse, the surviving spouse, without developed social support, can become even more at risk. Single, widowed and divorced daughters living alone with an ill parent are also vulnerable to depression and poor physical health. Having social support and emotional outlets is especially important for the caregiver.

Increasingly, concern is expressed that those caring for th
the community are carrying an inordinate burden. Much of t
been focusing on the families of Alzheimer's victims. It is
families play a major role in the care of such persons (Ellio
adequate social and medical support is lacking (Wasylenki, 198_). ... __
for physical care alone can lead to exhaustion and despair (Brocklehurst, 1977).
The caregiver has also to cope with the relative's memory loss, emotional
outbursts and personality changes.

Concern has also been raised for family and friends of institutionalized elderly persons. The extent to which the caregiver burden is decreased when the
patient becomes institutionalized is not well understood. Smith and Bengtson
(1979) argue that reports of renewed closeness after admission suggest there
is now time for socioemotional involvement as the more physical needs are
met by facility staff. However, a longitudinal study by George and Gwyther
(1984) does not find increases in well-being for caregivers after institutionalization of the patients. The authors suggest that their study may not have allowed
a sufficient lapse of time for the caregivers to relinquish the caregiving role
and adjust to a new relationship.

More research is required to understand evolving relationships between
family and friends and older institutionalized persons. There is some suggestion that friendships with other residents and staff are an important factor
for the resident's well-being (Harel and Noelker, 1982). Little, however, is known
in this area.

CONCLUSIONS

The lives of elderly people are filled with social relations.
There is a tendency for the elderly not to live with their children, and to that
extent the nuclear family persists. Nevertheless, aging family members are
not discarded and are not abandoned in long-term care institutions. Rather,
a modified extended family appears to be thriving. The term intimacy at a
distance aptly describes the dual desire for independence and relationships
with others. The trend among elderly persons, and in particular among
widowed elderly women, towards living alone therefore should not be interpreted as isolation. Living alone can be viewed as increasing independence
welcomed and chosen with a modest amount of economic independence that
permits this life-style.

An area about which relatively little is known is that of friendship and
neighboring. Some recent data suggest that this is an important area for further study. Peers as friends share common experiences, such as the fact that
they have reached old age in our society. While there is some suggestion that
friends provide both emotional and instrumental support, more research and
understanding is required.

The widespread belief that families, and for that matter friends, do not provide for one another in our fast-paced modern industrial society appears un-
founded. Interactions and relationships are preserved and developed, and most
care for elderly members comes from informal sources, both family and friends.

Much remains unknown in the area of informal care. As society evolves, these, like other areas, will change in unforeseen ways. Whatever specific changes the future holds, one can argue convincingly that the area of informal social support will become more important for elderly persons generally and for elderly females in particular. As the costs associated with formal health and social services continue to escalate, current concerns over economic restraint have brought more attention to informal support of the elderly.

Formal care is provided to only a minority, and only a small portion of the care actually provided comes from formal sources. Among those receiving formal care, even more care comes from family and friends. The provision of formal care and the interface between informal and formal systems is elaborated in the next three chapters.

■ CHAPTER 6 ■

THE FORMAL CARE SYSTEM

Even though most elderly individuals are engaged in informal relations and are not isolated from family and friends, health problems are commonly experienced. In addition, individuals' informal networks differ in the types of assistance and amount of care provided. The formal care system is the societal response to health care need. It assumes an obligation on the part of society as a whole for the provision of care for those needs. As such, it carries with it ethical overtones; the formal provision of health care is considered something different from other commodities, such as automobiles, houses or clothes.

The formal care system refers to all governmental and voluntary service agencies, as well as health and other service professionals and paraprofessionals that work on their behalf. This definition includes traditional medical services, such as physician and hospital services and long-term institutions. Community and social services, such as home care and community care that may be provided formally within a government program and/or by volunteer organizations, are also included (Branch and Jette, 1981). The formal system includes all health services delivered organizationally, where health is defined in a broad sense. Admittedly, there are grey areas, especially self-help and volunteer groups.

The focus of this chapter shifts somewhat from preceeding discussions. Here we are interested in the adequacy of the formal care system in meeting the needs of an aging population. Although the experiences of elderly individuals within this system are implied throughout, most of the discussion refers to the operation of the system. The central question addressed in this chapter is, "Does the formal care system adequately meet the needs of an aging society, given the social context, health status and informal relations discussed in preceeding chapters?"

This chapter examines the formal care system, as it exists today, and the role it plays in the provision of care to elderly individuals. It begins with a brief discussion of the establishment of federal programming in this area, programming which has had a sizeable effect on the type of health care systems which have developed.

THE DEVELOPMENT OF FORMAL CARE SYSTEMS IN CANADA AND THE U.S.

Volunteer organizations provided services long before governments in either Canada or the United States entered the arena. It is equally true that instances of local government involvement were evident prior to major efforts, especially national efforts, in the provision of services. Examples include worker's compensation medical services; hospital outpatient departments for the indigent and near-indigent; public clinics for VD, TB, child welfare and so on; federal medical services for war veterans; and health plans operated by numerous industries.

Public effort was most effective in the area of public health or preventive medicine, such as the collection of vital statistics; sanitary inspection; supervision of water, milk and food; disposal of sewage and garbage; and so forth. In addition, national governments by and large became involved, first, in income security legislation and, later, in health service legislation.

The development of the formal care systems in both countries is tied to the development of the medical profession. Most writers place the inception of the public acceptance of medicine around the late 1800s and early 1900s (Brown, 1979; Enos and Sultan, 1977). It was the late 1800s when Pasteur discovered that each disease had its own microorganism, and when Lister advanced techniques for sterilizing operating procedures. It was also the late 1800s when the vaccine for smallpox was used and when the stethoscope, the clinical thermometer, the hypodermic syringe, and other medical devices were invented. It was during the first two decades of the twentieth century when medical licensing laws were passed, medical schools were standardized, restrictions on entry into the medical field were enforced and the income and status of the medical profession increased.

It was in the Depression of the 1930s, which demonstrated the vulnerability of private schemes and the social nature of human poverty — well after the public acceptance of medicine had begun — that an interest in health insurance developed in both countries. This was a time when private enterprise dominated the field of health. Doctors, dentists and nurses sold their services privately. Drugs and medications were sold on the market. It is important to remember that medicine as we know it today is a relatively recent phenomenon.

With the Depression, thousands of individuals could not afford care. The lack of standardization of services from one area to another and the lack of central coordination became evident. In addition, social services were unable to meet the growing demand (Bryden, 1974). It resulted in the breakdown of the fiscal independence of many municipalities and certain provinces or states (Sirois, 1940).

The experience of other countries was also available for comparison. In Great Britain, Prime Minister Winston Churchill appointed Lord Beveridge to chair an interdepartmental committee on social insurance and allied services. The resulting report argued that the state could and should accept responsibility for the relief of its citizens. It argued for universal coverage, with the same basic provision for all individuals. This, it will be recalled, was at the time of World War II. White papers of 1944, proposing a National Health Insurance plan, were supported by Churchill (Walley, 1972). The National Health Services Act was passed in 1946, by the Atlee government, adding a health scheme to unemployment and old age pension schemes, which were national, irrespective of wages (Sirois, 1940). However, developments differed somewhat on the North American continent.

Canada

According to Granatstein (1975), Mackenzie King's decision to stay on as prime minister of Canada in the 1940s was related to his dream of making a complete program of social security. He wanted to add health insurance to old age pensions and unemployment insurance (the latter was established at the beginning of World War II). In addition, individuals in government, the civil service and industry feared possible dislocations in returning to peace time: massive unemployment and popular unrest. After the prosperous wartime years, people would not willingly return to the depressed conditions of the 1930s. Social welfare legislation could dampen unrest and possibly aid in the re-election of the Liberals under King's leadership.

In 1940 Prime Minister Mackenzie King set up the Rowell-Sirois Commission to study the economic problems of Canada and the nature of federal-provincial relations. This Commission recommended that medical care stay a provincial responsibility with the federal government sharing the cost. Regional differences in the delivery of medical care added support for leaving it as a provincial responsibility.

A Committee on Reconstruction was established in 1941, with Leonard C. Marsh as research director. Marsh was a British-born economist, who had worked for Beveridge at the London School of Economics. Two weeks after the release of the Beveridge Report in the United Kingdom, preparation of the Report on Social Security for Canada, the Marsh Report, by the Committee on Reconstruction began. Marsh argued that the basic soundness of social security was that the universal risks of sickness, invalidity and old age were underwritten by the community as a whole. The first suggestion was for a national health insurance scheme. However, implementation of other recommendations began in 1945, specifically a research and training program and assistance in hospital construction (Marsh, 1975).

It was not until 1957 that the Hospital Insurance and Diagnostic Services Act insured hospital care for the entire population through a fiscal policy in which the federal government agreed to share the cost of running hospitals (excluding tuberculosis hospitals and sanatoria; institutions for the mentally ill; and care institutions, such as nursing homes and homes for the aged). In 1965-66 the Medical Care Act was passed (implemented in 1968), providing a national insurance scheme for physician services.

The 1966 Canada Assistance Plan, based on income, provided social assistance to anyone in need, irrespective of their age or the reason for their lack of income. The Canada Assistance Plan was intended to fill gaps, paying for health care services not covered by hospital insurance and medicare (for example, homes for the aged and nursing homes). The Plan replaced the 1956 Unemployment Assistance Act, old age assistance, and blind and disabled persons allowances. However, each province administers its own social assistance programs, there is no uniformity across provinces, and not all provinces use money from the plan to pay for nursing home costs. (Lee, 1974; LeClair, 1975).

By 1972, all provinces and the territories had joined the federal government's cost-shared comprehensive medical insurance program. To be eligible for federal cost-sharing, any provincial health plan must include universal coverage, reasonable access to services, portability of benefits, comprehensive services and nonprofit administration by a public agency. More is said later in this chapter and in the next chapter regarding access and the comprehensiveness of services.

Before 1977, federal-provincial cost sharing was 50/50, with the federal government matching every dollar the provinces spent on approved services. This, in effect, meant the provinces controlled overall health expenditures. In 1977, this was changed to a system of cash grants from the federal to the provincial governments, based on population, gross national product and the transfer of specific taxing powers to the provinces. By divorcing funds from specific health expenditures, the rate of growth of federal costs was limited. The change also gave the provinces more control over specific health expenditures within their own territories, since transfers were no longer dependent on the use of specified services.

Much debate has arisen around extra-billing by physicians (additional charges to patients over and above the payment schedule) and hospital user fees within provinces to help finance their share of health insurance costs. Concern arose that reasonable access was being threatened. This resulted in federal government legislation, and the passage of the Canada Health Act of 1984. This act provides for a reduction in federal financial contributions to provincial health plans by the amount of extra-billing and user charges implemented in the province.

The United States

By the early 1930s, there was also an evident emphasis on medical care in the United States. The American Medical Association (AMA), however, would not support a national insurance scheme because of fear of socialized medicine (Perkins, 1948). In 1935, the AMA passed resolutions reversing its prior total opposition to all forms of health insurance, endorsing experimentation with voluntary plans under the control of national and state medical associations. This unified doctors aganist compulsory health insurance (Witte, 1963).

It was, in fact, pressure from the AMA that defeated sickness and health insurance as part of the 1935 Economic Security Act. This act, as discussed in Chapter 4, provided a national contributory system only for old-age income insurance. It did not include either unemployment or health insurance.

Voluntary health insurance therefore grew rapidly in the United States, especially among private business. Although many national health insurance schemes were proposed during the 1940s and 1950s, none were passed. Opposition was too great, especially from the AMA (Kayser-Jones, 1981). Some movement did take place in the 1950s, when Congress extended old-age and survivors' insurance to include more workers, raised benefits and remove some inequities.

It was not until 1965, however, that legislation for medicare and medicaid was passed. The medicare program covers nearly all persons aged 65 and over, the disabled and those with end-stage renal disease who meet certain qualifications. It consists of two parts: Hospital Insurance (HI) for services in hospitals, skilled nursing facilities and home health services and Supplementary Medical Insurance (SMI) for the services of physicians, home health visits, outpatient services, medical equipment and prostheses. Enrollment in HI occurs at age 65; enrollment in SMI is contingent upon payment of a premium. Some of the more important features of medicare are freedom of choice of providers, cost-based reimbursement for institutional providers and fee-for-service reimbursements based on charges for local physicians. Among elderly persons, it is estimated that 95 percent are covered by medicare.

Medicaid was developed to provide medical care for those persons who lack their own financial resources. Aged recipients must meet the Supplementary Security Income eligibility standards. For those who are eligible for both medicare and medicaid, medicare is the first payer of services and medicaid the second. Medicare covers most health care costs related to acute illness, with a major focus on hospital care, and medicaid has become the primary source of public funding for long-term nursing home services for aged persons. Medicare is a national program wherein everyone receives the same benefits. Medicaid is jointly operated by the federal and state governments. Although the federal government sets minimum standards, both eligibility criteria and benefits vary by state. Medicare and medicaid, like old-age insurance, are entitlement programs; that is, costs vary according to use (Lave and Silverman, 1983; Harrington and Newcomer, 1982).

In addition, the Older Americans Act of 1965 (with subsequent amendments in 1973 and 1978) is intended to provide for the special needs of elders in a less restricted and more comprehensive fashion. Unlike medicare and medicaid, which provide financing for medical care, the Older Americans Act includes nutrition, housing, opportunity for employment and the pursuit of meaningful activities in its general goals. This act provides funding to establish state units and local area agencies on aging to act as advocates and coordinators of services (Branch, 1980; Tenhoor, 1982).

In 1975, the Social Security Act was again amended with Title XX. This title authorizes the federal government to reimburse states 75 percent of the costs for discretely defined social services, that is, Title XX provides noncash benefits for recipients. These services include transportation, homemakers, emergency assistance and some kinds of counseling (but not housing subsidies or home health aides). These services, unlike those covered by medicare and medicaid, tend to support those still living in the community. Generally speaking, recipients must be income eligible. Title XX is paid for through a block grant from the federal government to the state.

In summary, Canada and the United States exhibit many similarities in their social security programs. The recognition of the high association between poverty and old age in both countries was a major force in the development of social security legislation. In addition, both countries introduced old age pensions before health insurance.

Both countries began health coverage with the provision of medical services and hospital services. Both now provide a mix of federal and provincial or state programs focusing on the income and health areas. Both provide medical services and some social services. Both have programs based on age, as well as others based on needs and means. Both provide noncash benefits as well as cash benefits. In fact, Leman (1977) claims there are roughly similar levels of benefits in the United States and Canada, supplied through their social security programs.

The development of national health insurance schemes in the two countries, nevertheless, reveals considerable differences. In the United States, the major development occurred with the 1935 Social Security Act. It was three decades before further major developments took place. These, in the form of medicare, medicaid and Title XX, evolved by amending the 1935 act, while leaving the basic contributory premise intact. In Canada, legislation was passed earlier (starting in 1927) and evolved more steadily from that time, with an underlying principle of universality frequently evident.

In the United States, the private sector contracts for the functions of insurance administration with the public sector subsidizing the cost. Generally, those who do not qualify by age, poverty, illness or other special status do not receive assistance. In Canada, the hospital and medical care delivery systems contract with the public insurance scheme to provide care at specified rates of reimbursement. In fact, hospitals in Canada, unlike their private sector counterparts in the United States, are somewhere in between public agencies and private firms. Decision-making is shared among hospital management, governments and physicians. Both contrast with Great Britain, where their nationalized health service provides public insurance and public provision; that is, all three countries differ in the underlying principles on which their legislation rests. The countries also differ in the role played by the medical profession in the development of national insurance schemes. The following section gives a more elaborate comparison of the systems.

SOME UNDERLYING PRINCIPLES OF THE SYSTEMS

The underlying principles upon which the social security programs, including both income and health policies, are based diffently. In Canada, the Old Age Security (OAS) payment is universal, with a flat rate to everyone aged 65 and over. The guaranteed income supplement, given in addition to the OAS, is based on a means test that establishes economic need. Health care is universal, based on need and available to everyone irrespective of age. In the United States, old age pensions are based on age, but payments vary depending on the individual's contributions while working in paid labour. This is similar to the Canada-Quebec pension plans. As for health care, medicare is provided to those who are elderly, while medicaid is provided to the poor. In both instances, provision is based on need.

In other words, while both countries exhibit a variety of policies, Canada's are more likely to be universal, to be based on need rather than on age and to be uniform rather than based on past income differences. In this regard, Canada is more similar to Great Britain than to the United States. It is generally accepted that Great Britain and Canada have more extensive public programs than the United States (Weller and Manga, 1982). In Great Britain, the 1946 National Health Service Act established a universal health service regardless of income, and nationalized hospitals.

Age versus Need

The issue of age- versus need-based programs has been evident as these policies have evolved. It has been highlighted as financial pressures have resulted in a search for less costly alternatives, including decreasing the size of the eligible group, encouraging more efficient use of services, decreasing the level of reimbursement to providers, increasing the cost to the patient and increasing the efficiency of the overall health services delivery system (Lave and Silverman, 1983). Rationing scarce health care resources and reorienting them to an aging society has become of major importance.

Categorical programs can be defined as those that provide benefits on the basis of individual or group characteristics (such as age). They differ from selectivity in that benefits in the latter case are assigned after determining the eligibility of the recipient, usually through income testing. Categorical programs are universal to the extent that all persons with certain characteristics receive the same benefit (Hum, 1984).

As Neugarten (1982a; 1982b) points out, the argument in favor of age-based programming relies, to a considerable extent, on the disproportionate numbers of older persons who live in poverty, have comparatively bad health and fail to receive proper medical and health services when age-based policies do not exist. Without such policies, proponents argue, a redistribution of society's resources will not take place because of ageist attitudes and structural constraints preventing full participation by elderly people in society.

It might also be noted that policies based on age are administratively efficient and have low administrative obtrusiveness. Furthermore, Kutza and Zweibel (1982) note that it is not politically hazardous to support age-based programming for elderly persons. In 1976-77, a survey of a large urban population in the United States indicated the public's willingness to support elderly persons in relation to most, although not all, services. Life-supporting services in the areas of income, nutrition and transportation were generally accepted. Proponents also argue that policies based on age have a lower level of stigma associated with them, since everyone within that age bracket receives the same benefit or service. One does not have to be frail or disabled to receive the service (Estes, 1979).

Individuals arguing against age-based policies and in favor of need-based policies believe the former policies do not lessen the stigma. They say such policies segregate and stigmatize the entire group, imply that all elderly persons are a problem and encourage the view that everyone 65 and over is alike (Branch, 1980).

It is further argued that the circumstances and status of elderly persons in society have improved sufficiently over the last few decades that such programs are now providing benefits to individuals who do not require them. As a result, many who desperately need services, the poor and the frail elderly, do not have all of their needs met. It has been argued that 15 to 20 percent of the elderly population require some form of special health or social services and will have their needs obscured by the other 85 percent who do not require such services (Branch, 1980).

Indeed, Austin and Loeb (1982) note that elderly persons as a group appear to use more health care services because the health care costs of the most sick and most disabled are extremely high. It is misleading, therefore, to say that elderly people as a whole use more health care services than other age groups (Kane and Kane, 1978; Kammerman, 1976). Estimates are that only around 17 - 20 percent of elderly people are the major users of health care services.

The argument that age is a valid predictor of need may decrease as new cohorts enter old age. Neugarten (1982c), for example, believes the status of old age has changed considerably and that age per se is becoming less relevant as a predictor of life-style and of need. She states that the 70-year-old student, the 30-year-old college president, the 22-year-old mayor, the 35-year-old grandmother, the 55-year-old retireee, the 65-year-old father of a preschooler and the 85-year-old mother caring for her 65-year-old son are more frequent now than in the past. While her examples may be somewhat over-drawn, her point, nevertheless, appears valid. Few would quarrel with her argument that retirement, not chronological age, defines old age in society. Major deterioration in health, not chronological age, distinguishes the old-old from the young-old, although it may be the sudden loss of informal support that precipitates dependency.

Most would agree that age norms and expectations are in flux. The extent to which their importance as regulators of behavior is waning, however, is a topic for much debate. Some who agree with these arguments, such as Kutza and Zweibel (1982), suggest 70 rather than 65 should be the age for age-based policies. They argue for raising the age of eligibility for age-based policy rather than adopting need-based policies.

Policies based on need have a major difficulty — the definition and measurement of need. Needs can refer to a multitude of areas, including functional capacity, physical disability, psychosocial functioning, living arrangements, transportation and nutrition. After specifying what needs are to be included and how they are to be measured, they must be translated into a package of services, a care plan (Austin and Loeb, 1982). If this can be successfully accomplished, programs aimed at such demonstrated need are "target efficient" compared with programs provided to everyone based on attributed need. Need-based policies, however, are not easy to translate and require skilled personnel for their implementation. One of the few extensive attempts to establish criteria based on a broad definition of need is reported in Branch's (1980) monograph on vulnerable elders.

While the issue is far from being resolved, at least in the area of health care, it would appear there are good reasons for need-based rather than aged-based policies. Extreme caution, however, is required in the measurement of needs and their translation into services.

It is not as clear that need should be used in the economic area. Some argue the tax structure permits (even if it is not used) equalization, so that means testing can be avoided. Those who do not require economic transfers from the government can pay it back in the form of taxes. In health care, provision on the basis of need can be applied universally, so that anyone requiring the service would receive it, irrespective of economic circumstance. To be needy because of declining health appears not to carry the same stigma as to be chronically poor.

The issue of need versus age based policies is relevant to federal policies in the United States and Canada and is currently receiving increased attention as economic constraints continue to be felt. The evolution of the formal care systems in the two countries represent different combinations of policies with age and need bases.

Community versus
Institutional Care

There are also national differences in the extent to which health care pro-grams support community services or institutional care. Once again the United States and the United Kingdom stand at the extremes with Canada in the mid-dle. Neither Canada nor the United States provides community services to the extent evident in the United Kingdom.

Health care in the United States has emphasized short-term acute and long-term institutional care. The development of community and home health ser-vices has not been supported. A major problem is the lack of funding for needed services. Both medicare and medicaid fund services for acutely ill elderly but not for the chronically ill, who may have some functional impair-ment. These restrictions and deficiencies in home health services have led to the institutionalization of individuals who require relatively inexpensive assistance from homemaking services to enable them to remain in their homes.

Most home health services are dependent on the patient's need to be house-bound and to have skilled nursing. Housebound can refer to patients who are confined to their homes except for short periods, usually leaving only for medical care. Some of these benefits are given only if recipients have been hospitalized, which excludes from assistance many who are in need of home health services (Beatty, 1980).

Restrictive policies under medicare and medicaid are the major reasons for this lack of services. Medicare provides for 100 days of home health care per episode of illness. Only those who will become rehabilitated with the provi-sion of services are eligible; the chronically ill are excluded. Services must be medically necessary and include nursing care, physical, occupational or speech therapy but do not include personal, supportive or homemaker ser-vices. Medicaid is less restrictive; however, only 2 percent of medicaid's budget is allocated for noninstitutionalized health services, including homecare (Har-rington and Newcomer, 1982).

Even with Title XX and the social service amendments, there is wide varia-tion among states. With the Older Americans Act, service availability and coor-dination depend on local agencies. Little money has been provided, and home health services have not been seriously considered as an alternative to in-stitutional care (Trager, 1980). Nevertheless, some services are available in different states.

In Canada, a global concept of health is more evident than one based on purely medical needs. However, the independence of the provinces and their jurisdiction in health matters makes generalization to the entire country dif-ficult (Gomers et al., 1979). A national scheme covering community based care, similar to that for physician and hospital services, does *not* exist. As of the early 1980s, three provinces (British Columbia, Manitoba, and Saskat-chewan) had coordinated home care and community support systems (Robert-son, 1982), which included homemaker services, home nursing, therapy ser-vices, medical services, social workers, meals-on-wheels and some household

repair services. Even here, recent political developments in
involving monetary cutbacks question the future viability o
that province. Other provinces offer some such services on
   The United Kingdom, however, offers community servic
national program. They were insured simultaneously with hos
tional care under the National Health Service (NHS). The primary goals of social
services in the United Kingdom are assistance in maintenance of family ties,
living in one's own home and participation in the community (Ginzberg, 1983);
that is, public policy in the United Kingdom stresses community-based services
over institutional care. The four home-based health services in the NHS plan
are general practitioners, home nurses, health visitors and chiropody services.
   One of the more important features of the NHS is provision for the development of community health services, as well as practitioner and hospital services. Some of the community and social services developed through this act
are domiciliary services (home helpers, meals-on-wheels, home nursing services,
volunteer friendly visitors, podiatry services, home physiotherapy and occupational therapy); sheltered housing; geriatric day hospitals and day centers.
   Another service developed through the NHS is the geriatric service. The
geriatric service consists of three types of wards: assessment, rehabilitation
and continuing care. The rehabilitation ward receives most of its patients from
the acute ward with the goal of returning them to the community. If it appears
that rehabilitation will not occur, the patient is transferred to the continuing
care ward.
   While few dispute that the United Kingdom is further advanced in legislation in the social service area than Canada and the United States, most also
recognize important difficulties within that system. Some of the problems that
have been identified include a shortage of geriatricians, a shortage of appropriate bed and facilities for the aged and difficulties associated with the
provision of geriatric care in the community. Townsend (1981) notes that even
in Britain, where community services are included in the national scheme
of social insurance, the majority of medical and nursing staff work in hospitals
and the majority of local authority care staff work in residential homes, suggesting that the extent to which this country has been able to provide adequate
community services requires greater study.
   In the North American countries community services are less entrenched
within national legislation for health care than they are in the United Kingdom.
The first national insurance schemes determined the institutional focus within
the North American health care systems. Schwenger and Gross (1980) claim
that in the past the Untied States has had too few institutional beds and virtually no community services. Recently, the number of nursing homes has
risen dramatically. Canada, they point out, has opted for the two most
expensive forms of care: institutional care and medical care. Because of the
historical development of formal care in Canada and the United States, community based programs have tended to develop as "add-ons" to the cost of
existing institutional and medical care. More is said about this in chapter 7.
   It can be hazardous to examine cross-national figures for community

vices. They are not provided here. Differences may reflect different definitions; comparable data do not always exist; the reliability and validity of the
data are seldom without question; availability does not necessarily mean services are accessible. In fact, conclusive figures on a national level do not exist
in Canada and the United States, where there is considerable variability from
province to province and state to state.

It is the existing formal health care system in the two North American countries, with their medical and institutional focus, to which we turn next. It is
through an understanding of the current systems that their inadequacy for
meeting the needs of an aging society becomes evident.

The Resultant Systems: Medical Care

Despite their differences, the formal health care delivery systems in the
United States and Canada have resulted in remarkably similar medical care
systems. This section discusses those similarities in terms of the systems' major
emphases, some reasons for the development of these emphases and their
implications for an aging society. A fuller discussion of alternative forms of
health care is presented in chapters 7 and 8.

Physicians

The major focus of both countries' systems is medical. In the United States,
the medical model for health services is evident in both the medicare and
medicaid programs. All services, even home care services, received under
these two programs, must have authorization from a physician. In Canada,
the initial Medical Care Act of 1965-66 provided a national insurance scheme
for physician services.

Evans (1976) demonstrates the major role of physicians in cost figures. Physicians control approximately 80 percent of health care costs. Even though in
Canada only about 19 percent of total health care expenditures go directly
to physicians, this group largely controls hospital use (accounting for about
half of all health care costs), prescribing of drugs and so on. (Bennett and
Krasny, 1981; Detsky, 1978). To put it another way, the decision to use expensive health services is not made primarily by the individual patient, or client;
the decision is made primarily by medical doctors. They are the major
gatekeepers to use of the system. Physicians (and other providers) have expert knowledge, not shared by patients, and make decisions on patients' behalf.

While physicians are central in this system, hospital costs represent about
one-half of the total health care expenditures in both Canada and the United
States. Increased use is often cited as the reason for these increasing costs.
However, Marmor (1975) comments that in the United States increased use
accounts for less than 7 percent of the growth in per capita hospital expenditures. Increased incomes of hospital laborers and increased costs of equipment have been major contributors to the increased cost of hospital services.

Detsky (1978) also points out increases in relative wage gai
in 1975 compared with wage gains of 16 percent in 196⁵
laborers, whereas increases in utilization rates were less tl
1970-71. Furthermore, Bennett and Krasny (1981) estimate .
took 6 percent more hospital workers and 80 percent more drugs, X-ray ₁₁₁...
and other supplies to treat the average hospital patient in 1975 than it did
in 1965.

In Canada, there has been a leveling off of both physician and hospital
workers' salaries since the 1970s. Hospital space and resources have been
relatively stable since that time as well. The number of physicians, in comparison, has grown rapidly, with a resultant increase in pressure for hospital
capacity (Evans, 1984). The extent to which physician practices can be disen-
tangled from independent hospital use is not clear. Physicians play major roles
in the use of hospitals in our society. Patients usually have access to hospital
benefits only if admitted by a physician.

The pervasiveness of the medical profession is evident in its official role
at birth, at death and in between. Increasingly, areas previously outside the
jurisdiction of medicine are coming under its aegis: alcoholism and other addictions are viewed as illnesses, mental illness is considered a disease and
death and dying now take place in hospitals. Physicians make critical decisions in relation to worker's compensation, maternity benefits and other "cer-
tifying" roles. They are well represented on critical policy and planning committees throughout society. They are heavily involved in research. Then there
are their obvious roles as educators of future physicians, certifiers of illness
and so forth.

The reliance on physician-centered services reflects an acceptance of a
medical interpretation of health and illness. There is a tendency to equate
good health with proper medical care, to identify health with medicine and,
therefore, to imply that an extension and expansion of health care services
will be accompanied by rises in health levels within the population (Mishler,
1981a). Indeed, some authors, such as Hokenstad and Ritvo (1982), use the
terms medical services and health services synonymously. The central role
played by physicians, and the medical emphasis, are evident within the very
naming of our health care systems as medicare.

In other words, our system provides a healing approach rather than a health
approach (Eisdorfer and Cohen, 1982). A healing approach aims to restore
a sick individual — one who has been diagnosed as ill by appropriately sanc-
tioned experts — to a state of optimal health. Programs emphasizing healing
will focus on medical care within a health services delivery system.

The medical interpretation of health and illness relies on a biomedical model.
The model assumes etiology is biologically specific, that disease is accounted
for by deviations from the norm of measurable biologic (somatic) variables.
Medical care and treatment are defined primarily as technical problems, and
the goals of medicine are viewed in terms of technical criteria, such as validity, diagnosis, precision of disease-related treatment, symptom relief and ter-
mination of disease processes. This technical orientation is reinforced by

ning received in large teaching hospitals filled with large-scale medical echnology (Mishler, 1981b; 1981c).

This biomedical perspective focuses largely on cure and acute care, rather than on chronic illness and coping with permanent conditions. Indeed, some argue that it has resulted in old age itself being defined as a problem considered solvable through the receipt of services, essentially medical services, at the individual level (Estes, 1979).

The medical orientation has also been associated with a growth in the use of drugs and medications. This growth is evident among the population as a whole, but especially among elderly persons (Chappell and Barnes, 1982). Although elderly individuals constitute only about 10 percent of the population in the United States, they receive approximately 25 percent of all prescriptions written in 1967. In that same year, the average person over 65 was prescribed roughly three times as many drugs and spent more than three times as much for her or his drugs as did someone less than 65 (Peterson, 1978). As a group, elderly people are the largest consumers of legal drugs and are increasing the number of prescriptions they purchase annually (Guttman, 1978).

More recent Canadian data from the Canada Health Survey show elderly men and women are more likely to take medications (including prescription and nonprescription drugs) than is true of younger age groups. They are more likely to use pain relievers, tranquilizers, heart or blood pressure medication, stomach medication, laxatives and other drugs. They are no more likely to be using antibiotics, cough or cold medicines, skin ointment or vitamins and minerals (see Table 6-1). Overall, elderly women are more likely to be using medications than are elderly men.

Examining only those medications taken on the advice of a physician (see Table 6-2), elderly men and women are more likely than younger age groups to be taking drugs for fewer of the categories. They are more likely using pain relievers, tranquilizers and heart or blood pressure medication only. For these categories, elderly women report using more medications than do elderly men.

Institutions

Concomitant with the rise of a physician focus, there has developed an institutional bias within health-care services. Indeed, the development of medicine as a profession has been tied to the development of short-term institutional services, specifically with hospitals.

In both Canada and the United States, it was after World War II that hospitals developed and signaled a break with the home, where illness had traditionally been treated. By this time, hospitals were viewed not as places where the poor went to die but where skilled medical specialists practiced and complex diagnostic technologies were used (Coburn et al., 1983). As noted at the beginning of the chapter, hospital growth in Canada was federally supported in the 1940s and 1950s through contributions towards construction.

Crichton (1980) tells us that hospitals received such federal support because people in local communities saw them as a safety net; doctors appreciated

TABLE 6-1

PERCENTAGE OF POPULATION IN SELECTED AGE GROUPS USING DRUGS* BY GENDER, CANADA, 1978-79

	Male				Female			
	<25	25-44	45-64	65+	<25	25-44	45-64	65+
Pain relievers	7.0%	11.4%	13.3%	16.4%	10.6%	20.3%	23.3%	26.3%
Tranquilizers	.6	2.6	6.7	10.9	.9	5.4	14.3	19.2
Heart/blood pressure	.1	1.4	12.7	30.1	.1	1.8	17.5	42.6
Antibiotics	2.8	1.8	2.4	2.4	3.4	3.5	2.3	2.0
Stomach	.8	3.9	4.9	6.2	1.0	3.7	5.8	7.3
Laxatives	.3	.6	1.8	8.2	.8	2.8	6.7	11.9
Cough/cold	7.7	4.4	4.3	4.9	8.5	5.5	5.3	5.4
Skin ointment	4.8	3.6	3.2	4.9	6.8	6.9	6.4	7.1
Vitamins/minerals	22.2	13.9	17.2	17.6	26.0	24.3	23.2	23.8
Other	1.9	2.9	8.3	16.5	4.1	9.2	18.4	21.2

*Using drugs refers to use of prescription and nonprescription drugs including vitamins and minerals.

SOURCE   Health and Welfare Canada and Statistics Canada *Canada, Health Survey Public Use Tape,* 1978/79.

TABLE 6-2

PERCENTAGE OF POPULATION IN SELECTED AGE GROUPS USING DRUGS ON MEDICAL ADVICE* BY GENDER, CANADA, 1978-79

	Male				Female			
	<25	25-44	45-64	65+	<25	25-44	45-64	65+
Pain relievers	1.3%	2.0%	4.5%	8.9%	1.8%	3.9%	8.9%	15.3%
Tranquilizers	.6	1.9	5.1	7.8	.5	3.3	8.7	12.5
Heart/blood pressure	.1	1.0	8.9	17.4	.1	1.1	10.3	23.9
Antibiotics	2.2	1.3	1.3	.8	2.5	2.2	.7	.6
Stomach	.2	1.4	1.6	1.5	.3	.8	1.4	1.2
Laxatives	.1	.1	.2	1.1	.1	.5	.8	.9
Cough/cold	1.6	.5	.5	.4	1.5	.5	.3	.6
Skin ointment	1.9	1.4	1.2	1.2	3.0	2.4	1.7	.8
Vitamins/minerals	4.5	1.3	1.8	2.3	5.9	5.0	2.6	1.9
Other	.8	1.5	.3	.5	1.9	3.4	5.5	3.7

*For those reporting use of drugs, respondents were asked whether or not this was on the advice of a physician.

SOURCE   Health and Welfare Canada and Statistics Canada Canada Health Survey Public Use Tape, 1978/79.

the sophisticated technology they would house; busines
would be profits from construction, equipment and dr
viewed hospitals as bringing employment and trade to th
The federal government saw hospital construction as a w
cohesiveness, redistribute wealth across the country anc
proving health.

The growth of hospitals encouraged the development of hospital insurance, since the costs could be high, and the effects devastating, especially for an uninsured patient. As hospitals increased, physicians became increasingly specialized, hospital-minded and accustomed to expensive therapies, for which dollars flowed readily from the public purse (Tsalikis, 1982).

The public financing of hospitals reinforced the move from the patient's home and the doctor's office to hospitals as the major place for treatment. At the same time, the public financing of hospitals gave rise to the growth of paramedical workers to assist in the tasks performed in this milieu. Public funding ultimately was a major factor in transforming doctors from independent entrepreneurs to participants in a complex medical-industrial institution.

Hospital utilization statistics are shown in Table 6-3 for bed days, discharges and length of stay. Canada's elderly population has more bed days per 1,000 population per year than does that in the United States. This is not true of Canada's younger population (those aged 64 and less). The figure for the younger age group is more comparable to the figure for the United States. It is, however, elderly persons in the United States who have more discharges per 1,000 population per year. This is true of both the elderly and the younger populations in the United States. In both countries, hospital use for persons aged 65 and over is substantially greater than for those younger.

The focus in the systems on hospitals reinforces short-term acute care. However, as noted in chapter 3, the major illnesses among elderly persons are chronic. Long-term institutions (referred to variously as nursing homes, personal care homes and so on) have been the major service provided for such needs. Both types of institutions, hospitals and long-term institutions, have been criticized as being oriented towards institutional management rather than to the individual and his or her needs.

The percentage of elderly persons in long-term institutional care (excluding hospital care) was shown in the previous chapter. It will be recalled that only a small proportion of elderly persons in each of the countries is in long-term institutional care at any one time. It is just as true that increasing proportions are found in such facilities as one examines older age groups. Approximately one-fifth to one-quarter of elderly people can expect to spend some time in a long-term care facility before they die.

The funding of long-term institutional services generally came after that for short-term hospitals. In Canada, reimbursement of the cost for long-term institutional care is still not guaranteed, but the Canada Assistance Plan sometimes covers this service. In the United States, medicare and, more so, medicaid provide public funds for such care.

Long-term institutional care has also become a major concern for those

TABLE 6-3

SHORT-TERM HOSPITALIZATION IN TERMS OF BED DAYS, DISCHARGES AND LENGTH OF STAY IN CANADA AND THE UNITED STATES

		Canada 1978-79	United States 1980
Bed days per 1,000 population per year*	≤64 65+	1161 5186	1212 4125
Discharges per 1,000 population per year	≤64 65+	119 280	167 386
Average length of stay (days)**	≤64 65+	9.7 18.0	7.3 10.7

* Bed days refer to the total number of days spent in hospital per year.
** Average length of stay refers to the mean number of days spent in hospital per admission.

SOURCES: Harris, C.S. *Fact Book on Aging: A Profile of America's Older Population*. Washington, DC.: National Council on Aging, 1978 and Statistics Canada *Fact Book on Aging in Canada*. Ottawa, Ont.: Minister of Supply and Services, 1983.

involved with mental illness. This is partly because of the shift in funding to nursing homes. During the 1950s and early 1960s in the United States, one-quarter of all first admissions to state hospitals—for psychiatric care—was for patients aged 65 and over, and half of all state hospital populations were in this age group (Eisdorfer and Cohen, 1982). Only 2 percent of psychiatric out-patients' care was provided to aging individuals during this period. Elderly individuals received little preventive or outpatient therapeutic care and were at heightened risk for long-term custodial placement.

It was during the late 1960s that the transfer of elderly individuals from state hospitals to nursing homes and other long-term care facilities took place. Direct admissions, however, from the community to nursing homes rarely involved mental health evaluations. The shift took place with no provisions to determine level of psychiatric services needed for nursing home inpatient care or mental health intervention.

Eisdorfer and Cohen (1982) also inform us that by 1967 there were more mentally ill aged in nursing homes than in psychiatric inpatient facilities. Most nursing homes, however, do not have identifiable ongoing psychiatric care.

Greater reliance is placed on tranquilizing and sedating with psychotropic medication. Care within nursing homes reflects more of a custodial system than a system of diagnosis and treatment. Nevertheless, chronic conditions are three to four times more frequent among individuals in nursing homes than among those in the community.

Neugarten (1982a) estimates about half of those in nursing homes have primarily mental health illnesses. Robertson (1982) presents a similar picture for Canada, estimating that 30 - 50 percent of those in institutions have some psychiatric conditions.

This focus on institutional rather than community services is evident in the next section providing utilization and cost figures.

Utilization Figures

Utilization figures confirm the focus of Canadian and American health care systems on medical care, acute care and institutional care. In terms of physi-cian services, the Canada Health Survey (Health and Welfare Canada and Statistics Canada, 1981) reports one or more visits by 85 percent of elderly persons in 1980. Kovar (1977) reports the figure for the United States as 79 percent.

Figures for community care are difficult to obtain but are instructive. For the United States national statistics are not collected (Lutz, 1984). In Canada, it is estimated that in 1981, 0.8 percent of elderly persons received meals-on-wheels, 3.5 percent transportation services, 4.3 percent homemaker or home help services, 4.3 percent assistance with shopping and banking and 3.7 per-cent receive nursing or other medical calls at home (Statistics Canada, 1983).

In the United States, in the early 1970s, elderly people occupied 30 percent of the one million general hospital beds (Gomers et al., 1979). This rate of hospitalization is two-and-a-half times greater than for younger people. Fur-thermore, Solomon and Hirt (1979) note that for 1977, average length of stay was twice as long for those 65+ than for those younger. In 1981, elderly per-sons accounted for 11 percent of the noninstitutionalized population and con-sumed 29.8 percent of short-stay days of hospital care (Rice and Feldman, 1983).

In Canada, in the early 1970s, Gomers and associates report elderly people occupied 22 percent of acute hospital beds and 76 percent of chronic beds. In 1976, elderly people constituted just under 9 percent of the population but used about 34 percent of patient days in hospital (Rombout, 1975). It will be recalled from the previous section that in both countries, elderly persons had more bed days and more discharges per 1,000 population and longer average length of stay than those younger.

Most telling are the proportions of total expenditures within the system. In Canada, for the period 1970-79, 50 percent of total health care expenditures went to hospitals and nursing homes (institutional care), 25 percent went to salaries for professional services (including but not exclusive to physician ser-vices), 10 percent went for drugs and appliances, and 15 percent to all other costs (Statistics Canada, 1983). Similarly, the majority of total health care expenditures in the United States in 1977 was spent on hospital and nursing home care (54 percent). Salaries of physicians and other professionals made up 31 percent of the expenditures, with the remaining consisting of 12 percent for drugs and appliances and 3 percent for other health costs (Fox and Clauser, 1980).

Looking specifically at public health expenditures for elderly people, figures are similar to those just noted for the total population. In the United States, 46 percent of these expenditures were for hospital utilization, 22 percent for physician services, 10 percent for nursing homes, 8 percent for drugs and 14 percent for all other services (Waldo and Gibson, 1982). Comparable Canadian figures for elderly persons only are not available.

Both utilization and cost figures confirm the focus within the systems in both Canada and the United States on institutional care rather than community care, on acute care rather than chronic care and on medical care rather than health care broadly defined.

The biomedical approach inherent in the current system, as well as several other aspects of that system, has come under heavy attack from several quarters. We turn now to a discussion of those criticisms.

THE CURRENT SYSTEM UNDER ATTACK

The biomedical model has come under heavy attack. One of the primary criticisms is its failure to take into account the fact that meaning is socially defined. Even the definition of a biological norm or deviation must incorporate information about specific populations and their sociocultural characteristics in order to be accurate (Mishler, 1981b).

Furthermore, it is argued (see, for example, Ehrenreich, 1978; Estes, 1979) that physicians do not only apply technical knowledge but also impart social messages that incorporate specific ideologies. The structure within which medical services are delivered, including the doctor-patient relationship, are social relationships. As such, these relationships reflect the social relationships of the larger society with their class, racial, gender and age differences.

A prime example, cited by these authors, is the treatment of menstruation and pregnancy in the latter part of the nineteenth century. Both were considered signs of illness; rest and passivity were prescribed as treatment. In addition, this "illness" was used as a reason for excluding women from paid labor. In other words, both diagnosis and treatment reflected male dominance in society. The medical profession not only reflects but also promotes the belief that elderly individuals are in need of services, in particular health services, which are equated with medical services.

The medical profession has also come under attack as empirical evidence has demonstrated the falsity of the popular belief that modern decreases in the death rate are due to scientific medicine (Dubos, 1963; McKeown and Lowe, 1966). McKeown and Lowe examined numerous factors as possible determinants of the long-term downward trend in mortality. They conclude that the primary factors were first, a rise in the standard of living of which the most important feature was probably improved diet; second, hygienic changes introduced by sanitary reformers; and third, a favorable trend in the relationship between infectious agent and human host, that is, specific preventive and curative therapies. The authors conclude that medical measures had a minor effect on the reduction of death rate, with the exception of reducing deaths due to smallpox. General improvements in social and environmental conditions provide a more adequate explanation for improvements in longevity. Said another way, public health measures rather than curative medicine account for the improvements.

Similarly, Evans (1984) notes that most of the preventive interventions that have been effective have been largely outside of the clinical field. Water flouridation is effective and inexpensive; tax and regulatory policies control smoking, alcohol consumption and seat belt use; and mass immunization works. Clinical strategies in these areas are more expensive and not necessarily as effective. This is not to deny that some forms of clinical intervention are useful and important, but to point out that other measures can and often are effective.

Health Care Costs and Health Status

In addition to arguments concerning the social definition of meaning and improvements in the environment, there are arguments that the costs of health care are not necessarily related to health outcomes. Recently, attempts have been made to relate costs to health outcome.

Both developed and less-developed countries show a high correlation between life expectancy and number of physicians, up to 100 per 100,000 population. Beyond this ratio, the relationship is not clear. The ratios for both Canada and the United States exceed that figure. Similarly, amount of dollars spent on overall health care is not related to life expectancy. Canada's health expenditures are higher than the United Kingdom's, but Canada has a lower life expectancy. Similarly, the United States spends a higher proportion of gross national product (GNP) on health care than any other country in the world but has the next to worst mortality rate among western nations (Maxwell, 1975).

Taking into account labor power, facilities and other aspects of the delivery system, as well as individual expenditures, best estimates suggest the United States spends proportionately more on health care than any country. Canada's expenditures are high but less than those of her neighbor to the south. In 1975, Canada spent 7.2 percent of the GNP, or approximately $495 per capita, on health care. In 1976, the United States spent 8.3 percent of GNP, or $650 per capita. The United Kingdom, however, spent $160 per capita in 1976 and only 5.4 percent of its GNP (Bennett and Krasny, 1981). Administrative costs are considerably higher in the United States (about 16 percent) than they are in the more centralized bureaucratic systems of the United Kingdom (2 - 4 percent) and Canada (2 - 4 percent) (Weller and Manga, 1982).

Cost arguments are critical. They have become a major concern, reflected in increasing debates and moves to control expenditures. However, as argued so convincingly by Evans (1984), no one part of the formal health care system has responsibility for ensuring either cost effectiveness or effectiveness of treatment. Neither physicians, nor hospital management nor other sectors within the system have any incentive or pressure to adopt less costly types of care. Despite the billions of dollars spent each year to improve the health of its citizens, no comprehensive, systematic effort is made either to measure results or account for costs in terms of outcomes. The United States does conduct periodic national health surveys; Canada does not even do this. Despite the frequently made assumption that more dollars spent on health care will lead to better health status, no good evidence exists to support this claim. Indeed, solid arguments can be made that this is not the case.

Increased capacity tends to lead to increased utilization, without corresponding price decreases. Bed capacity seems to be the single best predictor of hospital utilization (and estimates suggests this would continue to double or triple current need estimates). Once hospitals are built, they are seldom closed or reduced in capacity. A hospital is often the only industry in a small community and therefore a major source of employment. As well, a hospital may be the only way of attracting a physician to a rural area (LeClair, 1975). The concern, therefore, in reducing hospital costs is not always over patient care but rather is a political concern over loss of jobs or the inability to attract physicians to remote areas.

Innovations that free capacity have the same effect; they induce more utilization. New procedures, which become implemented because they are less expensive, more effective, less dangerous or more comfortable, become utilized to meet capacity. The result is that the overall cost exceeds that of the techniques it replaces. For example, one frequently hears the argument that the provision of more extended care for elderly persons and those chronically ill would reduce pressure on acute care facilities. But as such facilities are built, they become filled and acute care hospitals remain full.

Nor does a third party insurance system encourage cost-effective utilization. It pays physicians on a fee-for-service basis, an incentive for physicians to provide the best regardless of cost and to adopt a treatment-just-in-case attitude (Bird and Fraser, 1981). A combination of self-regulation and relatively generous insurance coverage without direct controls means price escalation is unlimited.

The argument that extra-billing reduces frivolous demands on the system and heightens the public's awareness of the cost of services is false. It is physicians, not patients, who decide utilization of the system. Studies on utilization and public medical insurance suggest such insurance results generally in making medical care more available to those with lower incomes (Evans, 1984); user charges will deter the poor, not the frivolous users, and it is frequently the poor who are sickest.

Suggestions for greater accountability and effectiveness (both clinical and cost) are discussed in chapter 8, where changes to the current system are examined in more detail.

Shift in the Nature
of Illness

In addition, the nature of illness has shifted. Infectious diseases have been replaced as major causes of death by heart disease, cancer and other chronic conditions, as well as accidents and other life-style-related causes. More dollars spent on the current medical care system are unlikely to overcome these causes of death. Furthermore, clinical intervention is largely ineffective and very expensive for life-style-related illnesses.

Questions are being raised about elderly people's use of medication. Because of their decreased physical reserve, they are twice as likely to react adversely to medications, even in normal doses, than is true of younger populations, and they experience side effects from a wider variety of medications (Schuckit, 1977). Further, iatrogenic hazards from polypharmacy and from drugs interacting with alcohol are known to exist. Some medications interfere with laboratory tests, resulting in a delay in discovering, or masking altogether, some illness; and some medications are known to be addictive. Research suggests elderly people are largely unaware of such dangers. Another problem is the significant amount of errors in taking medications, especially when multiple medications are prescribed (Chien et al., 1978; Lamy, 1981). These problems, together with general concerns that many medications affect the symptoms, not the cause of the symptoms, and that many lack long-term effectiveness, have raised concerns that medication therapy is not always the best therapy during old age.

Still other observers have presented a more extreme argument: not only is medicine not responsible for many of the improvements in life expectancy and in health, but modern scientific medicine can have a negative impact on health. Perhaps best known in this regard is Illich (1977) and his concept of iatrogenesis. Iatrogenesis refers to diseases and other individual and social problems resulting from the practice of medicine itself. Examples include side effects and addictions associated with drugs, unnecessary surgeries, accidents, injuries and infections resulting from hospitalization. Clinical iatrogenesis refers to specific diseases resulting from deficiencies in medical practice. Social and cultural iatrogenesis refers to the medicalization of life that is, to the extension of medical definitions of health, illness and treatment into all aspects of our lives.

Illich argues that the expansion of medicine by the definition of more and more aspects of life in medical terms erodes autonomy for self-care and of community processes for mutual care. Individuals become less and less competent to take care of themselves. Crichton (1980) suggests that we have become dependent on expertise. The centrality of the physician-patient relationship means the patient is considered as an individual, and the family and the wider social context are considered irrelevant to health.

The argument that there are negative side effects from the practice of medicine is important for at least two reasons. It means, like those technologies and treatments that simply do no good (as opposed to doing harm), there is room for improvement within the current system. Many argue, including Evans (1984), that withdrawing or redeploying resources will not reduce anyone's well-being and indeed will lead to benefits; for some forms of diagnosis or therapy, more is not always better. The argument that one cannot put a dollar value on health, presented in favor of the current system, is a false argument when that system can be restructured to provide better health care, more closely related to health outcome, at no extra cost. As Evans points out (1984), "It is easier to justify interventions as the organism slowly deteriorates — there is always something wrong." As a society, we have not yet dealt with the issue — especially during old age — "When is health care servicing inappropriate or too much?"

Negative consequences from the practice of medicine are important for another reason. They magnify the distinction just mentioned between health care and health outcome or status. That distinction is especially important when health professional and client disagree on the value of the outcome. Especially with a focus on curing illness rather than on overall well-being, a health professional may assume a treatment to cure the illness would be appropriate. The patient, however, may consider that the resulting quality of her or his life, especially if there are serious side effects from the treatment, will be insufficient to warrant the cure, even it it may add years to his or her life. This is a decision only the patient can make — with appropriate information.

In sum, while the medical model is inherent in our health care system and is equated with health in our society, it has, nevertheless, been subject to vigorous attack, especially in the last decade. This is not to attack individual physicians or to criticize their efforts for care and healing. It is, rather, to recognize the biases of the medical perspective and to recognize that the perspective is no more objective and value free than any other orientation.

As Mishler (1981a; 1981b; 1981c) says so well, the criticisms of the biomedical approach are not simply an argument to incorporate epidemiological or other social variables into a consideration of the biological. Nor are they simply an argument that one should be aware of both the effect of medical practice on institutional and organizational factors and of the effect of these factors on the practice of medicine. Rather, the meaning of health and illness is itself socially constructed. Diagnosis, therefore, is interpretive work; it is one of several different ways through which reality is viewed. While physicians have expert knowledge in a particular area, they do not necessarily know the preferences of the patient. Nor is there incentive or pressure for physicians to be economical.

One way of understanding the relevance of a biomedical model for aging, and of recognizing it as only one among several perspectives, is to look at its consequences in terms of institutional placements. The assumption that illness is the criterion for institutional placement underlies the management, funding and staffing of nursing homes, which concentrate on needs classified as requiring medical care. There may be two individuals equally disabled by a stroke. One, however, may be without family and social supports and need placement, while the other, who has money, family and friends, may be able to cope well and, indeed, do better by continuing to live in the community. The need for institutional care in this example is determined not by medical need but by social circumstance.

The current formal health care system in both Canada and the United States is to a considerable extent centralized around a medical model of health and illness and, in particular, around the services of physicians and hospitals and long-term institutional settings. An understanding of these foci within the current system is central for examining health care in an aging society.

‖ CONCLUSIONS ‖

Following from chapter 5, which focused on informal relations and the informal care system for elderly individuals, this chapter has focused on the formal care system. The formal care system exists to provide for those in need. The first part of this chapter briefly recounted the development of that system, primarily on the North American continent. Canada and the United States share many similarities but also differ considerably from one another.

One of the main differences concerns the crucial role played by groups and associations in the development of federal policy that embraced the medical model. It is evident that Canada tends to fall between the United Kingdom, with its more unitary and universalistic system, and the United States with its more fragmented and targeted system. The recognition of these differences led to a discussion of need- versus aged-based policies, an issue relevant to many of the changes currently being proposed in the systems.

Nevertheless, the systems that have evolved in both Canada and the United States are inherently medical in focus. The medical care system, which is largely viewed as synonymous with the health care system, has come under attack from several perspectives. It has been forcefully argued that medicine is not synonymous with health and that the biomedical model of illness is ill suited to an aging society. The emphasis on acute care and acute episodes of illness is not consistent with the shift to chronic illnesses and conditions during old age and in society in general.

At the heart of the numerous attacks on the medical care system is a recognition of the social meaning and context of medicine. Arguments abound that the medical care system cannot, to any large extent, improve the health of the population. Futhermore, no part of the system is designed to ensure either clinical effectiveness or cost effectiveness. The system permits unlimited growth without sound evidence that growth is related to health outcome.

Part of the medical care system is biased toward institutions, including both acute care hospitals and long-term care institutions. Hospitals account for the major cost component of health care dollars. Within long-term care institutions which are important considering the aging population, care is primarily oriented towards custodial service.

As others have noted, the current formal care system is dominated by the medical profession with the acute care hospital as its key institution. It has been argued that the aging of the population brings the inherent inadequacies of that system to the fore. Community and home care services have not had a particular emphasis to date in national systems of health care in either Canada or the United States. The systems have been criticized for this neglect. The next chapter discusses community and home care services, and is followed by a chapter on creating an appropriate system for an aging society — one that facilitates the informal care system.

▪ CHAPTER 7 ▪

‖ COMMUNITY ‖
HEALTH AND SOCIAL
‖ SERVICES ‖

If the social meaning and the consequences of the biomedical model are not fully understood, the emphasis on technical expertise and bio-scientific knowledge to improve levels of health will be considered appropriate by policy makers, medical educators and health administrators. Energies and funds will be directed to improving the existing system, for example, through measures to ensure a more equitable distribution of physicians or the more effective application of scientific medicine. As long as it is assumed that the basic premises underlying the system are correct, current policies will not be questioned and more resources will be put into improving the existing system.

The basic question, which is critical to health care for an aging society, is well expressed by Estes (1979):

> This focus on the needs of the aged, rather than on the defects of the medical care system, has proved costly for the aged as well as for the general public . . . . To label aging as primarily a problem of personal functioning is to deny recognition of the aggregate marginal economic and social status of the aged, while drawing attention to individual problems.

The question is whether the current formal care system, as it is organized and delivered, is appropriate to an aging society. As Crichton (1980) notes, one can spend endless efforts increasing access to the current system, increasing patient satisfaction and physician distributions or increasing the utilization of hospital beds, but if these do not have much bearing on health outcome, the effort is not going to achieve its goal.

It is not difficult to find authors who argue that the major shortcoming in the current medical system is its failure to meet the needs of the chronically ill elderly and to develop programs that allow flexible relationships between caregivers, whether they be professional or nonprofessional, over a long period of time. The above argument assumes that the significance of chronic disease should be measured in terms of the extent to which an individual's ability to function is impaired. It also assumes that satisfactory care of the chronically ill involves many aspects, including income, housing and social support. In short, long-term care has both social and medical components.

As Branch (1980) points out, an older individual who requires help financing the cost of long-term care cannot reasonably hope to receive this care at home as the current system exists. Yet, in some cases, it is extensive home-care-based services that would better foster independence of functioning and life-style, better reinforce feelings of dignity and self-respect and better provide high quality care. Indeed, Branch argues that the lack of funding for home care is the basic flaw in medicare, medicaid and Title XX in the United States. Branch goes on to say that the neglected alternative in the formal care system is a program that would provide intensive support services for those elderly who are sufficiently frail and vulnerable and sufficiently limited in functional activities to require extensive aid, but not so badly off that they require institutionalization.

Because of the inherent biases within the biomedical model, this broader definition of health and, therefore, health care are neglected. Federal programming in the United States reimburses for the high cost of institutional services but there are restrictions on reimbursement for noninstitutional services (Harrington and Newcomber, 1982). Only about one-third of the noninstitutional population who are either bedridden or require assistance in basic functions of daily living receive some form of governmental assistance. Medicaid automatically covers nursing home care, but coverage for home health care is a state option (Estes, 1979).

It is only when health is not equated with medicine that health care is no longer equated with healing activities. A broad definition of health, such as that enveloped by the World Health Organization and discussed in chapter 3, aims activities and expenditures at preserving an acceptable equilibrium between the person and his or her environment. Programs directed towards health involve strategies of public health, preventive medicine and health maintenance. The heavy emphasis on payment for services of physicians and surgeons tends to obscure the importance of extending programs to include the whole spectrum of health services.

A formal health care system more appropriate for an aging society, it is argued, would still provide some institutional care services, both short and long-term. However, a more appropriate system would have at its core a broad definition of health and would make adequate provision for noninstitutionally based chronic care. A more appropriate system would take into account family and other informal supportive groups. A reorganization of the existing system should integrate formal and informal care systems. That integration would more adequately meet the needs of an aging population.

We can ascertain a direction for the evolution of the formal care system by asking, "What are the needs of the elderly population?" Much has been said about the dearth of community and social services. This chapter examines community social services as they exist within the current system. It includes a description of some of the services, an assessment of those services and a comment on the appropriateness of such services for an aging society. The next chapter presents a more detailed discussion of the interface between formal and informal care systems.

A CONTINUUM OF SERVICES

Kammerman's (1976) review of services for aged individuals in eight countries (Canada, the Federal Republic of Germany, France, Israel, Poland, the United Kingdom, the United States and Yugoslavia) concludes that needs are fairly uniform among these countries. The needs identified include income after retirement, medical and related health care and shelter. A common theme emerges: services should be designed to enable elderly persons to remain in their own homes for as long as possible.

The spectrum of services to meet needs and enable elderly persons to remain in the community for as long as possible can cover a seemingly endless variety of care. Kammerman's list includes the following (although the author finds different countries emphasize different programs, access criteria, fees and coordination):

- community support services (homemaker, senior centers, etc.)
- multifacility, or multifunction, living and care complexes providing a range of separate but related facilities with different levels of care
- congregate or sheltered housing for those who do not require total care but cannot manage on their own in their own home
- and, finally, long-term care facilities for the frail elderly.

A continuum of care is implied in this ordering. Coward (1979), adapting from the work of Beattie (1976), suggests the following continuum:

- adjustment and integrative services, such as preretirement and postretirement counseling, bereavement counseling, specialized recreational programs for the aging, etc.
- supportive services to assist the elderly individual in her or his usual living arrangement when help is not available from informal sources. Examples of supportive services include outreach services, organized day care, geriatric day hospital, homemaker/home health aides, friendly visiting, portable meal services, organized home care, substitute family care or foster care, transportation services, etc.

- congregate and shelter care services, which can also include day care and geriatric day hospitals; substitute family care; specialized housing including health, social and recreational services; in-patient long-term care and treatment facilities; and respite care
- protective services, including coordinated and focused organization of legal, medical, psychiatric and social services to manage such areas as fulfilling personal and physical needs, planning and decision-making and the handling of finance
- specialized terminal care facilities and services.

Harrington and Newcomer (1982) prefer to discuss a continuum of programs, from the most restrictive to the least restrictive settings. Blenkner (1977) considers a continuum in terms of sources of care, from self-care to kinship support to societal programs.

The alternatives to institutionalization, encompassed by the phrase continuum of care, however that phrase is conceptualized, may take many forms. Some programs may involve medical care as well as social services, while others may be viewed strictly as social service programs. Each type of program has a potential effect on the health of an elderly individual. The focus of this chapter is on the provision of health and social services (rather than the more traditional medical services) and on community care (as opposed to institutional care).

Despite the emphasis on medical care today, a variety of health and social services does exist. Many of these services are not new. Home health services were initiated in the late 1800s in Europe, the United Kingdom and, to some extent, in the United States. It was not until the 1970s, however, that a substantial increase in the development of such services took place in North America.

Recognizing the Need
for Community Social
Services

In the late 1970s, it became increasingly evident that existing residential resources for elderly persons were able to meet the needs of those at the extremes, either the very sick or the very well, but were less able to meet the needs of those in the intermediate range (Havens, 1977). It was also at this time that the numbers of people in personal care homes or nursing homes at the lowest levels of care were being examined. Dulude (1978) notes that 45 percent of the over 100,000 elderly persons in nursing homes in Canada in 1975 were in self-sufficient, or level 1, care. She argues they could probably live in the community if support services were available.

Recognition of the need for community social services, however, comes at a time of economic constraint and when the expensive medical and institutional care system discussed in the previous chapter is already in place. Community social services are offered as alternatives to institutionalization and are believed to be considerably less costly than long-term institutional care

(Lalonde, 1974; Weiner et al., 1978). Novak (1985) reports tha
study finds that home care costs 14 percent of institutional
foundland study finds it costs 11 percent of institutional care. .
reports it cost $6,800 in 1978 to keep a patient in an exten
tion, compared with $53.87 a year for home care (Toronto C
Services, 1978).

The existence of such services is also believed to enhance the probability
of elderly persons living independently and to reduce their need for
hospitalization or nursing home placement (Katz et al., 1972; Kraus et al.,
1976). The services are an alternative elderly persons themselves prefer.

Community social services could fill the gap between the extremes of hospital, nursing, and shelter care, where extensive services are provided, and con-
ventional housing with very little or no support, (Heumann, 1978). They are
often thought of as filling gaps in a continuum of care. It is argued that such
a continuum is required to meet the needs of a heterogeneous elderly
population.

The trend towards more home care services is consistent with the prevail-
ing view in the gerontological literature that long-term institutionalization is
undesirable for most elderly persons. Notwithstanding the contrary view held
by some, such as the proponents of the welfare model (Myles, 1978), the gerontological literature abounds with the assumption that institutions are detrimental for elderly persons, except for a minority who require such total care. This
assumption is tied to the belief that independence is desirable and that institutions restrict autonomy while encouraging dependence. Wolk and Telleen
(1976) claim that a necessary component for satisfaction in the later years
is "an environment which at minimum offers the potential for personal
autonomy. . . ."

While many favor the trend towards increasing the diversity of community
supports for elderly persons, there is by no means consensus. Some policy
makers fear community programs will destroy family responsibility, although
there is no evidence to support this claim (Biaggi, 1980; Kane and Kane, 1980).
(See the next chapter for a further discussion of this issue.)

In addition, community and social services tend to be equated with welfare.
In the United States, social services have been less likely to be universal or
privately provided, as compared to medical services. They have tended to
be publicly funded and means-tested, stigmatizing recipients (Tenhoor, 1982).
Eisdorfer and Cohen (1982) argue that many of the health services required
to maintain elderly persons in the community have more difficulty being
accepted as legitimate health costs because they include social programs. Even
though prevention is less costly than diagnosis and treatment, its efficacy is
often obscure. Because such programs are less likely to be accepted as
legitimate, they are in danger of being cut in times of economic constraint.

Several specific services can be discussed as examples of community social
services. We turn now to such a discussion.

Home Care

The provision of home care is considered by many as a basic component of health and social services. In its broadest sense, it includes any services that enable elderly persons to remain in their own homes. In Canada, the Federal-Provincial Working Group on Home Care (National Health and Welfare, 1975) defines home care as:

> A basic mode of health care that co-ordinates and/or pro-
> vides the variety of personal health and supportive services
> required to maintain or to help function adequately in the
> home, those persons with health and/or social needs related
> to physical or mental disability, personal or family crises or
> to illness of an acute or chronic nature. A pre-requisite is that
> the home is judged to be a viable place where treatment or
> care can be provided. Supportive services include social ser-
> vices and other services to assist such persons and their
> families.

Many of the early home care programs were established as posthospital care. Many had primarily a nursing function rather than a coordinated variety of services. One of the first programs with coordination as an objective was the Montefiore Hospital program in New York, developed in 1946 (Bluestone, 1957).

Today, home care programs are both hospital- and community-based. Some operate on public funds; others rely on private funds. Some are administered at the national level, some at the provincial or state level, some at the local and some at the agency level. The services offered within the programs are also diverse.

The Manitoba Home Care program is an example of a community-based program that has not been designed mainly for posthospital care. The program has a coordinated entry point, the range of services is available after an initial assessment by a nurse and/or a social worker. While the Manitoba program is far from flawless, it is often regarded in Canada as a model of the home care delivery system. There is no unilateral restriction by medical, nursing, social or financial condition.

A range of services is provided at no cost to recipients who require help to function adequately at home because they are deteriorating physically or mentally. Services include care by nurses, home aides and orderlies, social workers, homemakers, therapists and volunteers. Various facilities and equipment are also available. One service under the home care umbrella is respite care. Homemakers and/or other services are placed in the home to provide personal care and/or household management on a 24-hour basis for a limited period as substitutes for the care or supervision usually provided by the family (Government of Manitoba, 1983).

While numerous services can fall within formal home care programs, they can also be offered independently. Select services are discussed next.

Adult Day Care

Adult Day Care (ADC) programs may be offered within h within other programs, or stand independently. ADC prog been accused of having no clear philosophy and few guid and social service components of care (Weiler and Rathbone-McCuan, 1978). Nevertheless, as Ohnsorg (1981) points out, the programs do have a common goal: to provide noninstitutional support for those unable to remain in the community without it. In the United States, in 1979, the National Institute of Adult Day Care was established. That institute views ADC as a component in the continuum of long-term care. Ohnsorg (1981) defines ADC as:

> . . . a gamut of services in a congregate setting that enhances the daily lives of older people and supports their continued involvement in the community. Adult Day Care is a generic term for a variety of programs offering services that range from social and health related to the provision of active rehabilitation, physical and mental health care. Various terminology is applied: day care, day treatment, day health care, psychiatric day treatment, partial hospitalization, day hospital care, etc. It is co-ordinated with, and relates to, other agencies and services, such as senior centres, in-home services and institutional and hospital care.

Some, such as Weissert (1977), distinguish two types of ADC programs, both captured within the above definition. The first type is narrowly defined in its service objectives, targeted towards a homogeneous group who meet specific admission criteria concerning health. These programs are often established by health institutions for people they have discharged. Participants tend to have chronic disabilities. Services frequently include meals, social work services, physical and occupational therapy and periodic medical evaluation.

Weissert's second type serves a more heterogeneous group of participants and is more oriented to social needs. The participants tend to show fewer functional impairments and fewer diagnosed medical problems. Services tend to focus on social and recreational needs.

In the United Kingdom, ADC programs tend to be similar to Weissert's second type of program (Weiler and Rathbone-McCuan, 1978). These programs are generally aimed at the less functionally impaired considered in need of social stimulation. It is the social services that tend to be emphasized—custodial care, meals, bathing and social interaction.

In Canada, the same general principles apply. The primary goals of ADC are to meet the needs of those who require assistance in maintaining their social and physical functioning and/or whose families need some relief from this responsibility. Canadian ADC fits Weissert's second category. Programs similar to the first type are frequently referred to as day hospitals.

all three countries, these programs are designed to provide care to those .th physical, mental or social impairments who remain in the community. Services are provided during daytime hours and can serve as respite care for family members.

Transportation

Transportation is a service recognized as necessary but service providers still do not know how best to deliver it. Without transportation, participation in social and recreational activities and the use of health and social services may be hampered. Education and housing needs, among others, may not be met (Carp, 1979; Government of Canada, 1982).

Many older people do own and are able to drive their own cars. In Canada, 60 percent own their own cars, while in the United States, the comparable figure is 61 percent (see Table 7-1). However, as health deteriorates, reliance on friends, family and private/public transportation systems becomes increasingly likely. The usual sources of transportation for elderly persons have received some, but not extensive study. A Canadian study (Grant and Rice, 1983) reports that 51 percent of the rural elderly usually drive themselves, 17 percent usually ride with another household member and 33 percent ride with a relative or friend outside the house. In an American study, Gombeski and Smolensky (1980), asking specifically about the usual mode of transportation for travel to a physician's office for nonemergency health care, report that 62 percent use a private auto, 17 percent ride with relatives, and 9 percent ride with friends or neighbors.

‖ TABLE 7-1 ‖

PERCENTAGE OF POPULATION BY AGE OF HOUSEHOLD HEAD AND CAR OWNERSHIP: CANADA, 1983, AND THE UNITED STATES, 1976

| | Canada | | United States | |
	Own vehicle	Do not own vehicle	Own vehicle	Do not own vehicle
35-44	87%	13%	88%	12%
45-54	86%	14%	86%	14%
55-64	82%	18%	82%	18%
65+	60%	40%	61%	39%

SOURCES: Statistics Canada, *Household Facilities by Income and Other Characteristics, 1983.* Ottawa, Ont.: Minister of Supply and Services, 1984, Catalogue 13-567, Table 3.1, p. 84-103. and Harris, C.S., *Fact Book on Aging: A Profile of America's Older Population.* Washington, DC.: National Council on Aging, 1978, p. 212.

Although transportation has been identified as a major concern, estimates of the level of need vary considerably, according to geographical area and the wording of the question. Here are some available figures regarding transportation problems: 2 percent of the elderly people in a rural county in Texas have difficulty with nonemergency transportation (Gombeski and Smolensky, 1980); 18.5 percent of elderly individuals in rural Saskatchewan have serious transportation problems (Grant and Rice, 1983) as do 37.9 percent of persons in rural North Carolina (Kivett and Scott, 1979).

Much of the attention on the transportation issue has focused on the rural elderly population. Compared with their urban counterparts, rural elderly persons are likely to have less access to transportation (Lee and Lassey, 1980). Many small towns and villages do not have public transportation, and some do not have private transportation in the form of taxis. Lack of transportation has been reported as strongly associated with low life satisfaction and loneliness among the rural elderly (Kivett and Scott, 1979; Fengler and Danigelis, 1983). Generalizations about all rural elderly are difficult to make given the diversity of small towns and rural communities.

Other aspects of the transportation issue need to be considered. These relate to design, service and safety elements. More specifically, they refer to: providing priority seating and grab bars on buses; having transit stops where older people can easily enter the bus; designing vehicles with easy access, including hydraulically operated kneeling buses and wheelchair buses; and programs such as dial-a-bus (Beattie, 1976; Government of Canada, 1982).

Participation in various health services may be dependent on having transportation available. For example, individuals who may benefit from a day hospital program may be unable to attend if transportation is not provided. Transportation needs are recognized as one of the greatest needs of elderly persons today, but strategies for solving such problems seem to be lacking.

Housing

Housing is another concern, central both to the ability of the elderly to remain independent in the community for as long as possible and to questions concerning cost. Increasingly the provision of community and social services within different housing alternatives is viewed by policy makers as a way of decreasing the use of costly medical services and long-term institutional care. The provision of community services spanning a spectrum of alternatives— represents an integrated approach combining housing and health services. It is also known as supportive housing.

As dollars are being spent on various combinations of services and housing, reliable data both on the benefits for recipients and on the cost of such programs is generally lacking. There are virtually no data on the effectiveness of alternative forms of service provision, including multilevel care facilities.

Reasons in favor of multi-level care facilities include economies of scale, provision of continual care and thereby a reduction of relocation trauma, adjustment of service levels to meet temporary changes in needs, maintenance of spousal relationships, flexibility of design to allow long-term changes in the facility's role, attraction of more qualified personnel, feelings of security and interaction among residents with different sorts of problems. Reasons against these types of facilities include their complexity, cost and size, their tendency to make their residents inward-oriented, and their encouragement of dependency among residents. Such facilities become funnels to care. Those requiring long-term care must enter at the lowest level or enter prematurely in order to ensure themselves a place at the highest level of care when it is needed.

Existing research is inconclusive. Gutman's (1978) study shows the multilevel tenants tend to exhibit higher morale and increased interaction with neighbors 18 months after moving into the building. The study also suggests no decrease in amount of satisfaction with or in visiting with friends after the move into such housing. In another study, Gutman (1980) reports tenants in retirement housing have more health problems and functional disabilities than do those of comparable age living at home, suggesting the need for special design features in retirement homes.

Defining "need" for housing is difficult. Varady (1980) reports that individuals may move from current housing to different types of housing for reasons other than health. They may move as they get older, when the racial mix in their neighborhood changes, to leave public housing, to avoid living alone and so on. Housing involves more than shelter needs, narrowly defined. It is an area which has much potential for innovative approaches.

In sum, a variety of services exist to meet the needs of an elderly population. Although a program may operate under a generic name, such as home care, the services may vary considerably. Several types of services, such as senior centers, educational experiences, meals-on-wheels, friendly visitors, financial planning and personal counseling may or may not come under the home care umbrella. Services can operate independently, or within some other program.

Some of the areas discussed here, like home care, respite care, and day care represent specific services. Other areas such as transportation and housing, represent needs for which the most appropriate forms of delivery have yet to be found. Part of the difficulty in this area is the heterogeneity of the needs of an aging population. There is confusion over the many similar programs and the diversity of services within programs. The effectiveness of many of these programs is unknown.

Literature assessing some of these programs appears later in this chapter. First, we turn to utilization of social services.

Utilization of Social Services

When one attempts to compare community programs in various countries, and indeed within a country, several difficulties arise. There is a lack of uniformity in program objectives, criteria, funding sources, services available, use of personnel and terminology (National Health and Welfare, 1975; Governoment of Canada, 1982). Trager (1980) summarizes the problems of the home health services in the United States as: complex and differing requirements of multiple reimbursement and funding agencies; confusing and contradictory target populations; varying definitions of services; inadequate, inaccessible or absent services; differing regulations with respect to the range of, duration of or access to, services; and inconsistency in the standards that regulate quality assurance.

A major problem when trying to collect even basic statistics on what programs exist is the lack of coordination and centralization. Beattie (1976) argues that one of the main barriers to the effective provision of services is the lack of organizational approaches integrating medical, health, and social services in a coordinated manner to meet the needs of the older individual and his or her family. Yet coordination and joint decision-making are essential for the effective operation of such programs. Only through coordinated efforts can continuity of care be provided, the appropriate level of care be assured and the individual be helped to remain at home for as long as possible. It is necessary to maintain a working relationship with all segments of health and social services in order to identify community needs and to meet the larger objectives of public policy.

Information and referral centers have been established to assist with information dissemination. They can take various forms. Zawadski and Ansak (1983) suggest that two models exist: the brokerage model and the consolidated model. The former refers to the channeling of existing services by a case manager or an advocate who links elderly persons to the services she or he requires. The consolidated model assesses clients and coordinates services within a single program that attempts to meet a variety of needs.

Not everyone agrees that such centers are the best solution. Critics argue that information and referral centers, especially the brokerage type, are more add-ons to the system. Silverstein (1984) discusses the need for more appropriate targeting of existing services. An example would be outreach aimed at members of elderly persons' informal networks, as well as at elderly individuals themselves.

Irrespective of the debate regarding the necessary mix of services for an aging population, or the mechanisms to best achieve coordination, there seems to be strong consensus that coordination is urgently required. Coordination is necessary not only among formal services within the institutional structure of the formal care system but between the formal and informal care systems as well.

Funding exemplifies some of the difficulties involved. Funding frequently comes from several sources, each with its own eligibility rules, and is frequently short-term. Community programs are operated by federal, provincial/state or local government agencies, voluntary groups, nonprofit organizations, outreach departments of hospitals and proprietary agencies. As a result, some critics (such as Zawadski and Ansak, 1983) argue that there are service overlaps and gaps, problems of access and a rigidity in programs which, once established, are difficult to adjust to meet the changing needs of clients.

A specific example of the dilemma faced when relying on such sources of money is presented by Matthews (1982). A transportation program was established in eight counties in a regional planning district in the United States. Between 1971 and 1977, funds were obtained from various funding sources: Title III of the Older Americans Act, Title XX of the Social Security Act, Title 16(b)(2) of the Urban Mass Transit Act and contracts with various agencies. The project had to be altered to fit the requirements of the funding agencies at the expense of the original philosophy, which was to provide transportation to anyone who met the age requirement. In the end, only the transportation disadvantaged were to be served. In other words, the program shifted from one based on age to one based on need as defined by the funding agency rather than by the community organizers. This problem is not unique to transportation. Nor is it unique to the delivery of health services. Indeed, anyone or any agency that relies on what is often referred to as "soft money," is well aware of the dilemmas faced.

Some Figures

Despite numerous problems, some investigators have attempted to compile utilization figures. LaVor (1979) suggests that approximately 3.4 million, or about 18 percent of the noninstitutionalized population aged 65 and over in the United States, need some form of continuing home care and support. Included in these estimates are the bedfast, the housebound and those having mobility-limiting conditions. However, Richmond (1980) argues there is a wide variety in the estimates of need, depending not only on the criterion used but also on the methodology employed. His review of several studies shows the variation. Estimates for nursing care range from 2 percent to 6.7 percent, for personal care from 5.2 percent to 14 percent and for homemaker and chore services from 11 percent to approximately 25 percent. Kovar (1977) suggests there are no good estimates of the number of individuals who could benefit from such services.

Similarly, it is difficult to determine how many individuals are served by home health services. Unless the program falls under governmental jurisdiction, figures are seldom available. Even when figures are available, it is difficult to draw comparisons because programs vary greatly. It tells us little if we know that in one state or province 12 percent of the population aged 65 and over is served by a home care program compared with 4 percent in another state or province unless we know whether comparable services are offered in the two locations.

Figures for home nursing and home helps, commonly referred to as homemakers in North America, are available for the United Kingdom. The National Health Service offers four home-based health services, which include general practitioners, home nurses, health visitors and chiropody. Provided by local authorities, and also mandated by legislation, are home helps, meals-on-wheels and counseling. In addition, there exists a wide variety of non-mandated services, including household aids and equipment services and day hospital centers. The majority of elderly individuals who receive these services pay no fee (Trager, 1980).

Figures for 1976 show that approximately 16 percent of the British population aged 65 and over used home nursing services and 8.1 percent used home helps. In Canada, 4.3 percent of the elderly population used homemaker or home help services in 1981, while 3.7 percent received nursing or other medical care (Statistics Canada, 1983). The United States does not collect such information (Lutz, 1984).

Little additional information is available on the number of individuals served by home care programs. While programs may record the number of clients served, this type of information is more likely to be contained in agency files and reports than in publications available to the public.

Despite the broad definition of health care and the eloquent speeches on the need for home care programs by groups, such as the Federal-Provincial Working Group on Home Care, this ideal is far from being reached. Even though in 1975, there were 2,254 home health agencies in the United States participating in the medicare program, all offered nursing care. Almost three-quarters (74 percent) offered physical therapy and almost three-quarters (71 percent) had home health aid services. Only 35 percent included speech therapy, 24 percent occupational therapy and 25 percent medical social services (U.S. Department of Health, Education and Welfare, 1975). That is, especially in the United States, nursing care is likely to be a common element, while social services are likely to be unavailable, reflecting the medical focus even in home care programs. Eisdorfer and Cohen (1982) note that the ratio of medical expenditures to health/social expenditures for long-term support in the community was a striking 30 to 1 in the late 1970s.

Because neither medicaid nor medicare provides the elements of home services, other than the skilled nursing component, many viable alternatives to institutional care remain financially impractical. Funding continues to go to institutions, while day care and home care services flounder (Binstock, 1978).

Although the Department of National Health and Welfare in Canada established a committee for developing pilot home care programs as early as 1957, there were only 26 programs operating in six provinces by 1967. While in 1978 most communities provided services by community health nurses, the Victorian Order of Nurses, the Canadian Arthritic and Rheumatism Society, the Canadian Red Cross Society and visiting homemakers, Manitoba was the only province to provide a universal home care program. In some provinces, medical authorization was still required for entry into the program (Shapiro and Roos, 1978).

As noted in chapter 6, the evolution of the formal care systems in the United States and Canada resulted in an emphasis on medical and acute care rather than on the development of either community and social services, or a system involving both. Widespread recognition that the existing system has an overemphasis on medical and institutional services, especially for an aging population, and a damaging underemphasis on community and social programs, coincides with periods of economic constraint. Economic constraint has led to a questioning of the existing system and some interest in the provision of community and social services, because the alternatives to institutional care may be less costly. In addition, moves to block funding of health services mean there is potential for greater flexibility in the provision of services by provinces and states rather than tying the funds to specific services, such as physician and hospital based services. Even though questioning has come at a time when a huge medical complex is already operative and when money is scarce, the criticisms nevertheless provide an opportunity for change. That opportunity should not be ignored but grasped to create a system more appropriate for an aging society.

Increased interest in community social services has been accompanied by a demand for greater accountability. This is tied to the period of economic constraint and the escalating costs of the medical care system. Studies examining the impact of various forms of care, especially alternatives to acute or chronic institutional care, are difficult to find. We do not know if participation in such forms of care in fact prolongs elderly persons' stay in the community or prevents long-term institutionalization altogether; nor do we know if it helps to prevent decreases in well-being or contributes to increased well-being; nor do we know if some community programs interfere with informal care. Is it monitoring by staff at any one program that leads to increased use of other services or is it the individual's increased knowledge of the system which can lead to increased use of other services? The next section examines available knowledge on benefits of community social services.

EVALUATING COMMUNITY PROGRAMS

By its very nature evaluation research is fraught with difficulties. The implementation of a rigorous design that would lead to answers for many of the vital questions is frequently close to impossible in the world outside of the controlled laboratory. The laboratory, however, does not simulate the complexity of the real situation. In fact, the lack of rigorous evaluation research has been attributed to the difficulty of designing research capable of assessing the questions raised by policy makers (Rossi and Wright, 1977). This, however, does not obviate the need for such studies. Chapter 9 discusses some of the important features of applied research and the difficulties of implementation.

Existing evaluations on health and social services suffer from many shortcomings. Many lack a comparison or a control group; some examine change over a relatively short time period, so it is difficult to assess long-term effects. Comparisons of results from various evaluations are difficult due to differences in outcome measures, time parameters, programs under study and other problems (Kelman, 1980).

So long as we recognize these limitations, existing evaluations tell us something about the effectiveness of the health and social programs available to an elderly population. A number of evaluations are discussed here in terms of the following outcome measures: institutional services, physical functioning, well-being and mortality.

Institutional Services

Some studies do explore the effect of a program on the participant's use of hospital inpatient services. Robertson et al. (1977), in their study of planned intermittent hospital readmission (similar to respite programs), report an average of 79.5 hospital bed days in contrast to the anticipated full-time occupancy (365 days) if the program is not available.

Fewer days stayed in hospital are also reported by Nielsen et al. (1972) in the United States for the recipients of home aid services as compared with a matched control group of nonrecipients. Similarly, Horowitz and Dono (1984) find that the average length of hospital stay per admission for individuals receiving community-based program services decreases, and increases for the comparison group not receiving such services. However, both groups experience declines in the mean number of admissions per person.

A Canadian study of ADC participants (Chappell, 1983b; Chappell and Blandford, 1983) reports mixed findings. When ADC participants are compared with two groups of controls matched on age, sex, functional disability and illness, no group differences emerge in terms of hospital utilization. However, all participants were in new programs. Later data from those attending ADC, after the program had been established for some time, reveals substantial and dramatic decreases in inpatient hospital utilization. No control group was used in this later study. Thirty-nine percent of the sample decrease their total number of admissions, and 42 percent decrease their total days stayed. The change in average days stayed shows the size of the changes taking place: in the year before entering ADC, each person spent on average 33 days in hospital. This drops to 13 days on average for the year July 1982 to June 1983. (Controlling for length of time in the program does not affect these results.) While these data are longitudinal, no control group was used in the study.

An explicit rationale for many community programs is a prevention, or postponement, of long-term institutional care. Examining experimental groups receiving home aid services and control groups not receiving such services, Nielsen et al. (1972) suggest that such services may reduce the likelihood of entering long-stay institutions. Matching the two groups on sex, diagnostic group (illness) and age, they report significantly fewer patients admitted to long-term care institutions among the experimental group, that is, the group receiving home aid services. The authors do note, however, that potential caregiving by a household member may be an important factor, which has not been taken into account.

Hodgson and Quinn (1980) report that 7 percent of users of a coordinated community services program are in nursing homes at any one time and that 41

41 percent of such residents return home. They argue that home care services can therefore enable individuals to use the nursing home temporarily rather than permanently.

Flatham and Larsen's (1976) study of day hospitals fails to show evidence that the program prevents, or retards, long-term institutional care. Their data are longitudinal but do not include a control group. Similarly, Weissert and associates' (1980) assessment of a day hospital demonstration in the United States fails to show support for the desired outcome. Their study did include random assignment to treatment and experimental groups. (See *Home Health Care Services Quarterly,* 1(3), 1980 for critiques of this study.)

Some studies (Chappell and Blandford, 1983) suggest there may, in fact, be a greater likelihood of long-term institutional placement among ADC participants compared with recipients of other types of home care services and, most notably, when compared with a group of matched controls not receiving any home care services. Whether the ADC participants are more in need because of some other factor, such as the unavailability of social support; whether they are just as in need but receive long-term institutional care because of appropriate monitoring in the ADC program; or whether they are no more in need than other groups but are simply known to the system could not be determined from the study.

Some support exists for the effectiveness of community social services in reducing hospital stay. The findings are more mixed in terms of postponing, or preventing, long-term institutional care. More needs to be known about the types of programs that are most effective in this area and how their effectiveness can be enhanced.

Even less research exists on the relationship between the use of community social services and other services, such as those offered by physicians. Some studies (Chappell and Blandford, 1983) suggest some decreases in physician services, mainly by type of visit rather than by type of doctor or disease category, but the relationships are not strong. More studies are needed in these areas.

Physical Functioning, Well-being and Mortality

Physical functioning, as noted in chapter 3, can be measured in a variety of ways. Many evaluations incorporate some measure of activities of daily living. In a project of coordinated home care services studied by Hodgson and Quinn (1980), 72 percent of the participants improved or maintained their ability to perform basic personal care functions, while 48 percent improved or maintained their ability in basic community living activities. The time period examined varied for each participant, as clients who began the program between 1974 and 1979 and survived until 1979 were included.

The time element can be important, particularly when considering physical functioning. For example, after six months Horowitz and Dono (1984) report no significant changes in basic or instrumental activities of daily living

(ADL-IADL) for either their experimental group, who received a variety of community-based services, or their comparison group. However, after one year the comparison group had improved its functioning, while the experimental group remained the same.

Similarly, Weissert and associates' (1980) evaluation of a day hospital demonstration project fails to show benefits for the functioning of its participants. Functioning is measured in terms of Katz' ADL scale. However, Flatham and Larsen's study does report improvements in patients' health status, the criteria being assistance with ADL, physical problems and last active treatment.

The enhancement of the participants' quality of life is frequently a stated goal of community social programs. Although accomplishment of this goal is more often assumed than validated, subjective well-being is an area where such programs may well be quite effective. Studies more consistently show improvements in this area, in contrast to the mixed findings reported for changes in physical functioning.

Nielsen and associates' (1972) study of home aide services for patients discharged from a geriatric rehabilitation hospital reports significant and favorable effects on contentment among arthritic or fracture patients receiving the services. Weiler and associates' (1976) comparison of ADC participants with a group of community living elderly persons shows no significant differences between the groups in satisfaction with life-styles, but it does report improvement among the ADC participants in the areas of emotional functioning and interpersonal relationships. Similarly, Flatham and Larsen (1976) report improvements in mental and social health among participants of day hospitals.

Chappell's (1983b) ADC studies also show increased life satisfaction among participants, an effect *contrary* to that evident among recipients of other home care services who are not attending ADC. The ADC program also shows a significant increase in the participants' social integration when compared both with recipients of other home care services and with nonrecipients of any such services. Participation in ADC also seems to lead to increases in specific types of recreational activities (indoor, outdoor and church related) compared to non-participation in the ADC program.

Mortality is another outcome sometimes examined. Once again the effects of home and community services are unclear. It is difficult to know, especially if recipients are frail, whether death should be considered bad. Someone who is severely disabled and suffering and who has little or no prospect for improvement, may well view death as the preferable alternative.

Looking specifically at home aide services, there are no significant differences in mortality rates between the matched experimental and control groups of patients discharged from a geratric rehabilitation hospital (Nielsen et al., 1972). Individuals who receive home aide services are no more or less likely to die than those who do not receive this particular service. Similarly, the participants in ADC, the recipients of other home care services and those receiving no such services reveal no significant differences in mortality rates (Chappell, 1983b).

Two other studies explore the relationship between mortality and the receipt of community-based program services. Both include experimental and control groups in their designs. However, the results do not concur. Skellie and Coan (1980) report individuals in the control group, who are matched on age, sex and illness with the experimental group, are more likely to die within the first six months (19 versus 6 percent) and during the first year (29 versus 15 percent). Horowitz and Dono (1984), on the other hand, report a higher incidence of mortality among the recipients of services but no significant treatment effects.

To summarize, the review of the evaluations of community and social services points out some of the difficulties involved in conducting such research and in comparing outcomes across programs. Obtaining adequate control groups is frequently difficult. The time element is also important; often the period of observation is too short for efffects to be seen. Furthermore, the effects of the program may not be measurable. Intangible benefits can exist. The standard measurements used may not be appropriate for the particular client group or for the particular service being evaluated.

The difficulty of disentangling possible age and illness effects, especially when studying an elderly population, is well known (Botwinick, 1982). Without a comparison group of individuals with similar health status and age, one is unable to determine the effects of the program versus progression of a disease or deterioration due to age.

Overall, existing evaluations show some support for the effectiveness of community social programs. They do not, however, show overwhelming support. Nor are they conclusive. Aside from the difficulties of design and measurement for assessing effectiveness, the evaluations face another inherent difficulty—trying to operate in a system ill-designed to meet the needs of an aging society. Before elaborating on possible improvements to this system, the topic of the next chapter, we turn to a discussion of the characteristics of users and determinants of utilization of existing services.

‖ PREDICTING UTILIZATION ‖

Assessing the effectiveness of community social programs is confounded by the debate on utilization of health services and need. A growing body of literature attests to the fact that variables other than need are associated with utilization of services. Said another way, need is socially defined, so that what one individual considers a need, another may not.

It has long been recognized that one of the reasons people with heart disease or cancer delay seeking medical advice is that they view the disease as incurable. They may avoid the physician so as not to learn the truth and because they believe the physician cannot do anything for them. Whether or not an individual under stress goes to a doctor reflects more her or his pattern of illness behavior than the nature and the quality of stress (Berkanovic, 1982).

Dean (1981) reviewed the literature on self-care, noting that the amount of serious illness experienced by individuals who regularly visit the doctor and those who seldom visit the doctor is no different.

Alternative belief systems regarding health and illness have been called various names, including professional and lay (Freidson, 1970); modern and traditional (New, 1977); and scientific, folk and primitive (King, 1962). Disease, defined within a medical model, refers to an abnormality in function and/or structure of body organs and systems. Illness in a nonscientific belief system refers to perceived changes in the individual's psychological well-being and role performance.

There seems to be general consensus that the folk, or lay, health belief system is related to both the social characteristics of the individual and the type of symptoms experienced. Although McKinlay (1980) notes there is still confusion over the importance of symptoms and the process of seeking help, few argue that, where symptoms are severe, there is little alternative but to recognize the illness and the requirement for some kind of formal help. Mechanic (1969) argues that social factors are much less important when symptoms are more severe. Conversely, McKinlay argues that social factors probably exert considerable influence in the case of known disabling symptomatology. Folk medicine is more likely to be involved if the condition is one for which scientific medicine has not been able to produce effective cures or controls.

Social factors include social class, ethnicity and gender, among others (Burke and Goudy, 1981; Kahana and Kijak, 1980). In trying to understand these factors, Zola (1964) delineates five triggers, or mediating factors, likely to influence an individual's decision to seek medical care: interpersonal crisis, social interference, the presence of sanctioning, perceived threat and the nature and quality of the symptoms. In later works (1966), Zola reports that interpersonal crisis and social interference are the most prominent triggers among Italians, sanctioning among the Irish, and the nature and quality of the symptoms among Anglo-Saxons. McKinlay (1980) argues that interference with everyday activities is one of the major criteria used by laymen to define illness. Generally, symptoms that are socially disruptive are more likely to be defined as worthy of some kind of lay or professional attention. Evidence documenting gender differences in health utilization behavior, particularly greater use among women, has been mentioned in chapter 3.

Existing research, then, suggests that numerous factors may be relevant in the elderly's utilization of formal care services. Factors include various aspects of the informal network, health beliefs, social and demographic characteristics, knowledge and need.

At least three theoretical approaches for studying health behavior have relative popularity in the literature. These include the health belief model; social network model; and a framework that distinguishes need, predisposing and enabling factors.

One of the more enduring conceptual frameworks for studying health related behavior is the health belief model, a psychosocial framework introduced by

Rosenstock (1966). Rakowski and Hickey (1980) inform us that the impetus for the development of the health belief model came from observations indicating the nonutilization of preventive health services was significantly related to personal attitudes and beliefs regarding health and health care assistance. This model assumes that good health is a goal more or less common to all, and that differences in preventive health behavior are due to different perceptions, which determine the individuals' motivations to engage in action and the specific decisions of what action to take to reach good health.

Four health beliefs that are fundamental elements of this model are (1) perceived susceptibility to a given illness, or re-susceptibility, (2) perceived seriousness of the target illness, (3) benefits that are expected to occur from contact with the health care system and (4) perceived barriers to and costs of contact with the health care system. Modifications have been suggested, including personal demographic characteristics, psychological and social variables and past and current experiences with the health care system.

Langlie (1977) notes that an alternate model, called the social network model, posits variation in preventive health behavior as a result of different characteristics of the social group to which the individual belongs, rather than to his or her personal attributes. Having empirically tested these alternative models, Langlie reports that a substantial proportion of variation in indirect risk preventive health behavior (such as seat belt use and medical check-ups) is accounted for by the joint effects of social psychological and social group characteristics. In contrast, appropriate direct risk preventive health behavior (such as personal hygiene and smoking) is mainly associated with older people and women.

Increasingly common, particularly for studying health service utilization behavior among elderly persons, is the paradigm initially posited by Andersen and Newman (1973). They first outlined the three main determinants of health utilization behavior as needs, enabling factors and predisposing factors. One has perceived needs as well as objective needs. Predisposing factors refer to the individual characteristics that may affect need, recognition or service utilization, such as demographic factors (gender, age and so on), social structural variables (education, ethnicity and so on) and attitudes and beliefs. Enabling factors refer to those circumstances or individual characteristics that either hinder or facilitate the use of an appropriate service once a need has been recognized. Enabling factors include, for example, financial resources, knowledge of services, ability to locate and travel to services, rural or urban place of residence and the organization of the delivery system (Ward, 1977). See Table 7-2.

Using this framework, Coulton and Frost (1982) study elderly persons and find the use of medical care and social services is largely associated with need factors. Enabling and predisposing factors tend not to be related. The only exception is recreational services, which are used most often by the least isolated. When Wan and Odell (1981) examine the use of health and social services among the noninstitutionalized elderly, they find that need for service (as evidenced by physical and psychological functioning) is the most

TABLE 7-2

INDIVIDUAL DETERMINANTS OF HEALTH SERVICE UTILIZATION

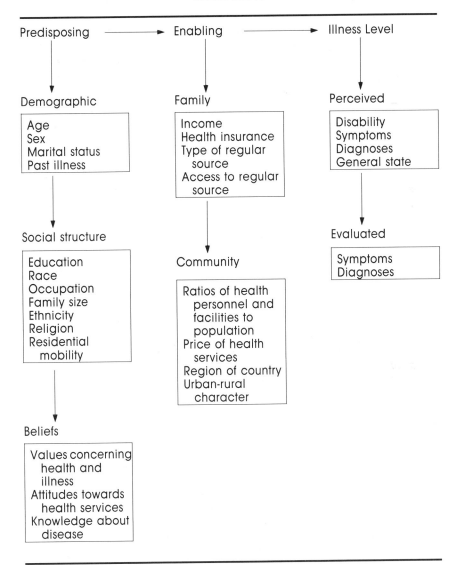

Predisposing ⟶ Enabling ⟶ Illness Level

Demographic

Age
Sex
Marital status
Past illness

Family

Income
Health insurance
Type of regular
    source
Access to regular
    source

Perceived

Disability
Symptoms
Diagnoses
General state

Social structure

Education
Race
Occupation
Family size
Ethnicity
Religion
Residential
    mobility

Community

Ratios of health
    personnel and
    facilities to
    population
Price of health
    services
Region of country
Urban-rural
    character

Evaluated

Symptoms
Diagnoses

Beliefs

Values concerning
    health and
    illness
Attitudes towards
    health services
Knowledge about
    disease

SOURCE: Andersen, R. and Newman, J.F. "Societal and Individual Determinants of Medical Care Utilization in the United States". *The Milbank Memorial Fund Quarterly*, 1973, 51, 1, pp. 95-124. Reprinted by permission.

important predictor of use of physician services and hospitalization. However, predisposing factors have the most effect on use of dental services. Knowledge of services, an enabling factor, is the most relevant for the use of social services. Similarly, George (1981) finds that demographic and enabling variables better predict service use among elderly persons than do need variables.

In a somewhat related, but different undertaking, Wolinsky (1982) examines the assumptions inherent in much literature studying the relationship of health status, or need, to the use of health services: that each of the three dimensions of health (physical, psychological and social) has an equal impact on the use of social services, and that the effect of these three dimensions of health is manifested in an additive rather than in an interactive function. Results suggest that the additivity assumption is correct but that the equality assumption is not. Contrary to Mechanic (1969), psychological health is found to have the least impact of the three.

As is true for so many areas examined here, there is more to know about utilization of health and social services. A major difficulty is whether or not those most in need are the recipients of the services. If it is not even those most in need who are receiving the services, is it right to ask about the effectiveness of those services for the current recipients?

‖ CONCLUSIONS ‖

This chapter has reviewed existing community social services. Neither Canada nor the United States has national insurance schemes to cover such services; nevertheless, such services do exist. National statistics do not exist; those that do exist do not apply to similar services. It would appear far fewer people use such services than use traditional medical services insured under national legislation.

Yet, community social services are viewed by many as a critical component in the provision of continuity of care, whether defined in terms of a health-illness continuum, a dependence-independence continuum or a source-of-care continuum. Many others consider them welfare programs performing functions that should be provided by the individuals themselves, their families or friends. Part of the debate concerning these programs involves their effectiveness in maintaining or improving the participants' quality of life (measured variously) and in reducing the need for other more expensive services, such as hospitalization and physician services and/or long-term institutionalization. Rigorous research in this area is difficult to find. Knowledge to date is inconclusive but suggests the potential of such programs.

One must recall, however, that the formal care system is not the only source of assistance for elderly persons. Informal networks have important contributions to make, as discussed in Chapter 5. One element in a changing system is an increase in the interface between this informal network and the formal system of care. The notion that the formal and informal systems can and should work together is not new. As Froland and associates (1981) point out, the use of the informal network by formal agencies can be traced back to the turn of the century in North America, when settlement house workers assessed the feasibility of enlisting the help of the informal network. Recently, assistance from family and friends has received increased attention, in part because of the rising costs of formal care for an aging population and in part because of concern that current economic circumstances will not allow utilization of the current system by more and more elderly persons in the future.

Governments, as well as others, are shifting their concern to the potential role informal caregivers can play. The American government has issued policy statements regarding the development of the relationship between formal and informal systems of care (Task Force on Community Support Systems, 1978). Similarly, the Canadian government has recognized the importance of this interface (Government of Canada, 1982).

Collaboration not only is considered potentially cost effective but also has the potential to minimize the possible devastating effects of political change every few years, to enhance the natural support system and to encourage contact between individuals (Maguire, 1983; Silverstein, 1984). It is the facilitation of natural support groups that is the topic of the next chapter.

- **CHAPTER 8** -

‖ FACILITATING ‖ APPROPRIATE COMMUNITY ‖ SUPPORT ‖

This chapter discusses some changes to the current system to better serve the needs of an aging population. Many of the criticisms of the existing system noted in the preceding chapters are accepted. However, the underlying principles of universality and equal access inherent in the current system are not questioned. Nor are the important contributions of clinical medicine and a medical perspective dismissed. We are arguing for less dominance by the medical profession than is evident today. We are also arguing for a greater emphasis on the autonomy of the patient, on the inclusion of the informal support network in the care of elderly people and on social and community services.

Such changes to the system would include a greater emphasis on chronic care, specifically chronic care in the community. Also necessary is a greater emphasis on meeting the needs of the patient, and a recognition of the potential for rehabilitation of elderly persons. Increased flexibility within the system, especially within long-term institutional care, so that individuals can return to the community, is also warranted. All these changes assume a broad definition of health.

More interface between the formal and informal systems of care is needed, recognizing that the informal care system includes self-care. It is frequently forgotten that self-care, not professional care, constitutes the majority of personal health care; that people usually try to treat problems themselves before seeking formal medical care; and that among those who seek formal care, a combination of the formal remedy and their personal remedy often occurs (DeFriese and Woomert, 1983). Most elderly persons are capable of caring for themselves, and do so, on a day-to-day basis.

Change from the existing *medical* care system to a *health* care system is desirable. The critical issues are not the existence of health insurance or state involvement (Coburn et al., 1981). Principles of universal access and the right to care are assumed. The critical issues for an aging society surround the development of a health care system and the delivery of services to maintain and improve the health status of individuals.

This chapter examines the likelihood of change in the system, then discusses various ways to enhance an interface between the informal and formal care systems, including ways to facilitate self-help and care from family, friends and community support groups.

‖ HOW LIKELY ‖
IS A CHANGE?

Whether one believes appropriate changes can, or will, take place, varies depending on one's beliefs about the root causes of the problems within the system. Illich (1976), for example, believes iatrogenesis is caused by industrialization and the monopoly powers of medicine. Iatrogenesis is solved, therefore, by demystifying and dismantling the monopoly of medicine, by deindustrializing and debureaucratizing society and by encouraging more individual responsibility for health.

The emphasis on individual responsibility is also at the forefront of the life-styles argument exemplified, for example, in Canada in the Lalonde report, *New Perspectives on the Health of Canadians* (1974). A life-styles approach, by emphasizing illnesses, mortality and chronic conditions caused by drinking, smoking, accidents and so on, places responsibility with the individual.

Others, such as Navarro (1976) and Estes (1979), see the root cause in capitalism and the capitalist class system. In a capitalist society, the corporate elite controls the power, with medicine either an influential intermediary or a part of that elite. From this point of view, medicine helps maintain the status quo and existing inequities in illness, in access and utilization of the system. This perspective demands change in the very structure of society. Life-styles are not simply a matter of individual choice, since individual choices and life-styles are inherently part of one's culture and social class. A life-style perspective, on the other hand, blames the victims for behavior chosen within cultural and societal constraints.

These viewpoints all agree the medical profession is dominant in the current system but see the sources of the problem differently. The likelihood of deindustrialization or a shift away from capitalism appears unlikely in the foreseeable future. Some (Coburn et al., 1983), however, argue that physician dominance has already seen its heyday. Coburn argues that its peak has been reached, and the first signs of decline in power are evident.

Several factors for the decline are cited. While the medical profession has been successful in maintaining control over health care services and confining government to a financial intermediary, it has failed to prevent a goverment funded and administered health insurance scheme. Other health occupations, such as nursing, pharmacy, psychology and chiropractics, among others, assert that many tasks currently performed by physicians could be performed by them. Evidence continues to accumulate on the failure of medical efficiency. Self-help and consumer groups have been increasing in the health field.

Coburn argues that medicine met its setback in moving into the arena of political influence. It lost substantial ideological and political influence in non-clinical areas when it opposed universal, portable, compulsory and publicly administered health insurance. Such opposition suggested to the general public that medicine had its own interests at heart. In addition, Coburn points out that the fee-for-service system administered publicly, together with computer technology, has resulted in a surveillance (of salaries, utilization and so on) hitherto not contemplated. In addition, bureaucratic and managerial experts, rather than those trained in medicine, are filling various positions in the complex organization of the hospital. Even Coburn grants the medical profession is still dominant. His position is that it is not as dominant as it once was.

The increasing medicalization of life, what Illich calls social or cultural iatrogenesis , is a distinct concept. One can envision a system with a medical perspective but in which several groups, or a group other than the medical profession, are dominant. If the medical profession is replaced with another group just as medically oriented, little change in the system will result. Some, such as Harding (1981), argue that the pharmaceutical industry is well on its way to replacing medicine in its place of dominance.

Alternatively, those groups currently dominant could change their focus considerably. Indications of this can be found, for example, in the interest expressed in holistic medicine. In this instance, the same groups would maintain their power within a changing system by evolving with, and indeed being at the forefront of, that evolution. The profession of medicine might remain dominant but place a decreased emphasis on a medical and a clinical orientation and advocate less medicalization of life.

In any case, changes in the system are required to meet more adequately the needs of an aging society. Furthermore, fundamental change in the system will not only meet needs better but can potentially curtail costs while providing more health care services.

Given cost concerns surrounding the existing system, perhaps implementing more community and social programs at this time simply represents add-ons to an already expensive system. If the current medical care system remains as it is or continues to grow, new community and social services will represent additional cost. This is because the current system operates on provider demand, not user demand, that is, use of the system is decided by the providers of the services. This is evident, for example, in the variation of surgical rates, by the interests, preferences and beliefs of the local medical community rather than indicators of need by community dwellers (Evans, 1984). As discussed in chapter 6, there are no sectors of the health care delivery system with explicit responsibility to ensure either clinical or cost effectiveness.

It must be emphasized that appropriate community and social services are considered a necessity in the provision of adequate care in an aging society. A move to deinstitutionalize without adequate community support is not a viable alternative. Indeed, recent attempts (Carbonara, 1980) to return the mentally handicapped to the community out of long-term care institutions without adequate support have demonstrated the unacceptability of this strategy.

Evans (1984) suggests ways by which changes can be brought about in the system, without advocating more radical changes in industrialization or the structure of society. He argues that no one innovation will have a major impact, but that viewing the system as a whole and treating it in its totality can make a difference. If all forms of questionable utilization are dealt with, savings could be great. The change, however, must be global not partial. If substitutes for inpatient care are introduced, a corresponding component of inpatient capacity must be withdrawn simultaneously.

Part of the problem with the current system lies in the many health care interventions that have not been evaluated at all or only improperly. Despite the billions of dollars spent on health care, little goes into research. The effectiveness of treatment in preventing, postponing or lessening morbidity or mortality is what should be assessed. Even if treatment delays death or some illness, side effects and decreasing quality of life have to be considered. Good evaluations must include baseline population data and comparisons with proper control groups. The system must then have a mechanism for change that responds to the effectiveness and ineffectiveness of various interventions.

We now turn to a discussion of the ways to improve the system, including an interface between the informal and formal care systems. Self-care is examined first, followed by ways to facilitate care from informal sources.

‖   SELF-CARE   ‖

Self-care can refer to those activities individuals undertake to promote their own health, prevent their own disease, limit their own illness and restore their own health without professional assistance (Levin and Idler, 1983). Some (Illsley, 1981) use the term synonymously with self-help groups. Others, such as Williamson and Danaher (1978), distinguish between the two, defining self-care as the individual's own efforts to maintain her or his health, and self-help as care given by other nonprofessionals.

Butler and associates (1979-80) propose three concentric rings to explain the concept. The inner ring consists of personal health practices associated with daily living. The second ring includes health education and prevention, and the third ring refers to formal programs that teach relevant skills. DeFriese and Woomert (1983) offer still another distinction. They define self-help groups as individuals with mutual concern over needs related to a similar health problem and self-care groups as individuals in programs that train them to perform activities usually conducted by professionals.

Despite the proliferation of definitions, there is increasing recognition of the role of self-care in improving health. This has been part of a general trend towards more interest in health and self-reliance in health care matters. Some of the reasons offered for this interest include increased awareness that self-care, not professional care, represents the majority of personal health care;

increased awareness that among most who seek formal care, some form of self-treatment has been tried; the lack of effectiveness of many clinical interventions especially for older people; and promotional material on nonprescription drugs (Dean, 1981; DeFriese and Woomert, 1983).

Research in the area is still sparse but growing. Haug (1984) asks respondents how they would react to five symptoms: depression, difficulty sleeping, gas in the stomach, a heavy cold and an infected cut. Her analyses uncovers seven distinct self-care practices: use of ingested over-the-counter medicines, use of ingested home remedies, use of noningested over-the-counter medicines, use of noningested home remedies, change of activity, fighting it off and doing nothing. The same author (Haug and Lavin, 1982) reports that it is those in better overall health and with less convenient access to formal services who are more likely to engage in self-care.

Fleming (1984) has examined self-care practices of elderly persons (including nonprescribed home treatments, such as herb tea, and lay consultations) in relation to use of formal services. Three measures of use were examined: whether there had been contact with a physician during the year, the number of physician visits for those who had at least one visit and whether or not the respondent was hospitalized. The findings indicate that those less severely ill and those having a stronger sense of control are more likely to use nonprescribed home treatments. For both elderly and nonelderly individuals, those using nonprescribed home treatments are significantly less likely to contact a physician. Findings for hospital admissions indicate that those who practice self-care are less likely to be hospitalized. The author concludes that among elderly individuals there may be two types of self-care users, those who shun medical care when possible, and those who use both medical and self-care.

About self-help groups, DeFriese and Woomert (1983) report that many such programs for elderly persons represent a continuum from disease-specific self-management to generalized health promotion/disease prevention goals. The programs frequently include training in the self-management of diabetes, the management of hypertension or the use of drugs. There is, however, a reported preference among elderly persons for programs dealing with medications, diet and nutrition, and exercise.

While we know self-care dominates personal health care, knowledge about particular practices, by whom, in what circumstances, and related to what outcomes is lacking. Several specific areas need clarification. What self-treatments are supplements to, or substitutes for, professional services? What factors shape self-care practices? What are the jurisdictional boundaries of self-help groups and of professionals? How self-care interests of patients are affected by professional values are unknown. Are professionals even aware of the self-medication or remedies of their patients, not to mention broader health practices? The area of self-care needs to be researched, particularly concerning its development as a component of the care system, as well as its effect on use of formal medical care, such as physician visits.

Self-care, however, does not occur within a vacuum. It is part of a complex network involving various degrees of assistance from family and friends. A facilitation of these different aspects of the informal network to maintain elderly persons in the community calls for an interfacing of the formal and informal care systems. Interface can take various forms. The informal network may act as an information source regarding the formal care system. To use formal services, one must have information about and access to these services. A second form of interface involves the provision of assistance whereby the use of the informal network would act as a complement to formal services.

Collaboration can also occur between the formal and informal systems within the various programs. Programs such as neighborhood intervention network progams are gaining in popularity and often involve a formal service provider collaborating with the informal helping network to provide assistance and services. A fourth interface lies in the provision of support and education for the caregiver. Some formal programs, such as respite care and adult day care, assist these caregivers.

One of the difficulties in examining the topic of interface, however, is the lack of rigorous evaluations that would indicate the benefits and drawbacks associated with various types of collaboration. This chapter reviews existing literature in these areas, but it must be noted that the interface between the informal and formal systems offered to the elderly is an area where relatively little is known.

‖ INFORMATION SHARING ‖

To use the formal system of health and social services, an individual requires information about those services and must make a decision to use them. Some argue that the modern day bureaucracy is too complex and confusing and that many elderly people are bewildered in attempts to obtain assistance to which they may be legally entitled (Auerbach et al., 1977).

Available resources are not always accessible (Government of Manitoba, 1973). As Brody (1973) points out, even when services are available, they tend to be complexly organized, physically dispersed, inadequately advertised or encrusted with eligibility requirements, all of which discourage their use by the elderly people for whom they are designed.

Hobman (1975) argues that advertising through the media, leaflets and traditional forms may be inadequate for those with faulty eyesight, difficulties with hearing and limited primary education completed more than half a century ago. For such individuals, there may be no alternative other than an explanation one-to-one. Furthermore, hearing about a program does not guarantee knowledge of what the program is or does, where it is located or how to become involved with it.

Sources of information about services may include the mass media, health care professionals, families, friends or neighbors. Silverstein (1984) reports that individuals she studied often use a combination of sources and that some individuals know about a wider variety of available services than others. The concept of the broker role (also referred to as the instrumental relationship) captures this idea of information sharing. Wellman (1981) argues that the largeness of our social system means that much social support is intercorporate rather than interpersonal, so that personal networks spend much time helping an individual deal with corporate bureaucracies, as well as directly providing assistance.

Lin (1982) argues that there are advantages to weak ties (which are characterized by infrequent interactions and peripheral relationships among dissimilar individuals), as opposed to strong ties (which are characterized by an intimate social circle of individuals with similar characteristics). Weak ties can involve linkages between individuals who are dissimilar and can provide access to information or to influence not usually available.

Not enough is known about the dissemination of information about health care services. Sound arguments, however, can be made that it is critical, especially in modern society. A host of services can exist in any particular community, but if an individual in need is unaware of their existence or does not know how to gain access to them, she or he will not have her or his needs met. Lopata (1984) believes much of individuals' outreach ability depends on the coping styles they have developed throughout their lives. Strategies to inform people of services will have to take different styles of coping into account.

‖ DECISION-MAKING ‖

The importance of the informal network in the decision-making process to use services is acknowledged by many, although studies on the details of how the process works are few. Friedson (1961) coined the phrase the "lay referral structure" to refer to the network of consultations, from intimate and information exchanges within the nuclear family, to more select and distant authoritative laymen, to professionals.

McKinlay (1972) argues that most available studies tend to be concerned with decision-making by individuals alone, ignoring the important influence of the individual's kin and friendship networks. Studies concentrate on the individual's decision to seek care rather than on the process of seeking care.

Much of the empirical work about decision-making asks who the person would turn to for advice, rather than how he or she decides to seek the service and who influenced him or her in this regard. For example, Shanas (1962) asks older people who, other than their spouse, they would turn to in a health crisis. In nine out of ten cases, an older person with a child says he or she would turn to a child. Auerbach and associates (1977) report most respondents could not answer immediately when asked who they would turn to if they were sick. The majority say they would contact a hospital, and about one-fifth state they would call on a friend or relative.

Similarly, Snider (1981) reports 67 percent say they would contact nobody for ordinary health advice (not an emergency); 18 percent would contact nonkin (including physicians, friends and neighbors); and 15 percent would consult kin (including spouse, child, sibling or other relative). When very sick, fewer than 1 percent would contact no one; 73 percent would contact nonkin;

and 27 percent would consult kin. It should be noted that nonkin includes physicians, a grouping not used by most other studies.

Perhaps one of the more indepth studies available is that conducted by Evans and Northwood (1979). This study, including but not restricted to elderly persons, asks about numerous types of personal problems, such as medical emergencies, family crises, money and legal difficulties and housing problems. Questions are asked about who first noted the problem, who gave information about where to go for help and who or what agency is turned to first. Informal networks help to identify personal problems and provide information concerning sources of assistance.

These authors also compare elderly and younger respondents and report that informal networks have somewhat different utility for those aged 65 and over. Elderly persons tend to turn first to relatives for medical and financial help and to friends and neighbors for help with housing. Evans and Northwood report that many elderly people feel they have no one to turn to when faced with a family or legal crisis. Fewer younger people say they are entirely lacking in social resources needed for confronting all types of personal problems. In short, not only formal care providers but also family and nonfamily provide information and aid. Individuals utilize an array of relationships in help-seeking and utilization.

Other studies examine the quantity of interaction with the informal network in an attempt to discern whether those with more informal supports are more or less likely to access and utilize the formal system. Results are inconsistent. Some studies (Brody, 1978; Shanas, 1979b) indicate that those who do not have support are more likely to become institutionalized. George (1981) reports that an older person who is isolated and does not have family members who are willing or able to provide support is more likely to use agencies providing personal care services.

On the other hand, Simon and associates (1970) find that the majority of elderly hospitalized mental patients are brought in by family members. In a 1981 study of son and daughter caregivers, Horowitz reports that 74 percent of these caregivers provide a linkage to formal services, helping their parents negotiate with the formal service sector. However, Wan and Weissert (1981) indicate that the availability of children and grandchildren has no effect on the hospitalization of the participants of day-care and homemaker programs.

Rundall and Evashwick (1980) incorporate both the quantity of and satisfaction with interaction in the network into their analyses. They try to assess whether the lay referral system will be ignored if the person feels forced to interact with the network to a greater or lesser extent than desired. In terms of visits to physicians, those who are engaged with families (high interaction, high satisfaction) are more likely to use health care services than others. Networks consisting of friends are not significantly related to physician visits. This suggests that friends may be less influential, or less instrumental, in mobilizing older people to use health care services.

Wagner and Keast (1981) find that self-referral is common for elderly people trying to find sources of assistance concerning residential relocation and housework. Self-referral or referral through formal sources dominate over referral through informal sources for services such as physical therapy, visiting nurses, legal aid, eyeglasses, dentures and hearing aids, braces and walkers and group meals.

These authors suggest a picture of self-reliance. Even in their sample of "at risk" elderly, those who use services appear to function independently in securing assistance. When a basic service is required, they are just as likely to go directly to a service provider, be it formal or informal, as to seek referral assistance. The relatively low incidence of informal group referrals could reflect a lack of knowledge on the part of the group as much as a preference on the part of the individual. In the case of complex services, their data suggest little evidence that informal groups assist elderly people in negotiating the complexity of help-seeking behavior. The informal group is more likely to function as a buffer than as a link to formal groups.

In sum, Gourash's (1978) review of the literature on help-seeking among persons of all ages appears to be more or less confirmed for elderly people. People tend to turn to an informal network initially, to family and friends, and to contact relief agencies or professional service organizations only as a last resort. The sole use of formal services is found much less frequently than is either exclusive reliance on the informal network or help-seeking from both sources. An understanding of the role of the informal network in the decision to use formal services is not well understood. Studies tend to focus on the end decision rather than the process which takes people to that point.

Individuals who seek help within the social network represent a cross-section of the general population. However, those who eventually utilize formal service agencies (discretionary medical and dental care, mental health services, social services, legal facilities and self-help groups) are repeatedly reported to be young, white, educated, middle-class and female.

In addition to the question of information concerning formal services and the role of the informal network in the decision to use such services, increasing attention has focused on the coexistence of assistance from both of these sources. The question addresses not which services come from each source but rather the interplay between each as potential service providers. This topic is discussed next.

‖ SUBSTITUTION OR COMPLEMENTARITY? ‖

Concern and research are increasing (Clark and Rakowski, 1983; Johnson and Catalano, 1983) about the provision of informal support in relation to the receipt of formal services. However, little is known about it. One argument is that formal support substitutes for informal care in the absence of an informal network to supply such care. Evidence for this argument includes documentation that older people with few or limited family relationships are prime candidates for institutionalization when they become sick (Shanas, 1979a). Furthermore, Lowenthal and Haven's (1968) study of intimates shows that a relationship exists between social resources and good morale. Blau (1973) emphasizes not so much the importance of a single intimate (unless that person has little interaction with others) as extensive social ties.

Wan and Weissert (1981) report that social networks have a positive effect on a patient's physical and mental functioning in a day care and homemaker experiment. Pilisuk and associates (1982) find that a supportive network is critical in the maintenance of health. Recent studies focusing on the caregiver, rather than on the receiver of care, suggest that a spouse or household member may be the critical factor as the care receiver's health deteriorates (Cantor, 1983).

Of more concern than evidence that those without extensive social ties are the ones who tend to utilize formal services is the argument that formal services directly replace available informal care. The remarks of some congressmen in the United States (Biaggi, 1980) represent this view. These congressmen argue that the provision of more community and social services for the elderly will lead to a "shirking of family responsibility."

This position assumes that such programs provide services which can and should be provided by the informal network, and that families will not provide such care if it can be obtained elsewhere. While studies are currently lacking to assess this position, recent data suggest the concern is unwarranted. These investigations are discussed later after a brief reiteration of an alternative argument, since the data are relevant to both points of view.

A contrary position (for example, Sussman, 1976) is that although modern society has freed grown children and aged parents from economic dependence on one another, social security and medicare have not usurped family responsibilities for the care of aging family members. This creates a new role for children as mediators between institutional bureaucracies and elderly parents. In favor of this view, it will be recalled that Rundall and Evashwick (1980) report that elderly people who are more engaged with their families are more likely to use health and social services. (See discussion in previous section.) This position assumes complementarity between the formal and informal care systems.

The two systems can be complementary in several ways, some of which may include the linking function just discussed, some of which may not. The systems can be complementary if some services are provided by family and friends and some by the formal system; or if care is initially provided by informal sources and then by the formal system as required, or as family and friends can no longer manage. The latter suggests individuals are assessed and screened into the formal care system based on need. This would also be the case if families care for their elderly members and mobilize home care services for them, whereas the childless aged would more likely become institutionalized if ill.

To understand the relationship between these variables, a multivariate model taking both need and informal support into account is necessary, since the need for formal care may be heightened in the absence of informal sources of care. Studies focusing in particular on the linking function are scarce. Studies on the coexistence of the informal and formal care system tend to be cross-sectional, single-sample studies. Nevertheless, those that do are informative and suggest the potential complementarity of the two systems. Few longitudinal and comparative studies exist.

A recent study (Chappell, 1985) discussed in chapter 5, examined this interface. As noted earlier, 80 percent of those receiving formal home care services are also receiving care from informal sources; that is, these data confirm the provision of informal care even when formal care is provided. Noelker and Poulshock (1982) studied family caregiving (defined as receiving assistance with personal care activities, for example, dressing, shampooing and toileting) for impaired elderly persons. They found that over half of these elderly people receive assistance with at least four personal care tasks and that 38 percent are completely dependent in the area of personal care. Families have been providing care on average for six years, and are the major source of assistance, and assist with three personal tasks three hours a day. In addition, 60 percent of the elderly people that receive personal care also receive formal services. This generally consists of in-home health care. Two-thirds of this group receive formal services on a weekly basis and one-fifth receive one to four hours of formal services per week. That is, formal services total a fraction of the hours per week when compared to the care provided from informal sources.

In one of the few longitudinal studies in this area, Horowitz and associates (1983) examine the question of short-term substitution. They use initial assessment and six-month follow-up data for participants of a community-based long-term home care program and participants in a comparison group of people meeting home care eligibility criteria. Recipients of home care services are the frail and homebound. Both groups have family and friends available for support. The groups are compared in terms of assistance with five basic ADL tasks and eighteen instrumental activities at the time of assessment and after the six month follow-up.

For both groups, caregivers not assisting with basic ADL at initial assessment are not providing assistance at follow-up. Caregivers providing a moderate level of assistance initially, and then receiving assistance from the formal home care program, show increased support over time compared with the control group. Caregivers who provide maximum informal assistance initially and who received formal assistance from the program show *no reduction* in the provision of informal care at the time of follow-up. The control group, however, providing maximum care initially and receiving no formal support, show a reduction in care over the six month period. In terms of basic ADL, the provision of formal home care can apparently increase, or at minimum show a reduction in, the provision of informal care.

These authors also look at service-specific substitution. In terms of basic ADL, the project group report a significant increase in the informal provision of assistance in feeding and toileting, a slight but significant decrease in assistance with bathing and no change for transfers and dressing. The comparison group shows no increases in any basic ADL tasks and significant decreases in both feeding and dressing.

While analyses involving instrumental ADL are not as conclusive, the findings add support to the position that the provision of formal services can encourage the continued involvement of informal caregivers among older people. As the authors themselves note, the study does not support the notion that community-based long-term care programs will necessarily substitute for family support.

The issue of whether or not community support services simply substitute for care from family and friends in giving assistance to the elderly is an important one. While more research is required in this area, the initial studies suggest community and social services in no way must substitute for informal assistance. Indeed, evidence is emerging that suggests the informal network will continue its history of involvement in this area.

Given Evans' (1984) argument (discussed at the beginning of the chapter) that new programs are likely to be add-ons because of the piece-meal way in which they are implemented and the lack of simultaneous changes in corresponding parts of the system, one might expect less complementarity between informal care and the provision of formal social services. Empirical studies attest to the desire and commitment of informal caregivers to provide care to their family and friends.

Formal care, for informal caregivers, is an area that refers not only to assistance in the formal provision of services to the frail elderly person but also to the provision of care designed specifically to reduce the strain and ensure suitable relief for the caregiver. It is an area frequently referred to as respite care and is discussed next.

‖ **CARE FOR THE CAREGIVER** ‖

Concomitant with an emphasis on community programs and a trend away from long-term institutional care, increased attention has been directed towards the needs of the caregiver, the individual(s) who assists an elderly person to remain in the community. Caregiving, as noted earlier, is substantially more common than previously assumed.

Caregiving tasks frequently fall first to the spouse, who is also elderly. If a spouse is not available, children frequently assume such responsibility. These children are themselves increasingly young elderly and, therefore, at risk of deterioration in their own health. (Sources of care in terms of specific aspects of the informal network are discussed in chapter 5.)

While informal care varies across a spectrum of tasks, there are at least three major types of care for the caregiver. One type is respite care, providing relief from caregiving responsibilities. There is little argument that this type of support is required. As already elaborated, informal caregivers are not asking to relinquish the caring role; they are asking for relief, so that they can conserve their limited resources to maintain this function (Cantor, 1983).

The logistics of programs differ, but the primary goal is to relieve family and friends who are giving total, or close to total, care to an elderly person. Respite care can involve the placement of homemakers and/or other services in the home to provide personal care and/or household management on a 24-hour basis for a limited period of time. In other instances, the elderly person may be taken into hospital or a personal care home for a specified period to serve the same function.

A second type of service directed primarily to the caregiver is a process of educating that person in the provision of care. Caregiving can involve specific skills. A wife, for example, may benefit from some training when her spouse is discharged from hospital. This idea is not new and has been conducted on an individual basis in the past. A wife is often shown how to change a dressing prior to her husband's discharge from hospital. A home nurse will visit the home to ensure that any necessary equipment is functioning.

Education needs of caregivers vary. Basic information about the aging process may be needed, or more hands-on practical training, such as how to change dressings, bathing and assisting with lifts. Nutrition information is sometimes valuable. Another critical area is information about services and resources that are available.

A relatively new concept is cooperative care. It is worthy of mention because it attempts to educate the informal caregiver and, at the same time, integrates the caregiver with the formal agency. Cooperative care brings the primary caregiver into the hospital to live prior to discharge of the patient. To the extent possible, it incorporates self-care of the patient and care by the primary caregiver. A primary rationale for the program is an attempt to bridge the gap between hospitalization and life in the community because of an assumed direct relevance for the long-term outcome of the patient's illness or disability (Stewart and Ufford, 1981).

While the particular program of cooperative care is new, the idea of bringing families into the care of the ill has been gaining in acceptance for some time. For example, the belief that families are valuable in treating and rehabilitating the mentally ill is evident. Hatfield (1979) argues that frequently when the patient returns home, the family is not prepared for the patient's poor functioning, resentment and anger. Similarly, Carbonara (1980) argues that disregard for the family context of the psychiatric patient sharply reduces the probability of continuity of care and long-term resolution of the problem. The importance of bringing the family into care when children are involved has also been acknowledged (Luciano, 1972; Deakers, 1972).

Clearly the success of any such program is dependent on those involved. Evangela (1968) discusses the attitude of nurses towards family members and the importance of that attitude in determining the extent to which family members feel free to participate. Getzel (1981) discusses the role of social workers within the natural support system. If professionals and paraprofessionals adopt an attitude that families cannot cope with aging individuals, this will have a negative influence on the outcome of any such program.

A cautionary note is in order. Family members and others in a person's informal network are not always preferred nor appropriate for assistance. Getzel (1981) talks about caregivers giving too much, assuming more dependence on the part of the elderly person than necessary. Scharlach (1983) has studied strain between elderly women and their daughters. Fischer (1983) reports that objective accounts of caregiving are poor indicators of the burden felt by the caregiver. This is an area about which we are just starting to learn. Any enthusiasm for caregivers must not neglect the elderly person's autonomy, dignity and preferences.

A third type of care or service for the caregiver, sometimes overlapping with the other two, refers to support groups. Caregivers may learn specific skills from these groups which may be coordinated by a professional. Support groups can also be self-help volunteer groups whose primary function is emotional support for the caregiver. Farquharson (1981) defines self-help groups as group efforts of lay citizens to cope with personal and social concerns. He notes, furthermore, that common reasons expressed for joining such groups include ineffectiveness of professional help, lack of professional expertise regarding their problem, the need for social contact and the perception that there is less stigma attached to group membership than to seeking professional help. Sometimes the caregiver is unable to leave the elderly person long enough to attend a support group or educational seminar. Either the provision of care in the caregiver's absence or the provision of in-home educators and visiting programs would alleviate this problem.

The extent to which the three types of services for caregivers discussed here may overlap should be emphasized. This point is demonstrated in Noelker and Poulshock's (1982) discussion of alleviating caregivers' stress. They note that at times it may be more effective to alter the caregiver's perceptions that assistance with personal care is difficult, tiring or upsetting. Where feasible, an impaired elderly person might be rehabilitated to greater independence in task performance. Assistive devices, such as lifts and bedside commodes, could be used. Learning how to handle incontinence or how to assist a confused or "acting out" elder can reduce stress experienced by a caregiver.

While the need for more support for caregivers is becoming obvious, Clark and Rakowski (1983) illustrate many difficulties in assessing programs designed to meet this need. Often, no specific learning objectives are stated; evaluations in terms of either process or outcome are seldom undertaken. The majority of the programs focus on providing social support to caregivers and assisting caregivers to cope with feelings associated with the caregiving role. Short-term benefits are often identified, although they have not been subjected to rigorous testing. These benefits include respite from continual responsibility, emotional support, the opportunity to express and share common concerns and information gathering and learning of skills regarding aging and service availability.

A great deal more information is required to assess the benefits, if any, of such programs. It is not known what benefits exist in the long-term. It is not known whether certain types of individuals are attracted to such programs and indeed whether those who least require the support are the most likely to participate. Whether programs should be on a continuous basis is not known. The benefits and/or costs for the recipient of care need further study. Sufficient information does exist to guard against what Cantor (1983) refers to as "the danger of global solutions." Needs vary tremendously and change over time.

Frequently one hears the suggestion that financial incentives should be given to caregivers. It is worthy of note that the idea of financial support to the caregiver does not tend to receive support in existing studies. The matter of financial remuneration is repeatedly raised as an option. Tax concessions and/or special allowances to caregivers have been suggested as a means to promote and maintain support from the family (Sussman, 1976; Government of Canada, 1982).

Arling and McAuley (1983) examine the feasibility of payments in a state where the general assembly pays family members, as service providers under contract, through the state department of welfare. The results indicate that finances are not among the major sources of stress or strain. In fact, only 10 percent of those in the study report a strain on finances due to caregiving. The greatest strains reported are emotional, and restraints on time and freedom.

Sussman (1976) reports about 19 percent of families studied would not care for elderly members under any circumstances. He argues that for those willing to provide care, incentives may speed up the process but would not change the initial willingness. As Noelker and Poulshock (1982) note, financial incentives to motivate or sustain primary caregiving by family members are not relevant.

A number of difficulties are encountered in the provision of financial relief, including some form of administrative mechanism to determine need, regulate access and determine actual cost. Informal support appears to come from a variety of sources, so that a decision would have to be made in terms of which sources are financially rewarded.

This section has examined an area of increasing concern, especially given the tendency for elderly people themselves to be informal caregivers for elderly spouses, parents, siblings or friends. Informal care is frequently preferred as more humanistic than formal care, not to mention the cost effective nature of this care. If, however, the health of the caregiver is not protected, both patient and former caregiver could well require extensive formal assistance.

Before leaving this chapter about the interface between informal and formal care systems, we turn briefly to a discussion of such an interface in long-term care institutions. It is a minority of elderly people who reside in such residences. Nevertheless, they are an important group, in a setting that poses special problems for facilitating informal relations.

LONG-TERM CARE INSTITUTIONS

As illustrated in chapter 5, the informal network appears to maintain its level of involvement when an elderly person is placed in a long-term care facility. The nature of this involvement, however, depends to a large extent on the attitude of facility staff towards the informal caregiver's involvement. Many authors (Smith and Bengtson, 1979; Harel and Noelker, 1982) suggest that institutions should encourage family involvement. The facility can provide assistance to the informal network; as well the family can offer assistance to the institution.

Group sessions where family members can meet with others in similar situations may involve discussing feelings of guilt or learning more about the aging process. York and Calsyn (1977) argue that many families need help in learning ways of making visits more productive. Many express a need to be more involved and knowledgeable.

Staff training is also required. This may include sessions on the complexities of the family-resident relationship and communication skills. Families need to be included in the development of care plans, and provisions made for activities and meetings of families only. Rules and regulations of a facility can either deter or enhance family involvement. Open visitation hours, arrangements for family dining and such are likely to enhance the relationship (Montgomery, 1982).

Litwak (1977) suggests family and staff have complementary functions. Facility staff can best provide technical tasks, while families can best provide nontechnical tasks, such as gifts for special occasions and outings. Both types of tasks are important. However, studies undertaken to address this sharing of tasks suggests there may be some ambiguity over such responsibilities between facility administrators and families of residents (Shuttlesworth et al., 1982; Rubin and Shuttlesworth, 1983).

While the potential for family involvement is great, there may be limits to their involvement. Adult children or other kin may not be available to provide any nontechnical tasks. However, other members of the informal network such as friends and neighbors may be available to interface with nursing home staff.

Ombudsman programs in nursing homes are becoming more popular, particularly in the United States where the mandate of the Older Americans Act provides such services. Few studies of these programs are available (Monk and Kaye, 1982), although program descriptions do exist. Many programs involve recruiting and training volunteers to act as ombudsmen in the identification, investigation and correction of problems and complaints made by long-term care residents. The problems encountered range from relatively minor difficulties to complex legislative difficulties. Monk and Kaye (1982) report that the areas most often dealt with by the ombudsmen volunteers in their New York City study relate to health care, environment/sanitation, food/nutrition and administration, while the areas less frequently mentioned include patient rights, finances, interpersonal relations and legality.

As with the involvement of family members, there can be disagreements on the part of ombudsmen program volunteers and nursing home staff on how to operationalize the former's involvement. Cooperation of staff appears to be a key ingredient in these programs. Zischka and Jones (1984) argue that in order to have staff supporting the work, the ombudsmen must credit staff for their efforts and understand that staff often feel underpaid and undeservedly criticized by residents, families and the media. Training and support for the volunteer ombudsmen is also necessary. The effectiveness of such programs is mainly speculative.

In some situations, there is a potential for interface between the residents themselves and the formal care system, beyond the direct provision of care. One example is resident councils. These councils can serve numerous functions, such as improving communication, providing information and consultation, identifying grievances and channeling complaints and developing resident support. Furthermore, they can activate residents, open up the policy process and involve individuals who are traditionally excluded. For the residents, they provide an opportunity for involvement in policy formation and planning, the exercising of rights and responsibility and the development of leadership. This allows the resident to influence facility decision, improve quality of life, provide an exchange, and a mechanism for discussing grievances and complaints.

Whether the potential of such councils is reached is debatable. Devitt and Checkoway (1982) report that generally residents do not have much input. Such councils are often formed by administrators, with residents invited to participate in predetermined purposes and procedures. The problems in this area reflect the management of institutions, which are frequently not organized primarily for the comfort and benefit of the resident.

Little is known about the best ways of involving residents, families and friends in long-term care institutions. It is an area of much concern that has few definitive answers. Whatever strategies are employed, it is clear that autonomy and choice should be kept uppermost. Too many rigid rules and regulations, while well-intentioned, are unlikely to suit the needs of all residents and will not meet changing needs of residents and their informal networks.

‖ CONCLUSIONS ‖

This chapter has discussed some of the features of a formal health care system, which, it has been argued, would better meet the needs of an aging society than the current system. Such a system would preserve universality and equal access but would see less of a focus on a medical system, especially clinical intervention, and more of a focus on a health care system. Within such a system, community social services would have a more prominent place than they do now. These services are considered essential in the provision of continuity of care.

Brody (1973) makes a similar appeal for a system designed for an aging society. He gives several suggestions for solving the current health delivery problem. Money is not the issue. It is necessary to reconstruct the health delivery system. If the current disease-oriented approach is continued as the single approach, the needs of elderly people will continue to be unmet. Lastly, a balanced health system must integrate health and social services with reorganized medical institutions.

Similarly, an interfacing between the formal and informal care systems, whereby the formal system facilitates and supports the informal system, is considered paramount. The importance of appropriate community support cannot be overemphasized, especially given the history in the area of mental illness. Witnessing the deinstitutionalization of mentally ill patients into communities ill-prepared to accept or support them should serve as a red flag, warning that the same be guarded against with an elderly population. The key is appropriate community support. Deinstitutionalization cannot be allowed to become a cheap cost-cutting mechanism without the implementation of adequate community supports.

Part of the strategy for restructuring the system must, of course, include appropriate staff training at all levels, a topic not dealt with in this book. Serious attention has to be given to this topic. Virtually all health care workers could benefit from more knowledge about aging, including information about families and friends. These health care workers include physicians, nurses, social workers, administrators, volunteers and so on.

In addition, there is an unknown demand for such services. If programs are not carefully implemented, the demand could be overwhelming. No doubt, criteria for eligibility will require considerable thought. Services for those in need must be flexible enough to meet changing needs of the client not only in relation to the client's changing health status but also in relation to the changing social network and its ability to provide care.

The areas discussed here, and the suggestions for change, have focused on strategies that are considered feasible within our society. No attempt has been made to offer larger scale solutions, which would involve a shift from monopoly capitalism, or from an advanced technological society. However desirable the latter may or may not be viewed, it has been argued here that the health care system can be changed to better meet the needs of an aging society within the overall framework of society as it currently exists.

It is imperative, however, that within any changes taking place the individual's autonomy is not threatened in the process. Integrating formal and informal care, which meet elderly people's needs and preferences, is not an easy task. Education to inform individuals of their real choices will help guard against erosions into the person's freedom of choice. It is, however, the larger groups involved in the delivery of health care (governments, professionals and hospital managers) who must become involved if change to the system is to be meaningful.

A common theme throughout this book has been the importance of rigorous research in the accumulation of knowledge relevant to the area of aging and health care. A major task throughout has been to bring together existing knowledge to bear on issues of practical relevance. An implicit assumption has been that the building of an adequate knowledge base requires the collaboration of researchers and practitioners, administrators, policy makers, and the elderly themselves in this endeavor. Before closing, the book devotes one chapter to a discussion of this collaborative effort.

■ CHAPTER 9 ■

ADVANCING KNOWLEDGE THROUGH COLLABORATIVE EFFORTS

This book has focused on aging and health care from a social perspective. It has sought a rigorous discussion of salient practical issues within the topic area. Interest in such an approach arose largely from the lack of collaborative efforts between university researchers and community individuals. However, in the area of aging many of the crucial questions are applied and require contributions from various sectors if the research is to be relevant and advance knowledge. This chapter turns attention to collaborative research efforts among the various constituents. It begins with a discussion of some reasons for collaborative efforts and of the process of collaboration itself. Attention is then turned to types of research of relevance to practitioners and policy makers, wherein collaboration can be especially important.

JUSTIFYING COLLABORATIVE EFFORTS

Those working in the field of aging and health care, whether they be practitioners, policy makers, administrators or elderly individuals themselves add expertise in terms of knowledge derived from experience. Researchers bring expertise in methods of scientific enquiry, that is, ability in assessing various questions in the least biased way. In addition, they bring training in the ability to analyze and to conceptualize. All of these components are necessary to conduct relevant applied research.

Furthermore, knowledge about the real world is a necessary component to the testing and evolution of theories and concepts within academia. Concepts and theories must be empirically tested to assess their validity. Empirical endeavors can advance knowledge, for example, in the area of family/non-family relationships, in our understanding of instrumental and expressive relationships and in terms of differential models of the utilization of health services. While practitioners have much knowledge from their own experience, scientific methodology can help one discover how applicable these idiosyncratic and personal experiences are to other contexts.

Many research questions can come from discussions with those in the community-at-large. For example, staff of a community agency engaged in numerous outreach activities, such as counseling elderly victims of abuse and about retirement, note how little is actually known about the reasons why individuals choose to utilize various formal services and why they choose not to access others. Little is known about the decision-making process in this regard, except that the use of fliers and radio and television announcements is frequently ineffective.

What is the process involved in deciding to access formal services, in deciding to implement another remedy but not access the formal system or in deciding nothing is wrong or that nothing can be done? The particular role of the informal network in this decision-making process and, relatedly, of health beliefs is largely unknown.

Another example: some of those involved in community adult day care programs are wondering what effect, if any, length of time in the program has on a variety of outcome measures such as functioning, well-being, social integration and the use of other social services. Others want to know if rural-urban differences exist among this group and the reasons for them. A final example: native groups want to know how to conduct a needs assessment for planning health services.

Conversely, it is useful to give examples of how researchers help, or are beneficial, to nonresearchers in the community. A community agency is interested in evaluating the effectiveness of its victimization counseling program. If the agency is interested in assessing the effectiveness of counseling, an "outcome" measure is necessary. Some measure of effectiveness is required to do such an assessment. A control group for comparison is also required. It is essential to have individuals of similar age who have also been victimized but have not received the counseling service to conduct an adequate assessment of the program. Without such a control group, it cannot be shown whether the counseling is leading to various outcomes, or if individuals would arrive at that point irrespective of whether they receive counseling.

The evaluations of community programs examined in chapter 7 also provide examples of information useful to practitioners. Data from the adult day care (ADC) studies (Chappell, 1983b; Chappell and Blandford, 1983) demonstrate that most of the participants of ADC are Canadian-born, with the second largest group consisting of people of British origin. Given the ethnic diversity of the province's elderly population, this led to discussions as to why this was the case. It was concluded that the areas of the province in which the ADC programs were implemented, consisted mainly of elderly people of British origin. This led to discussions as to whether other areas desired such programming.

Last, but not least, is the issue of whether or not informal care is replaced when community and social services are provided formally. As discussed in chapters 5 and 7, research (Horowitz et al. 1983; Chappell, 1985) suggests this does not occur. These findings stress the importance of taking informal networks into account when determining formal service use. This has led to a discussion of the potential interface between the formal and informal support networks in order to meet the needs of an aging population.

In other words, knowledge gained in the real world from those who work in it is invaluable, both in terms of contributing to the advancement of knowledge and in terms of identifying questions that require research. Conversely, researchers have the skill to identify whether it is possible to design studies to answer those questions, as well as aid in alternative interpretations of that information. The collaborative dialogue between the various segments is an essential component for the advancement of knowledge for so many of the applied questions relevant to aging and health care.

THE COLLABORATIVE PROCESS

Collaboration is a process, a relationship among the individuals involved. It is a long, slow process. Those involved in the different sectors must first begin by talking to one another. Once the relationship is established, it evolves; it does not remain static.

Our experience suggests that when a group representing different sectors comes together over a particular issue or question, the initial discussions can be less than friendly. It is critical that the group remain together until the negativism is surmounted, and, furthermore, that the group stay together for a period after this, so that its members recognize some benefits of the collaborative process.

It should be noted that all groups have their own issues and questions of concern, and all sectors develop their specialized jargon; this is not particular to researchers. For example, when one looks at nurse assessment charts, one frequently comes across the initials BP. Though this may obviously denote blood pressure to a nurse, it is not necessarily obvious to an individual without this type of background. Similarly, the initials BM are not obviously an abbreviation for bowel movement if one is in a different line of work. Those not involved in research frequently misinterpret random sample to mean a haphazard or convenience sample, or statistical significance to refer to substantive significance. The point is that it is not only academics who develop specialized language; other sectors do as well.

Initial conversations with a group, including various constituents, are devoted largely to an effort to explain one anothers' language, to eliminate as much jargon as possible and to begin dialogue on the issue at hand. This requires skill at human interaction, a basic acceptance that others have something valuable to contribute and an acceptance that no one individual in the relationship knows everything.

The importance of the dialogue when initially determining a researchable question cannot be overemphasized. If the questions of real interest do not emerge, much time and effort can go into a data collection process, which does not yield data relevant to the critical issues. Say a group is interested in assessing satisfaction with housing. Upon additional probing and discussions, it turns out that the members are interested in housing conditions rather than housing satisfaction. Asking about general housing satisfaction would likely result in a large proportion expressing satisfaction, since individuals tend to adjust to whatever situation they are accustomed. According to an objective assessment, actual housing conditions may nevertheless be substandard.

If the researchers decide to undertake a research project, any of several alternative arrangements may be agreed upon regarding the role of each sector and the division of labor within the research process. Assuming that the researchers undertake the main effort of data collection and analysis, meetings are particularly crucial at the beginning stages when the research question is defined and operationalized.

When the researchers go into the field, there may be less contact with the representatives of various sectors, a distance that is frequently desirable to help maintain the impartiality of the research endeavor. The researchers may then computerize, analyze and write a first draft of the data findings. The draft is circulated, and a meeting once again called of the representative sectors. This meeting typically involves a long and lively discussion in which representatives from the various sectors argue for their points of view for additional analyses in areas pertinent to their concerns and for their own interpretation of the data.

When this session is over, the investigators conduct additional analyses, resulting from the questions and issues raised in the discussion. A revised report is written, circulated and another meeting called. Typically, this second meeting is less lively and more congenial. Most of the queries raised in the first session are now understood. Usually only minor editorial revisions are required after this meeting.

The effort that goes into establishing and then maintaining the relationship of the group is critical in permitting as many of the relevant constituents as possible to contribute to the unfolding of the research project. At the end of a tedious and occasionally frustrating process, all sectors nevertheless tend to be convinced of the value of the collaborative effort. The meetings to discuss the data analyses and interpretations provide an education for all concerned, individuals from various applied sectors can discuss the study and the relevance of the findings to their day-to-day work, as appropriate. They have an intimate knowledge of the study and a feeling of confidence when discussing its implications.

In addition, the audiences are more numerous and varied than implied in a simple researcher/community distinction. Among researchers there are real differences in interests and expertise; among the community there are real differences among practitioners in different settings, administrators, policy makers and elderly individuals themselves. In other words, there can be and usually are numerous agendas represented at any one gathering.

Most of us have full-time and legitimate occupations, which are time consuming and specialized. Other than in exceptional circumstances, full-time practitioners, administrators and policy makers need not, and indeed should not, become full-time researchers. If they become full-time researchers they will no longer be practitioners, administrators and policy makers. They can ask important research questions and begin devising information gathering systems, which would permit answering some of these questions within their own work setting. More concerning this will be discussed in the next section.

Similarly, if those expert in scientific research become too immersed within the day-to-day world of practitioners, they will no longer be researchers. It is not necessary for each to become expert at the others' occupational endeavors; rather, with some effort each can contribute in essential ways to the research process.

In addition, some practitioners may be interested in becoming more expert as consumers of research without taking the years of study necessary to become full-time researchers. There are few, but there are some, courses designed with this in mind. The objective of these courses is to teach a minimal amount of research language and to convey an understanding of the basic concepts and intent of research, so that these practitioners can be intelligent consumers of research, and not have to rely totally on the research author's interpretation of his or her data. By the same token, researchers in applied areas should learn a sufficient amount about the real world in their applied areas, so that they are familiar and comfortable with it. They have an obligation to listen to and learn about that world.

The process involves a basic respect and trust for others as well as a desire to learn and a commitment to a joint endeavor. Recognizing specifically what it is that we do not know when the occasion arises will aid the process. Collaborative efforts, we would argue, help make aging and health care an exciting area in which there is much to learn, and that offer directions to orient our efforts.

Having discussed some of the reasons why collaborative efforts are important and some of the processes involved in collaborating, the remainder of this chapter turns to a discussion of several types of research appropriate to applied questions. This discussion includes the use of agency records, evaluation research, needs assessments and other types of research.

‖ AGENCY RECORDS ‖

There is a great deal that nonresearchers can do to examine their own programs and prepare baseline data for research. They may begin by collecting information on the number and type of people who attend their programs. This may be mandatory for many agencies. However, a review of 63 voluntary agencies in one district of Ontario by Boucher et al. (1979) reveals that only 40 percent of the agencies reviewed could adequately provide information on the actual number of clients served. If this is any indication of trends elsewhere, there are many agencies that do not have basic information about their programs.

An agency can start by recording the number of clients entering or using their services. It may also be useful to know more about the clients being served. Is the agency reaching a certain age group, a certain socioeconomic group, a group with a certain disability? These restrictions on client groups may be appropriate if the program targets services. If there is not a specific target group, collecting and using such information as age, gender and other demographic characteristics may provide insights into gaps in service delivery.

An important consideration in collecting basic information is deciding which information will be most useful to the agency. There is little value in constructing a detailed intake data sheet only to find no one wants the information, or that only one or two aspects are relevant for the agency. The basic information an agency chooses to collect should relate to the needs of its program. No single set of questions meets the basic information requirement of all organizations. Each organization is different.

This basic record keeping is important and agency personnel must understand its importance. If the staff responsible for recording such information does not appreciate the need for the information, the record keeping may be viewed as useless paperwork. Similarly, there is a need for consistency in record keeping.

Record keeping is worthy of much consideration, especially if it is to be used for research purposes. Unfortunately, it is frequently not in useable form. Weiss (1972) summarizes the problem of organizational records in her discussion of their use in evaluations:

> Unfortunately, experience has shown that organizational records are nowhere as useful as they should be. The organization's record keeping, the transfer of intake and service information to permanent records, tends to be haphazard. Records are inaccurate, out of date, months behind on entries. Furthermore, the definition and categories used by the agency may be inappropriate for evaluation purposes. Vital categories of information may never have been requested, or records may be kept in a form (such as narrative case recording) that is inordinately difficult to reduce to items useable for research . . . . Incompleteness plagues many agency systems. If participants do not supply certain items of information or if staff fails to enter data, nobody checks on the missing items and follows-up . . . . Agencies sometimes change recording procedures. If this happens during the period under study, it can vitiate all attempts at

before-after comparisons. Just to add another horror to the gallery, there is the possibility of distortion. Agency records are often based on the reporting of practitioners, and when they know that they are being 'judged' by the data in the records, they may intentionally or unintentionally bias their accounts.[1]

Suppose an agency does have a record keeping system. A form has been devised and information about the client has been recorded. The age, gender, place of residence and so on are available for use. What does a practitioner do with it? The information is valuable for case study purposes. There may be interest in examining a small sample of individuals who share certain characteristics, resulting in a review of the clients' histories in detail. This information is also useful at a more practical level as another staff person taking over this client will have basic information to which to refer. It is also useful to prepare global statistics. These statistics do not have to be complicated. Just adding up the number of clients who share certain characteristics will be useful. Say, for example, an agency's board of directors is interested in knowing whether more of the clients are between the ages of 65 and 80 than over 80.

The importance of collecting such baseline information cannot be understated. Any agency can implement a basic record keeping system with little difficulty. First, however, a decision must be made in terms of what information will be useful. It is a waste of time, energy and money to collect information if it will serve no purpose. Further, input is required from all levels of staffing in this process, since each area of the organization potentially has something to offer.

‖ EVALUATIONS ‖

Often one is interested in going beyond a description of program participants or other program characteristics. Frequently one wants to know how successful a particular program is. Is the program effective? Is it efficient? These questions fall into the realm of program evaluation. Evaluations may involve an after-only design (collecting data at one time only, after the client has completed the program), a pre- and post-test (collecting information both before and after entrance into the program) or various other designs. Evaluation may entail examining records of the agency, relying on opinions of staff, collecting data from the client group and others. Each form of evaluation has something to offer.

An important starting point is defining the question to be answered. What information is being requested? Who wants the information and how will it be used? A number of factors have to be considered, and at least one individual

---

[1] Carol H. Weiss, *Evaluation Research: Methods for Assessing Program Effectiveness* (Englewood Cliffs, N.J.: Prentice-Hall Inc., 1972), pp.54-5. Reprinted by permission of the publisher.

was interested in why some evaluations were used, while others were not. Through discussions with both evaluators and decision makers, a key factor that arose in the actual use of evaluation was an individual(s) who "personally cared about the evaluation and the information it generated." Factors, such as methodological quality, appropriateness of methodology or positive or negative findings, are not as important as this personal factor.

The question "Is our program successful?" is too broad to be adequately researched. What is meant by success will vary, according to the individual asking the question. It may relate strictly to cost effectiveness, or what benefits and how many benefits accrue as a result of X amount of dollars. Someone may view success as having a certain number of people in a program at a particular point in time. Someone else may say that a home care program is successful if it reduces the rate of institutionalization. Each of these questions would result in a different study.

The importance of precision in delineating the question to be addressed is evident in the following example. Evaluations are often conducted at the end of workshops to determine satisfaction with the presentation. It is not known whether the satisfaction or the benefits derived from the workshop are related to the course material, or if they result from bringing a group of individuals together who share common experiences. Asking the general question "Were you satisfied with the workshop?" tends to result in positive responses. If asked "How did you benefit from the workshop?" more specific information would be provided. If one is interested in determining an appropriate length, geographical location, lecture content and time for social events for the workshops, very different questions would be asked.

The delineation of the questions to be addressed helps determine the methodology to be used. Often an agency will decide to evaluate itself or to have an outside evaluation conducted and measure its success against the formal objectives or goals of the program. This is known as summative evaluation (Scriven, 1967), but as Weiss (1972) points out, programs do not necessarily operate in a manner in which the formal goals would lead one to anticipate. Indeed, one of the first steps in undertaking an evaluation is to determine how the program operates in reality. Does it perform in a manner consistent with its goals?

Some agencies have established an agreed-upon criteria against which they assess their program. Many do not. Boucher et al. (1979), report that 80 percent of the agencies studied could *not* identify an established means of judging and evaluating the success of the program or the outcome for the client. Furthermore, among those who report their programs as successful, the researchers found it difficult to determine objectively how success was measured.

In order to assess the effectiveness of a program for its participants (on whatever criteria are decided upon), it is often preferable to have both comparison groups and information collected before and after entrance into the program. Without such a group, one does not know whether the effects are due to the program or to some other factor (Sherwood et al., 1975; Fitz-Gibbon and Morris, 1978).

A preferred method is to randomly assign individuals eligible for participation in a particular program, half to the program and half not. This allows one to see if the effect being measured is due to the program or to some other factor. However, this design is often not implemented. Random assignment means that individuals assessed as needing the program will not receive the services immediately if they are assigned to the control group. Service providers sometimes feel they face an ethical dilemma when someone assessed as needing the service is denied it for evaluation or research purposes (Cook and Campbell, 1979).

The presence of a waiting list may make it possible to use a control group of those assessed as requiring, but not yet receiving, the service. When there are only sufficient numbers to begin a program or where the program has already started, it is more difficult to overcome community, agency, policy and financial pressures. Rossi and Wright (1977) suggest that withholding a service may be illegal and unethical. Even though several persons and groups may believe in the value of a program and have fought for its funding, it is seldom pointed out that in most instances rigorous evaluations demonstrating benefits from these programs do not exist.

Given the difficulties faced when trying to implement a random trial, alternate designs are used. Often one can locate a control group that has similar characteristics to the group in the program, for example, in terms of age, gender, socioeconomic level and health conditions but who are not participating in the program. If the design is longitudinal (collecting data at more than one point in time), it would allow the investigators to examine the effects of the program and determine what changes, if any, result from the program.

In many studies, however, a control group does not exist. Increasingly, such studies are longitudinal, in an attempt to examine changes which occur. Individuals may be contacted initially and asked a series of questions about their situation. After a period of time, they may be recontacted and asked similar questions. By doing so, the researchers have some indication of the changes which are occurring. Without the control group, it is difficult to assess which factors contribute to these changes, despite the existence of statistical techniques such as multiple regression to assist in this regard. One can determine the factors associated with the changes, but not if these factors *cause* the changes.

The most commonly used design is the cross-sectional design. Here researchers take a snapshot of the situation and record what is happening at a particular point in time. It is a one-shot attempt at obtaining information. Such a design is useful in situations where little is known about the topic, or when it is impossible to conduct a longitudinal study due to both time and budgetary constraints.

Often respondents will be asked to comment on their situation prior to the present time. This retrospective information may be considered necessary if one wants to look at changes. Individuals may be asked to provide information about himself or herself prior to participation in the program. However, retrospective self-reports are not always reliable, particularly for attitudinal measures. Reports of the past often become distorted, usually to be more congruent with present attitudes. This does not mean that retrospective information should not be collected, but that some care must be exercised in interpreting answers. Such data can be useful when viewed as interpretations of the past from the present situation.

Thus far we have been discussing summative evaluations. They examine primarily outcomes of the program under study. Summative evaluations provide information about the effectiveness of a program as opposed to formative evaluations, which provide information to be fed back into the system to help improve the program (Scriven, 1967; Weiss, 1972).

Formative evaluations have also been referred to as process evaluations. Irrespective of the phrase used, the important aspect of this type of evaluation is its feedback into the system to improve it. The focus is not on the outcome of what happened but rather on what is happening.

Many (Austin et al., 1982; Patton, 1978) argue that providing information to fill knowledge gaps is one of the central purposes of conducting evaluations. The purpose is not necessarily to provide the definitive answer but to provide direction. Furthermore, no one study will provide direction for all questions. As Austin et al. (1982) write:

> Program evaluations rarely produce startling unexpected results requiring major program change. In reality there are few such surprises, since good administrators and workers will be 'in touch' with the results of their various programs and have a pretty good sense of what lies ahead. However, evaluation is useful in either confirming our suspicions or hunches or filling in some gap in our knowledge of how a program is working. In either case, we are talking about reducing uncertainty, not providing the final word.

Anyone who expects an evaluation to provide final solutions to their dilemmas will be disappointed. Individuals must recognize both the limits and the potential contributions of evaluations to the decision-making process.

‖ NEEDS ASSESSMENTS ‖

Needs assessments are different from evaluations. Needs assessments are conducted to identify the needs of a particular population and are sometimes required prior to the allocation of resources to meet those needs. They can be and are, however, conducted after programs have been established.

Suppose a group is interested in building a housing unit for elderly people. One would hope that some assessment of the need for housing by this particular population would be undertaken, prior to laying the foundation. The providers' perceptions of need may not be consistent with the perceptions of the elderly population. The organizing group may see a need for a high rise building with primarily bachelor apartments, while the elderly population may prefer a large, rambling house. Information regarding such preferences, as well as an objective assessment of need for more housing, canbe obtained through a needs assessment.

Needs assessments may take many forms and may examine a variety of topics. Difficulties arise, however, with the concept of need itself because it can refer to economic need, psychological need, housing needs and so on. An explicit conceptualization of need is not available (Havens, 1984; Lareau, 1983). There is no single definition that fits all situations. Operationalizing the concept or finding a way to measure it is frequently just as difficult. In attempts to use standardized measures, practitioners and researchers alike often neglect the potential differences in their study populations, such as cultural differences.

Needs assessments are conducted using a variety of data collection techniques. Some use face-to-face interviews; some use questionnaires and some use telephone interviews. We would argue that the personal interview situation is more congruent with the sensory and cognitive capabilities of older people when compared with a mailed questionnaire or a telephone interview. Some (Neuber et al., 1980) argue that in addition to providing policy makers with information about the needs of a particular client group, interviewing serves to increase the visibility of the agency and often helps to improve public relations. Indeed, interviewers are often asked about available services, even if the elderly respondent is currently receiving some services. The demands for information are relatively easy to meet if the interviewers are knowledgeable about the services in their area and are prepared to supply this type of information.

There are, in addition, a variety of other methods, which have been used for needs assessments. These include the town hall or community forum method, the key informant method and the use of census or other demographic material. Each of these will be explored briefly.

The town hall or community forum brings together groups or individuals to discuss and describe needs. It may take the form of a public or senate hearing, where citizens are encouraged to present their opinions and information in the form of a brief or testimony. The presentation of the brief allows the collective voice of the members to be heard. The group process or brainstorming session is a variation of this method. Interested individuals are gathered together to arrive at a consensus on priorities (Lareau, 1983).

The town hall or community forum method has both strengths and weaknesses. It allows for a variety of groups and individuals to express their views. However, someone must collect and evaluate these sometimes divergent opinions, which can be time-consuming and expensive. In addition, groups that present testimonies and briefs are likely to be well-organized and vocal, with particular points of view. It may be that the brief is endorsed by an executive committee of an organization, but it does not have the endorsement of the membership. The opinions expressed by these groups may not reflect the opinions of the community as a whole. Some groups, such as the frail and isolated, will probably not be represented.

The key informant method relies on knowledgeable individuals from the community or on professionals in the field. These individuals are approached for their opinion on the needs of the particular subpopulation. It is assumed that they have an understanding of their community (Lareau, 1983). Anyone who is believed to have valuable information may be considered. In some needs assessments, attempts will be made to contact all these key informants. In other assessments, a listing of the key informants may be compiled and a random sample will be drawn. The procedure selected depends on the number of key informants and on the resources available to conduct the assessment.

One must be aware of the potential biases of the key informants. A service provider may have a vested interest in identifying needs, which could be met by his or her services. Another may have a somewhat narrow picture of the needs, due to the clients with whom he or she has had contact. Individuals involved in a particular work situation may view their program in a biased manner (Weiss, 1972) and possibly report their program as successful in order to maintain their position. This does not mean that the individuals have no useful insights or that their opinions are invalid. It does mean that the information provided must be evaluated with its potential biases in mind.

Another method used in needs assessments is the use of census or demographic information. Such information is useful in providing a profile of the community or group under study. For example, census data tell us about the sex ratios, age-breakdowns, prevalence of chronic conditions and the rate of institutionalization.

Depending on the extent of available data, it may also be possible to use these figures for estimating the type and extent of problems. Suppose one is interested in the elderly population in a small rural community. Census data may provide a description of the population and inform one that elderly people residing in the community tend to be old elderly females who are widowed. Information about the prevalence of certain diseases may also be available.

However, it is only an estimate, and numerous events may occur that will affect these projections. One of the difficulties in using this type of information relates to the geographical area for which the information is collected. Information may be available on the age and gender of residents of a small hamlet, but more detailed information such as the prevalence of chronic conditions may not be. One may have to rely on state or provincial and, in some cases, national data and extrapolate to the community under consideration.

The best needs assessments will likely incorporate several of the methods discussed here. Regardless of the method used, determining needs cannot be equated with predicting service use. Because an individual needs a service, he or she cannot be assumed to use the service if it is available. Needs assessments are not equivalent to either service requirements or service utilization, unless they are specifically examined in the study.

‖ OTHER TYPES OF ‖
RESEARCH

Practitioners and policy makers are particularly interested in needs assessments and program evaluations. Often this type of research is thought to be more relevant than other types. However, other types of research provide valuable information for this audience in forms that may not be as apparently useful to these groups. Some of it may not be easily accessible or understandable. However, recognizing the potential of research, which does not relate directly to a program or service, is an important step towards a better understanding of the elderly population.

To illustrate the practical relevance of research, which does not fall into the categories of a needs assessment or a program evaluation, a few examples are provided. Concern was expressed by a practitioner that individuals most in need were not necessarily using their services. As noted in chapter 7, concern that utilization of existing services is not necessarily based on need is a topic of much debate. While there is a large body of research pointing to other factors that determine utilization of formal services, including knowledge of existing services, gender of the individual and so forth, one is still faced with the basic question: What is it that leads women compared to men to use more services? Why is it that some individuals are more knowledgeable than others about the services?

Assume there is a group of symptoms, which elderly individuals explain simply as old age, and about which they feel the formal system is ineffective. Assume this is the primary reason for not accessing the system. Assume it is known that formal assistance can aid in adaptation to coping with the symptoms, if not in their cure. This may be relevant information to target to those individuals. On the other hand, there may be illnesses or symptoms for which the individuals are correct in assuming that the formal system can do nothing for them. It may be individuals are accessing or being referred to the wrong aspect of the formal system. Those who are more successful could be compared in their access routes to those who are less successful, if this were the case.

Similarly, one wants to identify to whom elderly individuals go for information. It has been suggested by Silverstein (1984) that information about services should be targeted to family members or to friends who have input into the decision-making process. Depending on whether these individuals are key elements in the entire process, their input will only be as complete as the information they have. If these informal sources do not know about a particular service, they cannot provide the elderly person with program details.

These questions can be studied in a research design other than an evaluation or a needs assessment. Scientific research using stratified random sampling, indepth interviewing and statistical data analyses will answer some of these questions. Potentially, the research will offer information for both nonresearchers and academics. For practitioners, the results can be translated into practice and used in service delivery. However, there are certain assumptions being made. First, it is assumed that practitioners will make an attempt to understand the information provided by the research. A second assumption is that the researchers will attempt to present their findings in a manner that service providers will understand and use. The results are not simplified so the rigor is deleted; rather the results are translated into terminology that practitioners can understand. The potential use of the research depends upon both the researcher and the practitioner, policy maker and program administrator.

In addition to practical relevance, the research is important to the academic. For this audience, it will add to the body of knowledge on the utilization of formal services and the role of the informal network. As McKinlay (1972) stated over a decade ago, studies on the utilization behavior of individuals tend to isolate and assess differences between users and nonusers. Seldom is attention given as to how individuals are influential in making this decision or why one form of behavior is selected over another. This criticism is still valid today.

This particular project involves at least two specific enquiries of relevance to academics. First, are there identifiable steps, which develop from the initial awareness of a potential problem through to a resolution — whether that resolution be a decision that no problem exists, that the problem can be treated with no care or self-care or that formal care is required? Does this process vary by problem? If so, how? This question addresses itself to the organization and structure of the decision-making process, that is, the stages in the decision-making process. Second, what is the role of lay referral and health beliefs relative to other explanatory factors in this decision-making process?

The potential of scientific research for both audiences can be explored in another example. Although living arrangements (or household composition) are not well understood in relation to informal and formal care, the concept nevertheless emerges as a potential key factor in understanding the utilization of formal services. For example, sharing the same household is suggested by some as a prerequisite for basic hands-on care for those with substantially deteriorated activities of daily living skills and/or mental functioning. Living alone consistently emerges as a main predictor of long-term institutionalization.

A series of questions, which have relevance for both the academic and the practitioner, can be addressed: Does living with someone affect the type of care or assistance received? Said another way, is the critical factor having another household member, or is it the marital relationship? Are there others with whom we do not live who can and will provide similar types of assistance? Are these individuals restricted by distance created between separated households? Is that assistance, if it exists, tied primarily to family and in particular to children, or do others provide similar assistance in the absence of available children?

To understand adequately the relationships between informal and formal care, it is important to understand forms of living arrangements currently emerging for elderly people, such as shared housing and apartment living. Projections of increasing divorce rates and the continuing prominance of women among the old elderly suggest we should be examining some of these new forms now to understand how they may, or may not, be viable alternatives as the aging of our population continues. Societal changes appear likely to bring new forms of living arrangements, family structures (including nonblood families) and interpersonal relationships (Chappell, 1982b).

Neither of the two examples can be considered evaluations nor needs assessments. Each addresses issues of importance and seeks to add to the body of knowledge in subject areas. Each suggests the potential for enriching agency-based needs assessments and evaluations to provide information for broader research interests, as well as suggesting the practical saliency of nonevaluations conducted by researchers.

Other studies, however, combine different types of research. Suppose one is interested in knowing how effective certain types of housing are for an elderly population in terms of a variety of outcome measures. One might be interested in knowing about the housing needs of the elderly population in a certain community and include, within the design, individuals living in various housing situations. One may be interested in the substantive topic of housing for elderly people and design a study that will provide this data base, as well as answer the other two questions. Such a study is an example of a project that includes an evaluation component, a needs assessment component and a component that will add knowledge within a substantive subject area, but is not related to an evaluation or a needs assessment.

Housing and health care are two services that are central to the ability to remain independent in the community for as long as possible and to the rising cost of the provision of services. It can be argued that the provision of more community and social services, in combination with housing alternatives, has the potential for decreasing both the use of costly medical services and long-term institutional care.

Increasingly, health care facilities want to sponsor nonprofit senior citizens' housing with support services. Some argue for seniors' residences juxtaposed to personal care homes. Multi-level care facilities do exist where a variety of care services are offered. However, little is known about the effectiveness of multi-level care facilities. Similarly, there are virtually no data on the effectiveness of alternative forms of service provision. Currently, dollars are being spent on a variety of combinations of services and housing without reliable data on either the benefits for recipients or the costs of such programs.

By studying elderly people living in their own homes in the community, in senior citizens' housing where supportive services are provided externally, in senior citizens' housing where supportive services are provided from a different facility under a similar board and in senior citizens' housing where supportive services are provided internally, the groups can be compared in terms of a variety of outcome measures including: independence, feelings of security, social integration, extent of external relations (contact with the outside world), services received and overall well-being. These questions allow an evaluation of the various housing/supportive services arrangements. At the same time, the research acts as a needs assessment and provides information on gaps in service delivery.

The data from such a study will provide a base from which decisions in relation to supportive and housing services for elderly individuals can be made on the basis of cost effectiveness and the ability to maintain or enhance independence. As this study examines effectiveness in terms of both costs and effects on residents, it can be considered an evaluation. At the same time, it assesses the need for a variety of supportive services and housing arrangements and attempts to identify service gaps. This aspect may be considered a needs assessment. For the academic audience, this topic is broad, and the results are of potential interest to a variety of disciplines, including psychology, sociology, economics and architecture and to a variety of professions, such as social work and nursing. They have potential relevance for theory building and assessing the generalizability of various data and ideas.

These are but three examples of research in substantive areas, which have practical relevance and, at the same time, add to the body of knowledge on aging. Numerous other examples could illustrate the potential contributions of this type of work to practice and to academe. In many instances, the research can address questions of concern to both the practitioner and the researcher.

‖ CONCLUSIONS ‖

This chapter has focused on the importance of collaborative efforts between researchers and nonresearchers in applied areas of aging. Examples of how this process works and the benefits to both groups have been discussed. Different types of research such as evaluations and needs assessments have also been presented. Highlighted in these discussions is the role of the researcher, practitioner, policy maker, administrator and elderly people themselves.

The collaborative process involves a realization on the part of all groups that each has important knowledge and skills, which can be contributed to the research process. Once initial barriers to communication have been broken, discussions involving the research question being addressed and other such practical issues can take place. Importantly, it should be recognized that for successful research to be conducted, researchers need not become practitioners, administrators or policy makers, nor should the latter become researchers. Rather, basic respect and trust for others is essential. Establishing such a relationship may lead to future discussions. Practitioners may be more likely to approach researchers with a question they are interested in answering through research, and researchers may be more likely to take time to translate research findings into terms that the practitioner or policy maker can use.

With the increase in number of government funded programs, particularly for elderly persons, and the cry to fund more services for this group, there has also been a rise in the number of evaluations and needs assessments conducted. It is important to remember that the purpose of conducting evaluations is not to provide definitive answers but to provide direction that is useful in the decision-making process. It does not aid in the growth or development of programs if information obtained from evaluations is not utilized by practitioners or policy makers or administrators.

Needs assessments have the problem of defining the concept of need. Furthermore, the utilization of standardized questionnaires may not be appropriate for the population being studied. The results of needs assessments may indicate the service thought to be appropriate is not and that resources would be better utilized elsewhere.

The emphasis here has been on the importance of dialogue between researchers and nonresearchers. When successful, both benefit in terms of the knowledge acquired through research. The collaborative effort is difficult but also necessary. Opting for either basic research, not translated for the community, or programming and service delivery without adequate data bases is not likely to lead very quickly to improvements. Interaction between the different sectors at crucial periods in the process will be fruitful in advancing knowledge for those involved.

CHAPTER 10

MAJOR THEMES AND ISSUES
A SYNOPSIS

The focus of this book has been on aging and health care from a social perspective. A primary effort has been directed towards drawing a realistic picture of the experience of aging in society, without undue attention either on the most frail or on the most healthy. Furthermore, the book has tried to bring a rigorous and scholarly approach to the examination of issues salient for practitioners and policy makers. The preceeding chapter has discussed collaborative research between university researchers, practitioners and policy makers. The book has incorporated a comparative and an historical perspective where it was perceived important for an adequate discussion of the issues at hand.

The book began with a brief discussion of the societal context as an initial background to aging and health care from a social perspective. In particular, historical evolution to longer life was pointed out; that is, more people are living to old age in today's society than in any past society. As more people have been living to old age, so too has the meaning of old age and the roles for older people within society been evolving. While much has been written on the low status of elderly people in modern society contrasted with high status in preindustrial society, existing evidence is not at all conclusive as to the status of the elderly in past societies, relative to modern society. This is partly due to the sparsity of valid information in past societies but also due to the complexity of the question. As becomes clear later in the book, even in our own society the question of the status of older people is not straightforward.

Chapter 2 continued with a social background to issues to be discussed in aging and health care by turning attention to a demographic profile. That profile first discussed aging in the world-wide context, with some emphasis on distinguishing between the more- and less-developed countries. Canada and the United States, despite their youth as nations, share with other developed countries around the world the aging of their populations. Attention then turned to a discussion of some of the more traditional demographic indicators such as number and proportion of individuals who are elderly, the gender distribution of elderly individuals and their marital status. That chapter concluded with a discussion of some of the more social indicators of aging. While statistics for these indicators were not as readily available, the potential importance of factors such as retirement, formal education, subcultural groups and rural-urban differences does emerge.

Those statistics point to the importance of a detailed investigation looking at age and gender differences. They suggest that specific attention should be devoted to the old elderly and to elderly women. This is but one example of the eterogeneity among elderly individuals.

The third chapter explored in relative detail the relationship between health status and aging. While it is clear there are declines in the various aspects of health as we age, the later years are not totally devastating for most of us. In fact, national data for both Canada and the United States suggest that approximately 80 percent of elderly people have some chronic conditions and about 50 percent have some functional disability. However, only about 20 percent have major functional disability.

Interestingly, attitudes and subjective perceptions of health do *not* become more negative as we age. Rather, there is some suggestion that they decrease. This apparent discrepancy between the more objective measures of health and overall well-being has not been well understood and requires more attention. At the current time, it is believed that mediating psychological factors account for the discrepancy. Individuals assess their current situation against their own expectations and the situations of others to arrive at their own personal adjustment to their situations.

Chapter 3 ended with a discussion of the fact that measures of various aspects of health are not synonymous with dependency or the need for care. One of the major difficulties in studying aging and health is that the relationship between dependency and the need for care is complex. This fact plagues the assessment of formal programming, including community and social services for an aging population.

As decline in health is a major reason for concern with aging, so too are the various role transitions individuals experience as they approach old age. Chapter 4 presented first a brief historical overview of the development of income security legislation at the national level in both Canada and the United States. Social security legislation has decreed age 65 as the age of retirement and, subsequently, the societal definition of the beginning of old age.

Research on the experience of retirement revealed that this is not the traumatic experience once believed. Indeed, most individuals adjust to retirement, and many consider it a positive experience. Although there is a dearth of literature on the empty nest experience when children leave the physical compounds of their parents' homes, that which does exist suggests this, too, is an experience that individuals adjust to without severe trauma and that many enjoy. The experience of widowhood does seem to be more traumatic, particularly in its initial bereavement stage. While there is much variety in individuals' styles of coping, here again most adjust and continue their lives.

In other words, the experiences characterized as role exits are ones to which individuals seem to make satisfactory transitions. While these areas are in need of more study — and it is true that most of the retirement literature focuses on men, while most of the widowhood literature focuses on women — nevertheless, it appears that individuals adjust to these life experiences.

These exits are from roles believed to represent major contributory functions for society. No other roles are available as replacement roles for most older individuals which represent primary contributory functions. Volunteer activity is not a major involvement during old age, or any other age.

The material presented in chapter 4 pointed to a discrepancy, analogous to the one which arose in the previous chapter. The lack of correlation between objective changes in health and attitudinal or subjective dimensions emerged in chapter 3. Chapter 4 pointed to a lack of correlation between the experience of various role transitions during old age and the objective circumstances that would lead one to expect more negative consequences for these individuals.

Those writing from the perspective of the political economy of aging, such as Myles (1984) and Guillemard (1984), point out that the conditions of aging in our society are largely negative. Individuals are excluded from paid labor; they live in relative poverty; their major functions of raising a family have come to an end; there are no other major roles to replace these; and their health is deteriorating. The health care system, by and large, has not evolved to best meet their needs nor to help them remain within the community. The structural position of elderly people in society is one of disadvantage. Nevertheless, evidence from the more social psychological literature on the experience of aging indicates that the aged adjust and cope fairly well. This discrepancy is not well understood and has not been adequately studied or explained within the literature.

Furthermore, as discussed in chapter 5, elderly people are not isolated from family and friends. Instead, they are involved within informal networks. While there is a trend towards elderly individuals to live alone, this emerges as independence freely chosen rather than isolation and alienation. Elderly individuals who live with someone by and large live with their spouse. There does not yet seem to be any major trend towards alternative living arrangements, such as families of choice, made so famous by Kuhn in the United States.

However, this does not mean that others outside the household ignore elderly individuals. Rather, interaction is fairly extensive. Relationships are maintained with children and grandchildren, although the extent to which the grandparenting role has primary importance in the lives of elderly people is not really known. The importance then of age peers also requires futher study.

The informal network is extremely important in the provision of informal care and assistance as people age. There is increasing evidence that most care for elderly people in society comes from family and friends, and not from the formal care system. Furthermore, even among those receiving formal care in the community, by far more care comes from the informal network. Those in long-term institutional settings still receive visitation and assistance from family and friends. These are areas of increasing importance, which require further research.

Chapter 6 then elaborated on the development of the formal health care system in North America. It is evident that despite various differences in the development of the health care delivery systems in Canada and the United States, both countries have medical care systems with physicians at the center. Acute care and institutional care is their major foci. Recently, this system has come under attack as reflecting a more narrow definition of health than is optimal. In addition, historical evidence suggests that some of the improvements in health, which are frequently attributed to advances in clinical medicine, are due more to environmental and public health measures.

The relationship between health care dollars and health status, especially in advanced industrial societies, has not been clearly demonstrated. There has also been a major shift in illness — especially during old age — so that there are now more chronic conditions than acute and infectious illnesses. These arguments suggest there is much room for improvement in our medical care systems to meet adequately the needs of an aging society. The chapter concentrated primarily on an exposition and a critique of the existing formal care systems with their medical focus.

Chapter 7 explored community social services, which currently exist, within the major focus on medical care in Canada and the United States. At the current time, arguments abound in favor of the establishment of more community social services. They are viewed as filling the gap in the provision of a continuum of services, which is largely lacking today. In addition, at least some of the current popularity of these services has arisen over concerns that the existing medical care system is simply too expensive when its efficacy is questionable. The chapter discussed some of the specific community social services that are needed for an aging society.

The important point is the provision of a range of services, which can include a host of workers, such as volunteers, therapists, homemakers, social workers, home aids and orderlies and nurses. Similarly, the types of programs can be offered in the community out of the home or in the individual's own home. They can include adult day care programs, providing monitoring of health conditions, senior centers providing primarily opportunity for socialization and day hospitals providing more medical care. Both transportation and housing needs have emerged as two areas of critical concern for an aging society.

While research is still lacking in the area of community social services, there is general consensus that the current provision of such services is inadequate. Obtaining data on the existence and utilization of the various services is difficult and drawing conclusions is hazardous at best. Nevertheless, it seems clear that far fewer of these services exist than do the medical and institutional services discussed in the previous chapter. Furthermore, evaluations assessing the effectiveness of these programs tend to be scarce. The data, which do exist, point to the potential benefits of these programs for an aging society.

Chapter 8 then discussed an alternative health care system, which would incorporate more community social services, and which would facilitate self- and informal-care. Such changes to the formal care system assume a broader definition of health than is reflected in the current medical care system. It calls for a greater emphasis on chronic care, rather than a primary focus on acute care, and an emphasis on community rather than institutional care. Whether or not such changes are likely is not known. However, arguments can be made that they will not only better meet the needs of an aging society but also will, at a minimum, cost no more than the current system. They could cost less. Such alternative health care systems assume, however, a restructuring of the system rather than a continuation of the current expensive system, with either little change or simply the provision of community services in the form of add-ons.

As argued by Evans (1984), there is room in the system for such reorganization which would incorporate accountability in terms of effectiveness of both services as well as costs. Services that are not effective in terms of health outcome should quite simply be terminated. A reorganization of the system to allow more totalistic rather than piecemeal types of changes, is also required. If community services are provided in the belief that they will ensure shorter stays in hospital or a prevention of long-term institutional care, then the corresponding sectors should have equivalent funds withdrawn. It is only through such a view of the system as a whole that cost measures can be taken.

The formal system also has to recognize the extent to which self-care and informal care are prevalent among elderly individuals. The task of the formal care system should be to facilitate that care, while maintaining the autonomy and dignity of the individuals involved. This is problematic, especially given that as a society we have not yet come to grips with questions basic to increased life expectancy with deteriorating health. How long should life be maintained and in what circumstances? Given a process of gradual decline, when is medical intervention warranted? Professionals can give technical information, but the decision regarding the value of the outcome should be the individual's. The formal system must also be flexible enough to change as the needs of the clients change, as they inevitably will. These are not easy problems to resolve. They must be looked at and treated seriously if the resolutions to these problems are ever to see the light of day.

Some specific areas requiring attention include informing individuals what services are available. As Lopata (1984) notes, even with our abundant society with all of its services, an individual who does not have the skills to reach into the community and discover what is available can be left without needed assistance. How individuals actually decide to use services, once they have the knowledge, is an area that is gaining in interest but about which there is much to learn. Individuals' informal networks appear to be a critical factor in this process.

An argument is being made by some politicians that community social services simply represent substitutions for informal care. Existing research suggests this is not the case. It is important, however, that this knowledge be shared with policy makers to ensure informed decision-making. An area that is especially vulnerable to these criticisms is the provision of relief for the caregiver. It is surely shortsighted to refuse such care if the lack of services results in a greater need for more intense care for both the original patient and the original caregiver.

This book has tried to present a realistic picture of aging in our society. In doing so, it assesses existing knowledge, surrounding issues of practical importance in an aging society. The common theme has been a focus on health and health care issues in an aging society, using a social perspective. Much remains unknown in the area of aging and health care. To advance knowledge, collaborative efforts among various constituents whether they be researchers, policy makers, administrators, practitioners or elderly people themselves is necessary. Chapter 9 discussed such efforts and explored different types of research where collaboration can be particularly important. In addition to gathering information, there must be an effort to disseminate it so as to minimize uninformed and partial judgements.

Given economic constraints, cost concerns surrounding the existing medical care system and the aging of society, these factors together present us with an opportunity to change our existing system to better meet the needs of an aging society. Whether or not the challenges will be met and a more adequate health care system will develop — to meet the needs of elderly individuals, while maintaining their autonomy, dignity and preferences — is unknown. The actions we take in the years to come will shape the health care system and the society in which we live our old age.

■ INDEX ■

▪ REFERENCES ▪

Abu-Laban, S.M. "Social Supports in Older Age: The Need for New Research Directions," *Essence*, 1980, 195–209.

Adams, B.N. *Kinship in an Urban Setting*. Chicago, Illinois: Markham, 1968.

Adams, D.L. "Analysis of a Life Satisfaction Index," *Journal of Gerontology*, 1969, 24:470–4.

Administration on Aging from RMC Research Corporation. *Assessing the Status and Needs of Older Americans: Questionnaire*. Washington, DC: U.S. Department of Health, Education and Welfare, 1975.

Andersen, R. and J.F. Newman. "Societal and Individual Determinants of Medical Care Utilization in the United States," *Milbank Memorial Fund Quarterly*, 1973, 51(1):95–124.

Arling, G. "The Elderly Widow and her Family, Neighbours and Friends," *Journal of Marriage and the Family*, 1976, 38:757–68.

Arling, G. and W.J. McAuley. "The Feasibility of Public Payments for Family Caregiving," *The Gerontologist*, 1983, 23:300–6.

Ashford, D.E., P.J. Katzenstein and T.J. Pempel. *Comparative Public Policy*. Beverly Hills, California: Sage Publications, 1978.

Atchley, R.C. "Selected Social and Psychological Differences Between Men and Women in Later Life," *Journal of Gerontology*, 1976a, 31:204–11.

_____. *The Sociology of Retirement*. New York, New York: Schenkman, 1976b.

_____. "Issues in Retirement Research," *The Gerontologist*, 1979, 19:44–54.

Atchley, R.C. and S.L. Corbett. "Older Women and Jobs." In *Looking Ahead: A Woman's Guide to the Problems and Joys of Growing Older*, edited by L.E.

Troll, J. Israel and K. Israels. Englewood Cliffs, New Jersey: Prentice-Hall, 1977, 121–5.

Atchley, R.C. and S. Miller. "Older People and their Families." In *Annual Review of Gerontology and Geriatrics*, Vol. 1, edited by C. Eisdorfer. New York, New York: Springer Publishing Co., 1980, 337–69.

Atchley, R.C., L. Pignatello and E.C. Shaw. "Interactions with Family and Friends: Marital Status and Occupational Differences Among Older Women," *Research on Aging*, 1979, 1:83–96.

Auerbach, M.I., D.W. Gordon, A. Ullman and M.J. Weisel. "Health Care in a Selected Urban Elderly Population: Utilization Patterns and Perceived Needs," *The Gerontologist*, 1977, 17:341–46.

Austin, C.D. and M.B. Loeb. "Why Age Is Relevant in Social Policy and Practice." In *Age or Need? Public Policies for Older People*, edited by B.L. Neugarten. Beverly Hills, California: Sage Publications, 1982, 263–88.

Austin, M.J., G. Cox, N. Gottlieb, J.D. Hawkins, J.M. Kruzich and R. Rauch. *Evaluating Your Agency's Programs*. Beverly Hills, California: Sage Publications, 1982.

Axelson, L.J. "Personal Adjustment in the Post Parental Period," *Marriage and Family Living*, 1960, 22:66–8.

Babchuk, N., G.R. Peters, D.R. Hoyt and M.A. Kaiser. "The Voluntary Associations of the Aged." *Journal of Gerontology*, 1979, 34:579–87.

Badgley, R.F. and R.D. Smith. *User Charges for Health Services*. Toronto, Ontario: Ontario Council of Health, 1979.

Barnes, G.E. and N.L. Chappell. "Old but Not Depressed." Paper presented at the annual meeting of the Canadian Association on Gerontology meetings, Winnipeg, Manitoba, November, 1982.

Barnes, J.A. "Class and Committees in a Norwegian Island Parish," *Human Relations*, 1954, 7(1):39–58.

Beattie, W.M. "Aging and the Social Services." In *Handbook of Aging and the Social Sciences*, edited by R.H. Binstock and E. Shanas. New York, New York: Van Nostrand Reinhold Co., 1976.

Beatty, S.R. "An Overview of Continuity of Care." In *Continuity of Care: The Hospital and the Community*, edited by S.R. Beatty. New York, New York: Grune and Stratton, 1980, 3–12.

Bell, M.J. and K.M. Schwede. "Feminist Attitudes of Older Women." Paper presented for the St. Michael's College Symposium: Women and Society, Vermont, March, 1979.

Bengtson, V.L. and N.L. Cutler. "Generational and Intergenerational Relations: Perspectives on Age Groups and Social Change." In *Handbook of Aging and the Social Sciences*, edited by R.H. Binstock and E. Shanas. New York, New York: Van Nostrand Reinhold Co., 1976, 130–59.

Bennett, J.E. and J. Krasny. "Health Care in Canada." In *Health and Canadian Society: Sociological Perspectives*, edited by D. Coburn, C. D'Arcy, P. New and G. Torrance. Don Mills, Ontario: Fitzhenry and Whiteside Ltd., 1981, 40–66.

Benson, R.L. "Misserrimi miserorum: bon compagno on the Evils of Old Age." Paper presented at Aging and the Aged in Medieval Society conference, University of Toronto, Toronto, Ontario, 1984.

Berardo, F.M. "Survivorship and Social Isolation: The Case of the Aged Widower." *The Family Co-ordinator*, 1970, 19:11–25.

Bergmann, K. "Dementia: Epidemiological Aspects." In *The Aging Brain: Neurological and Mental Distrubances*, edited by G. Barbagallo-Sangiorgi and A.N. Exton-Smith. New York, New York: Plenum Press, 1980, 59–69.

Berkanovic, E. "Seeking Care for Cancer Relevant Symptoms." *Journal of Chronic Diseases*, 1982, 35:727–34.

Biaggi, M. Testimony before the Select Committee on Aging, House of Represntatives, 96th Congress, Washington, DC, 1980.

Binstock, R.H. "Federal Policy Toward the Aging: Its Inadequacies and its Politics." *National Journal*, 1978, 10:1838–45.

Bird, R.M. and R.D. Fraser. *Commentaries on the Hall Report*. Toronto, Ontario: Ontario Economic Council, 1981.

Blau, Z.S. "Structural Constraints on Friendship in Old Age." *American Sociological Review*, 1961, 26:429, 439.

_____. *Old Age in a Changing Society*. New York, New York: Franklin Watts, 1973.

Blazer, D. and C.D. Williams. "Epidemiology of Dipphoria and Depression in an Elderly Population." *American Journal of Psychiatry*, 1980, 137:439–44.

Blenkner, M. "The Normal Dependencies of Aging." In *The Later Years: Social Applications of Gerontology*, edited by R.A. Kalish. Monterey, California: Brooks/Cole Publishing Company, 1977, 78–83.

Bluestone, E.M. "The Combined Hospital-home Program — a Critique." *Geriatrics*, 1957, 12:657–60.

Borland, D.C. "A Cohort Analysis Approach to the Empty-nest Syndrome Among Three Ethnic Groups of Women: A Theoretical Position." *Journal of Marriage and the Family*, 1982, 44:117–29.

Botwinick, J. "Method and Madness in Aging Research." Paper presented at Longitudinal Design and Data Analysis in Aging Workshop, Centre on Aging, University of Manitoba, Winnipeg, Manitoba, 1982.

Boucher, M.P., R.Y. Pablo and J.D.T. Roberts. "Voluntary Health Agencies — Who, What and Why?: A Survey of the Thames Valley District Health Council Area." *Canadian Journal of Public Health*, 1979, 70:183–98.

Bradburn, N.M. *The Structure of Psychological Well-being*. Chicago, Illinois: Aldine Publishing Co., 1969.

Braito, R. "Singles and Aging: Implications for Needed Research." Paper presented at the annual meeting of the Society for the Study of Social Problems, San Francisco, California, September, 1978.

Branch, L.G. *Vulnerable Elders*, No. 6, Gerontological Monographs. Washington, DC: Gerontological Society of America, 1980.

Branch, L.G. and F.J. Fowler, Jr. *The Health Care Needs of the Elderly and Chronically Disabled in Massachusetts*. Boston, Mass.: Massachusetts Department of Public Health, 1975.

Branch, L.G. and A.M. Jette. "Elders' Use of Informal Long-term Care Assistance." Paper presented at the annual meeting of the Gerontological Society of America, Toronto, Ontario, 1981.

Brocklehurst, J.C. "Brain Failure in Old Age — Social Implications." *Age and Aging*, 1977, 6:30–4.

Brody, E.M. "The Aging of the Family." *Annals of the American Academy of Political and Social Science*, 1978, 438:13–27.

_____. "Innovative Programs and Services for Elderly and Family." Testimony before the Select Committee on Aging, House of Representatives, 96th Congress, Washington, DC, 1980.

_____. "Women in the Middle and Family Help to Older People." *The Gerontologist*, 1981, 21:470–80.

Brody, S.J. "Comprehensive Health Care for the Elderly: An Analysis." *The Gerontologist*, 1973, 13:412–7.

Brown, E.R. *Rockefeller Medicine Men: Medicine and Capitalism in America.* Berkely, California: University of California Press, 1979.

Bryden, K. *Old Age Pensions and Policy-making in Canada.* Montreal, Quebec: McGill–Queen's University Press, 1974.

Bultena, G.L. "Age Grading in the Social Interaction of the Elderly Male Population." *The Gerontologist*, 1968, 18:556–61.

_____. "Rural-urban Differences in the Familial Interaction of the Aged." *Rural Sociology*, 1969, 34:5–15.

Burgess, E.W. "Aging in Western Culture." In *Aging in Western Societies: A Comparative Survey*, edited by E.W. Burgess. Chicago, Illinois: University of Chicago Press, 1960, 3–28.

Burke, S.C. and W.J. Goudy. "Older Men and Their Kinship Networks." Paper presented at the annual meeting of the Midwest Sociological Society, Minneapolis, Minnesota, 1981.

Butler, R.N., J.S. Gertman, D.L. Oberlander and L. Schindler. "Self-care, Self-help and the Elderly." *International Journal of Aging and Human Development*, 1979–80, 10:95–117.

Callahan, J.J. Jr., L. Diamond, J. Giele and R. Morris. "Responsibility of Families Caring for their Severely Disabled Elders." *Health Care Financing Review*, 1980, 1:29–48.

Campbell, A. *The Sense of Well-being in America: Recent Patterns and Trends.* New York, New York: McGraw-Hill Book Company, 1981.

Cantor, M.H. "Life Space and the Social Support System of the Inner City Elderly of New York." *The Gerontologist*, 1975, 15:23–7.

_____. "Neighbours and Friends: An Overlooked Resource in the Informal Support System." *Research on Aging*, 1979, 1:434–63.

_____. "Strain Among Caregivers: A Study of Experience in the United States." *The Gerontologist*, 1983, 23:597–604.

Carbonara, D.P. "Family Visits and Involvement in Treatment of Patients at a State Hospital." *Hospital and Community Psychiatry*, 1980, 31:854–85.

Carp, F.M. "Improving the Functional Quality of Housing and Environments for the Elderly Through Transportation." In *Environmental Context of Aging,* edited by T.O. Byerts, S.C. Howell and L.A. Pastalan. New York, New York: Garland Publishing Inc., 1979.

Carpenter, E.S. "Eternal Life and Self-definition Among the Aivilik Eskimos." *American Journal of Psychiatry*, 1954, 110:840–3.

Carveth, W.B. and B.H. Gottlieb. "The Measurement of Social Support and its Relation to Stress." *Canadian Journal of Behavioral Science*, 1979, 11:179–87.

Cassidy, H.M. *Social Security and Reconstruction*. Toronto, Ontario: Ryerson, 1943.

Cattel, R.B. *Abilities: Their Structure, Growth and Action*. Boston, Massachusetts: Houghton-Mifflin, 1971.

Chambre, S.M. "Is Volunteering a Substitute for Role Loss in Old Age? An Empirical Test of Activity Theory." *The Gerontologist*, 1984, 24:292-8.

Chappell, N.L. "Social Policy and the Elderly." In *Aging in Canada: Social Perspectives*, edited by V.W. Marshall. Don Mills, Ontario: Fitzhenry and Whiteside Ltd., 1980a, 35–42.

_____. "Re-examining Conceptual Boundaries: Peer and Intergenerational Relationships." *Essence: Issues in the Study of Aging, Dying and Death*, 1980b, 4:169–78.

_____. "Measuring Functional Ability and Chronic Health Conditions Among the Elderly: A Research Note on the Adequacy of Three Instruments." *Journal of Health and Social Behavior*, 1981, 22:90–102.

_____. "The Value of Research to Practitioners in Work with the Elderly." *Canadian Journal on Aging*, 1982a, 1:62–5

_____. "The Future Impact of the Changing Status of Women." In *Canada's Changing Age Structure: Implications for the Future*, edited by G. Gutman. Burnaby, British Columbia: Simon Fraser University Publications, 1982b, 203–37.

_____. *Peer and Intergenerational Support Networks Among the Elderly: Their Relevance for the Home Care Service Bureaucracy*. Final report. Ottawa, Ontario: Strategic Grants, Population Aging, Social Sciences and Humanities Research Council of Canada, 1982c.

_____. "Informal Support Networks Among the Elderly." *Research on Aging*, 1983a, 5:77–9.

_____. "Who Benefits from Adult Day Care: Changes in Functional Ability and Mental Functioning During Attendance." *Canadian Journal on Aging*, 1983b, 2:9–26.

_____. "Social Support and the Receipt of Home Care Services." *The Gerontologist*, 1985, 25:47–54.

Chappell, N.L. and G.E. Barnes. "The Practicing Pharmacist and the Elderly Client." *Contemporary Pharmacy Practice*, 1982, 5:170–75.

Chappell, N.L. and A.A. Blandford. *Adult Day Care: Its Impact on the Utilization of Other Health Care Services and on Quality of Life*. Final report. Ottawa, Ontario: NHRDP, Health and Welfare Canada, 1983.

Chappell, N.L. and B. Havens. "Old and Female: Testing the Double Jeopardy Hypothesis." *The Sociological Quarterly*, 1980, 21:157–71.

_____. "Who Helps the Elderly Person: A Discussion of Informal and Formal Care." In *Social Bonds in Later Life*, edited by W. Peterson and J. Quadagno. Beverly Hills, California: Sage Publications, forthcoming, 1985.

Chappell, N.L. and H. Orbach. "Socialization in Old Age—a Meadian Perspective." In *Advances in the Social Psychology of Aging*, edited by V.W. Marshall and A. Harris. Norwood, New Jersey: Ablex Publishing, forthcoming, 1986.

Chappell, N.L. and M.J. Penning. "The Trend Away from Institutionalization." *Research on Aging*, 1979, 1:361–87.

_____. "Informal Social Supports: Examining Ethnic Variations." Paper presented at the annual meeting of the Gerontological Society of America, San Antonio, Texas, 1984.

Cheal, D.J. "Intergenerational Family Transfers." *Journal of Marriage and the Family*, 1983, 45:805–13.

Chien, C.P., E.J. Townsend and A. Ross-Townsend. "Substance Use and Abuse Among the Community Elderly: The Medical Aspect." *Addictive Disease*, 1978, 3:357.

Clark, J.A. and W.E. Collishaw. *Canada's Older Population*. Ottawa, Ontario: Ottawa Staff Papers, Long Range Health Planning, 1975.

Clark, M. "Cultural Values and Dependency in Later Life." In *Aging and Modernization*, edited by D.O. Cowgill and L. Holmes. New York, New York: Appleton-Century-Crofts, 1972, 263–74.

Clark, N.M. and W. Rakowski. "Family Caregivers of Older Adults: Improving Helping Skills." *The Gerontologist*, 1983, 23:637–42.

Cleary, P.O., D. Mechanic and J.R. Greenley. "Sex Differences in Medical Care Utilization: An Empirical Investigation." *Journal of Health and Social Behavior*, 1982, 23:106–19.

Cobb, S. "Social Support as a Moderator of Life Stress." Presidential address, *Psychosomatic Medicine*, 1976, 38:300–14.

Coburn, D., C. D'Arcy, P. New and G. Torrance. *Health and Canadian Society: Sociological Perspectives*. Don Mills, Ontario: Fitzhenry and Whiteside Ltd., 1981.

Coburn, D., G.M. Torrance and J.M. Kaufert. "Medical Dominance in Canada: The Rise and Fall of Medicine." *International Journal of Health Services*, 1983, 13:407–32.

Cohen, C.I. and H. Rajkowski. "What's in a Friend: Substantive and Theoretical Issues." *The Gerontologist*, 1982, 22:261–6.

Cohler, B.J. and M.A. Lieberman. "Social Relations and Mental Health: Middle-Aged and Older Men and Women from Three European Ethnic Groups." *Research on Aging*, 1980, 2:445–69.

Conner, K.A., E.A. Powers and G.L. Bultena. "Social Interaction and Life Satisfaction: An Empirical Assessment of Late–life Patterns." *Journal of Gerontology*, 1979, 34:116–21.

Connidis, I. "Women and Retirement: The Effect of Multiple Careers on Retirement Adjustment." *Canadian Journal on Aging*, 1982, 1:17–27.

Cook, T.D. and D.T. Campbell. *Quasi-experimentation: Design and Analysis Issues for Field Settings.* Chicago, Illinois: Rand McNally College Publishing Company, 1979.

Copp, J.H. "The Rural Aged: What We Need to Know." *Social Abstracts,* 11343, 1980.

Coulton, C. and A.K. Frost. "Use of Social Services by the Elderly." *Journal of Health and Social Behavior,* 1982, 23:330–9.

Coward, R.T. "Planning Community Services for the Rural Elderly: Implications from Research." *The Gerontologist,* 1979, 19:275–82.

Cowgill, D.O. "Aging and Modernization: A Revision of the Theory." In *Late Life Communities and Environmental Policy,* edited by J.F. Gubrium. Springfield, Illinois: Charles C. Thomas, 1974.

Cowgill, D.O. and L.D. Holmes. *Aging and Modernization.* New York, New York: Appleton-Century-Crofts, 1972.

Crichton, A. "Equality: A Concept in Canadian Health Care: From Intention to Reality of Provision." *Social Science and Medicine,* 1980, 14C:243–57.

Cumming, E. and W.E. Henry. *Growing Old: The Process of Disengagement.* New York, New York: Basic Books, 1961.

Danis, B.G. and B. Silverstone. "The Impact of Caregiving: A Difference Between Wives and Daughters?" Paper presented at the annual meeting of the Gerontological Society of America, Toronto, Ontario, 1981.

Davison, G.C. and J.M. Neale. *Abnormal Psychology: An Experimental Clinical Approach* (3rd edition). New York, New York: John Wiley & Sons, 1982.

Deakers, L.P. "Continuity of Family Centered Nursing Care Between the Hospital and the Home." *Nursing Clinics of North America,* 1972, 7:83–93.

Dean, K. "Self-care Responses to Illness: A Selected Review." *Social Science and Medicine,* 1981, 15A:673–87.

DeFriese, G.H. and A. Woomert. "Self-care Among U.S. Elderly: Recent Developments." *Research on Aging,* 1983, 5:3–23.

Denton, F. and B. Spencer. "Health Care Costs When the Population Changes." In *Aging in Canada: Social Perspectives,* edited by V.W. Marshall. Don Mills, Ontario: Fitzhenry and Whiteside Ltd., 1980, 232–44.

Depner, C.E. "Health Networks in Later Life." Paper presented at the annual meeting of the Gerontological Society of America, San Francisco, California, 1983.

Detsky, A.S. *The Economic Foundations of National Health Policy.* Cambridge, Massachusetts: Balinger Publishing Co., 1978.

Deutscher, I. "The Quality of Post-parental Life." In *Middle Age and Aging,* edited by B.L. Neugarten. Chicago, Illinois: University of Chicago Press, 1968.

Devitt, M. and B. Checkoway. "Participation in Nursing Home Resident Councils: Promise and Practice." *The Gerontologist,* 1982, 22:49–53.

Dobrof, R. and E. Litwak. *Maintenance of Family Ties of Long-term Care Patients: Theory and Guide to Practice.* Washington, DC: U.S. Government Printing Office (DHHS Publication #81–400), 1977.

Dowd, J.J. "Industrialization and the Decline of the Aged." Paper presented at the annual meeting of the American Sociological Association, New York, New York, 1980.

Dubos, R.J. "Infection into Disease." In *Life and Disease*, edited by D.J. Ingle. New York, New York: Basic Books, 1963.

Dulude, L. *Women and Aging: A Report on the Rest of Our Lives*. Ottawa, Ontario: Advisory Council on the Status of Women, 1978.

Easterlin, R.A. "What Will 1984 Be Like? Socio-economic Implications of Recent Twists in Age Structure." *Demography*, 1978, 397–432.

Ehrenreich, J. (ed.) *The Cultural Crisis of Modern Medicine*. New York, New York: Monthly Review Press, 1978.

Eisdorfer, C. and D. Cohen. *Mental Health Care of the Aging: A Multidisciplinary Curriculum for Professional Training*. New York, New York: Springer Publishing Company, 1982.

Elliot, J. "Care for the Demented: It May Be up to the Family." *Journal of the American Medical Association*, 1979, 24:231.

Elwell, F. and A.D. Maltbie-Crannell. "The Impact of Role Loss upon Coping Resources and Life Satisfaction of the Elderly." *Journal of Gerontology*, 1981, 36:223–33.

Enos, D.D. and P. Sultan. *The Sociology of Health Care: Social, Economic and Political Perspectives*. New York, New York: Praeger Publishers, 1977.

Estes, C.L. *The Aging Enterprise*. San Francisco, California: Jossey-Bass Inc., 1979.

Evangela, Sister M. "The Influence of Family Relationships on the Geriatric Patient." *Nursing Clinics of North America*, 1968, 3:653–63.

Evans, R.G. "Does Canada Have too Many Doctors? Why Nobody Loves an Immigrant Physician." *Canadian Public Policy II*, 1976, 147–60.

_____. *Strained Mercy: The Economics of Canadian Health Care*. Toronto, Ontario: Butterworth and Company (Canada) Ltd., 1984.

Evans, R.L. and L.K. Northwood. "The Utility of Natural Help Relationships." *Social Science and Medicine*, 1979, 13A:789–95.

Farquharson, A. "Self-help Groups: A Health Resource." In *Health and Canadian Society: Sociological Perspectives*, edited by D. Coburn, C. D'Arcy, P. New and G. Torrance. Don Mills, Ontario: Fitzhenry and Whiteside Ltd., 1981, 313–21.

Fengler, A. and N. Danigelis. "The Shared Home: Assessment of Interest and Need." Paper presented at SYSTED '83, Montreal, Quebec, 1983.

Fengler, A. and N. Goodrich. "Wives of Elderly Disabled Men: The Hidden Patients." *The Gerontologist*, 1979, 19:175–84.

Ferraro, K.F. "Self-ratings of Health Among the Old and the Old-old." *Journal of Health and Social Behavior*, 1980, 21:377–83.

_____. "Widowhood and Social Participation in Later Life: Isolation or Compensation?" *Research on Aging*, 1984, 6:451–68.

Figner, M.A. "Honored Hoary Head: The Aged in the European Community." Paper presented at the Aging and the Aged in Medieval Society conference, University of Toronto, Toronto, Ontario, 1984.

Fillenbaum, G.G. "Social Context and Self-assessments of Health Among the Elderly." *Journal of Health and Social Behavior*, 1979, 20:45–51.

Fischer, D.H. *Growing Old in America*. New York, New York: Oxford University Press, 1978.

Fischer, L.R. "Elderly Parents and the Caregiving Role: An Asymmetrical Transition." Paper presented at the annual meeting of the Gerontological Society of America, San Francisco, California, 1983.

Fitz-Gibbon, C.T. and L.L. Morris. *How to Design a Program Evaluation*. Beverly Hills, California: Sage Publications, 1978.

Flathman, D.P. and D.E. Larsen. "Evaluation of Three Geriatric Day Hospitals in Alberta." Unpublished report, Division of Community Health Services, Faculty of Medicine, University of Calgary, Alberta, 1976.

Fleming, G.V. "The Elderly and Self-care for Serious Episodes of Illness." Paper presented at the annual meeting of the Gerontological Society of America, San Antonio, Texas, 1984.

Fox, P.D. and S.B. Clauser. "Trends in Nursing Home Expenditures: Implications for Aging Policy." *Health Care Financing Review*, 1980, 65–70.

Friedmann, E.A. and H.V. Orbach. "Adjustment to Retirement." In *American Handbook of Psychiatry* (second edition), edited by S. Arieti. New York, New York: Basic Books, 1974, 609–45.

Friedson, E. *Patients' Views of Medical Practice*. New York, New York: Russell Sage Foundation, 1961.

_____. *Professions of Medicine: A Study of the Sociology of Applied Knowledge*. New York, New York: Dodds Mead and Co., 1970.

Fries, J.F. "The Compression of Morbidity: Miscellaneous Comments About a Theme." *The Gerontologist*, 1984, 4:354–9.

Froland, C., D.L. Pancoast, N.J. Chapman and P.J. Kimboko. *Helping Networks and Human Services*. Beverly Hills, California: Sage Publications, 1981.

Gardner, M.A. "Caring and Sharing." *Perspectives on Aging*, 1981, X:4–7.

George, L.K. "Predicting Service Utilization Among the Elderly." Paper presented at the annual meeting of the Gerontological Society of America, Toronto, Ontario, 1981.

George, L.K. and L.P. Gwyther. "The Dynamics of Caregiver Burden: Changes in Caregiver Well-being over Time." Paper presented at the annual meeting of the Gerontological Society of America, San Antonio, Texas, 1984.

Getzel, G.S. "Social Work with Family Caregivers to the Aged. *Social Casework*, 1981, 62:201–9.

Gilbert, B.B. *The Evolution of National Insurance in Great Britain: The Origins of the Welfare State*. London, England: Michael Joseph, 1966.

Ginzberg, E. "The Elderly: An International Policy Perspective." *Milbank Memorial Fund Quarterly*, 1983, 3:473–88.

Gombeski, W.R. and M.H. Smolensky. "Non-emergency Health Transportation Needs of the Rural Texas Elderly." *The Gerontologist*, 1980, 20:452–6.

Gomers, A., B. Hankeme and B. Ragowski. "Help Structures for the Aged Sick: Experiences in Seven Countries." In *Reaching the Aged: Social Services in Forty-four Countries*, edited by M.I. Teicher, D. Thursz and J.L. Vigilante. Beverly Hills, California: Sage Publications, 1979, 117–38.

Goudy, W.J., E.A. Powers, P.M. Keith and R.A. Reger. "Changes in Attitudes Toward Retirement: Evidence from a Panel Study of Older Males." *Journal of Gerontology*, 1980, 35:942–8.

Gourash, N. "Help-seeking: A Review of the Literature." *American Journal of Community Psychology*, 1978, 6:413–23.

Gove, W.R. and M. Hughes. "Possible Causes of the Apparent Sex Differences in Physical Health: An Empirical Investigation." *American Sociological Review*, 1979, 44:129–46.

Government of Canada. *Canadian Governmental Report on Aging*. Ottawa, Ontario: Minister of Supply and Services, 1982.

Government of Manitoba. *Aging in Manitoba — Volume One*. Winnipeg, Manitoba: Department of Health and Social Development, 1973.

_____. *Continuing Care: Policy Guidelines and Program Manual*. Winnipeg, Manitoba: Manitoba Department of Health, Office of Continuing Care, 1983.

Granatstein, J. *Canada's War: The Politics of the Mackenzie King Government, 1943–1945*. Toronto, Ontario: Oxford, 1975.

Grans, A. and A.P. Fengler. "Vermont Elders — No Sense of Deprivation." *Perspective on Aging*, 1981, X:12–5.

Grant, P.R. and B. Rice. "Transportation Problems of the Rural Elderly: A Needs Assessment." *Canadian Journal on Aging*, 1983, 2:107–24.

Gratton, B. and M.R. Haug. "Decision and Adaptation: Research on Female Retirement." *Research on Aging*, 1983, 5:59–76.

Greenlick, M.R., A.V. Hurtado, C.R. Pope, E.W. Saward and S.S. Yoshioka. "Determinants of Medical Care Utilization." *Health Services Research*, 1968, 3:296–315.

Guemple, L. "Growing Old in Inuit Society." In *Aging in Canada: Social Perspectives*, edited by V.W. Marshall. Don Mills, Ontario: Fitzhenry and Whiteside Ltd., 1980, 95–101.

Guillemard, A. (ed.) *Old Age and the Welfare State*. Beverly Hills, California: Sage Publications, 1984.

Gurland, B.J. and J.A. Toner. "Depression in the Elderly: A Review of Recently Published Studies." *Annual Review of Gerontology and Geriatrics*, 1983, 3:228–65.

Gutman, G.M. "Issues and Findings Related to Multi-level Accommodation for Seniors." *Journal of Gerontology*, 1978, 33:592–600.

_____. "The Elderly at Home and in Retirement Housing: A Comparative Study of Health Problems, Functional Difficulties, and Support Service." In *Aging in Canada: Social Perspectives*, edited by V.W. Marshall. Don Mills, Ontario: Fitzhenry and Whiteside Ltd., 1980, 189–200.

_____. "Aging, Mirror of Humanity: The Psychologists' Perspective." Keynote address at the annual meeting of the Canadian Association on Gerontology, Moncton, New Brunswick, 1983.

Guttman, D. "Patterns of Legal Drug Use by Older Americans." *Addictive Diseases*, 1978, 3:337.

Haas-Hawkings, G. "Intimacy as a Moderating Influence on the Stress of Loneliness in Widowhood." *Essence*, 1978, 2:249–58. See Chappell, 1980b.

Harding, J. "The Pharmaceutical Industry as a Public Health Hazard and as an Institution of Social Control." In *Health and Canadian Society: Sociological Perspectives*, edited by D. Coburn, C. D'Arcy, P. New and G. Torrance. Don Mills, Ontario: Fitzhenry and Whiteside Ltd., 1981, 274–91.

Harel, Z. "Quality of Care, Congruence and Well-being Among Institutionalized Aged." *The Gerontologist*, 1981, 21:523–31.

Harel, Z. and L. Noelker. "Social Integration, Health and Choice: Their Impact on the Well-being of Institutionalized Aged." *Research on Aging*, 1982, 4:97–111.

Harlan, W.H. "Social Status of the Aged in Three Indian Villages." In *Middle Age and Aging*, edited by B.L. Neugarten. Chicago, Illinois: University of Chicago Press, 1968, 469–75.

Harrington, C. and R.J. Newcomer. "United States Co-ordinating Services to the Aged." In *Linking Health Care and Social Services*, edited by M.C. Hokenstad and R.A. Ritvo. Beverly Hills, California: Sage Publications, 1982, 241–78.

Harvey, C.D. and H.M. Bahr. "Widowhood, Morale and Affiliation." *Journal of Marriage and the Family*, 1974, 36:97–106.

Hatfield, A.B. "The Family as Partner in the Treatment of Mental Illness." *Hospital and Community Psychiatry*, 1979, 30:338–40.

Haug, M.R. "Doctor-patient Relationships and Their Impact on Elderly Self-care." Paper presented at the annual meeting of the Gerontological Society of America, San Antonio, Texas, 1984.

Haug, M.R. and B. Levin. "Self-care and the Elderly: An Empirical Assessment". Paper presented at the tenth word congress of the International Sociological Association, Mexico City, Mexico, 1982.

Hauser, P.M. "Aging and World-wide Population Change". In *Handbook of Aging and the Social Sciences*, edited by R.H. Binstock and E. Shanas. New York, New York: Van Nostrand Reinhold Co., 1976.

Havens, B. "Social Planning Implications of Needs Assessment." Paper presented at the World Conference on Aging: A Challenge to Science and Social Policy, Vichy, France, 1977.

_____. "The Relevance of Social Science Research in Aging." Paper presented at Towards a Mature Society, Conference on Research in Gerontology in the Social Sciences, Winnipeg, Manitoba, 1980.

_____. "Individual Needs and Community Resources." In *Health, Program Evaluation, and Demography: Research Instruments in Social Gerontology Vol. 3*, edited by D.J. Mangen and W.A. Peterson. Minneapolis, Minnesota: University of Minnesota Press, 1984, 137–74.

Havighurst, R.J. "Social and Psychological Needs of the Aging." *Annals of the American Academy of Political and Social Science*, 1952, 279:11–7.

Health and Welfare Canada. *Survey of Old Age Security (O.A.S.) and Canada Pension Plan (C.P.P.) Retirement Benefit Recipients*. Ottawa, Ontario: Minister of Supply and Services, 1981.

Health and Welfare Canada and Statistics Canada. *Canada Health Survey*. Ottawa, Ontario: Minister of Supply and Services, 1981.

Heltsley, M.E. and R.C. Powers. "Social Interaction and Perceived Adequacy of Interaction of the Rural Aged." *The Gerontologist*, 1975, 15:533–6.

Hendricks, J. and C.D. Hendricks. *Aging in Mass Society: Myths and Realities.* Cambridge, Massachusetts: Winthrop Publishers Inc., 1977, 1981.

Hess, B. "Friendship." In *Aging and Society Volume Three: A Sociology of Age Stratification*, Vol. 3, edited by M. Riley, M. Johnson and A. Foner. New York, New York: Sage Publications, 1972, 357-393.

Heumann, L. "Planning Assisted Independent Living Programs for the Semi-independent Elderly: Development of a Descriptive Model." *The Gerontologist*, 1978, 18:145–52.

Hirshfeld, R.M. and C.K. Cross. "Epidemiology of Affective Disorders: Psychosocial Risk Factors." *Archives of General Psychiatry*, 1982, 39:35–46.

Hobman, D. "Practical Care of Geriatric Patients: An Old Person's View of the Health Services." *Royal Society of Health Journal*, 1975, 95:21–5.

Hochschild, A.R. *The Unexpected Community.* Englewood Cliffs, New Jersey: Prentice-Hall, 1973.

Hodgson, J.H. and J.L. Quinn. "The Impact of the Triage Health Care Delivery System upon Client Morale, Independent Living and the Cost of Care." *The Gerontologist*, 1980, 20:364–71.

Hokenstad, M.C. and M.C. Ritvo (eds.) *Linking Health Care and Social Services.* Beverly Hills, California: Sage Publications, 1982.

Home Health Services Quarterly, 1980, 1:97–121.

Horn, J. "Human Ability Systems." In *Life-span Development and Behavior.* Vol. 1, edited by P. Baltes. New York, New York: Academic Press, 1978, 211–56.

Horowitz, A. "Sons and Daughters as Caregivers to Older Parents: Differences in Role Performance and Consequences." Paper presented at the annual meeting of the Gerontological Society of America, Toronto, Ontario, 1981.

Horowitz, A. and J.E. Dono. "The Evaluation of a Community-based Home Care Program: Findings After One Year of Service." Paper presented at the annual meeting of the Gerontological Society of America, San Antonio, Texas, 1984.

Horowitz, A. and L.W. Shindelman. "Reciprocity and Affection: Past Influence on Current Caregiving." Paper presented at the annual meeting of the Gerontological Society of America, Toronto, Ontario, 1981.

Horowitz, A., J.E. Dono and R. Brill. "Continuity or Changes in Informal Support? The Impact of an Expanded Home Care Program." Paper presented at the annual meeting of the Gerontological Society of America, San Francisco, California, 1983.

Hum, D.P.J. "Universality and Restraint in Income Security." *Western Economic Review*, 1984, 3:15–29.

Illich, I. *Limits to Medicine: Medical Nemesis. The Expropriation of Health.* London, England: Marion Press, 1976.

_____. *The Medical Nemesis.* New York, New York: Random House, 1977.

Illsley, R. "Self-care: What Is It and What Does It Mean for the Elderly and Health Care Providers?" Paper presented at the Intergenerational Research Colloquium on Self-care and the Elderly, University of Michigan, 1981.

Irving, A. "The Development of Income Security in Canada, Britain and the United States, 1908–1945: A Comparative and Interpretive Account." Publication Series, Working Papers on Social Welfare in Canada, University of Toronto, Faculty of Social Work, 1980.

Johnson, C.L. and D.J. Catalano. "Childless Elderly and their Family Supports." *The Gerontologist*, 1981, 21:610–8.

_____. "A Longitudinal Study of Family Supports to the Impaired Elderly." *The Gerontologist*, 1983, 23:612–8.

Jonas, K. "Factors in Development of Community Among Elderly Persons in Age-segregated Housing: Relationships Between Involvement in Friendship Roles Within the Community and External Social Roles." *Anthropological Quarterly*, 1979, 52:29–38.

Kahana, E.F. and H.A. Kiyak. "The Older Woman: Impact of Widowhood and Living Arrangements on Service Needs." *Journal of Gerontological Social Work*, 1980, 3, winter.

Kahn, R.L., A.I. Goldfarb, M. Pollack and A. Peck. "Brief Objective Measures for the Determination of Mental Status in the Aged." *American Journal of Psychiatry*, 1961, 107:326–8.

Kalbach, W. and W. McVey. *The Demographic Bases of Canadian Society*. Toronto, Ontario: McGraw-Hill Ryerson Ltd., 1979.

Kalish, R.A. "Social Values and the Elderly." In *The Later Years: Social Applications of Gerontology*, edited by R.A. Kalish. Monterey, California: Brooks/Cole Publishing Co., 1977, 64–9.

Kammerman, S.B. "Community Services for the Aged: The View from Eight Countries." *The Gerontologist*, 1976, 16:529–37.

Kane, R.A. and R.L. Kane. *Assessing the Elderly: A Practical Guide to Measurement*. Lexington, Massachusetts: Lexington Books, 1981.

Kane, R.L. and R.A. Kane. "Care of the Aged: Old Problems in Need of New Solutions." *Science*, 1978, 200:913–9.

_____. "Alternatives to Institutional Care of the Elderly: Beyond the Dichotomy." *The Gerontologist*, 1980, 20:249–59.

Kastenbaum, R. and S.E. Candy. "The 4% Fallacy: A Methodological and Empirical Critique of Extended Care Facility Population Statistics." *International Journal of Aging and Human Development*, 1973, 4:15–21.

Katz, S., A.B. Ford, R.W. Moskowitz, B.A. Jackson and M.W. Jaffee. "Studies of Illness in the Aged, the Index of ADL: A Standardized Measure of Biological and Psycho-social Function." *Journal of the American Medical Association*, 1963, 185:94.

Katz, S., B. Ford, T. Downs, M. Adams and I. Rusby. *Effects of Continued Care: A Study of Chronic Illness in the Home*. Washington, DC: United States Department of Health, Education and Welfare, Publication CHSMJ 73-3010, 1972.

Kayser-Jones, J.S. *Old, Alone and Neglected Care of the Aged in Scotland and the United States*. Berkely, California: University of California Press, 1981.

Keith, J. *Old People as People: Social and Cultural Influences on Aging and Old Age*. Toronto, Ontario: Little, Brown and Company, 1982.

Kelman, H.R. "The Underdevelopment of Evaluative Research on Health Services for the Elderly in the United States." *International Journal of Health Services*, 1980, 10:501–11.

King, S. *Perceptions of Illness and Medical Practice*. New York, New York: Russell Sage Foundation, 1962.

Kivett, V.R. and J.P. Scott. *The Rural By-passed Elderly: Perspectives on Status and Needs*, Technical Bulletin No. 260. Raleigh, North Carolina: North Carolina Agriculture Research Services, 1979.

Kovar, M.G. "Health of the Elderly and Use of Health Services." *Public Health Research*, 1977, 92:9–19.

Kozma, A. and M.J. Stones. "Some Research Issues and Findings in the Study of Psychological Well-being in the Aged." *Canadian Psychological Review*, 1978, 19:241–9.

Kraus, A.S., R.A. Spasoff, E.J. Beattie, D.E.W. Holden, J.S. Lawson, M. Rodenburg and G.M. Woodcock. "Elderly Applicants to Long-term Care Institutions." *Journal of the American Geriatrics Society*, 1976, 24:117–25.

Kuhn, M. Testimony before the Select Committee on Aging, 96th Congress, Washington, DC, 1980.

Kutza, E.A. and N.R. Zweibel. "Age as a Criterion for Focusing Public Programs." In *Age or Need? Public Policies for Older People*, edited by B.L. Neugarten. Beverly Hills, California: Sage Publications, 1982, 55–99.

Lalonde, M. *A New Perspective on the Health of Canadians*. A working document. Ottawa, Ontario: National Health and Welfare, 1974.

Lamy, P.P. "Editorial: The White House Conference on Aging — an Opportunity for Pharmacy." *Contemporary Pharmacy Practice*, 1981, 54:9.

Langlie, J.K. "Social Networks, Health Beliefs and Preventive Health Behavior." *Journal of Health and Social Behavior*, 1977, 18:244–60.

Lareau, L.S. "Needs Assessment of the Elderly: Conclusions and Methodological Approaches." *The Gerontologist*, 1983, 23:518–26.

Larson, R. "Thirty Years of Research on the Subjective Well-being of Older Americans." *Journal of Gerontology*, 1978, 33:109–25.

Laslett, R. "Societal Development and Aging." In *Handbook on Aging and the Social Sciences*, edited by R.H. Binstock and E. Shanas. New York, New York: Van Nostrand Reinhold Co., 1976, 87–116.

Lave, J.R. and H.A. Silverman. "Financing the Health Care of the Aged." *Annals of the American Academy of Political and Social Science*, 1983, July, 149–64.

LaVor, J. "Long-term Care and Home Health Care: A Challenge to Service Systems." *Home Health Care Services Quarterly*, 1979, 1:19–73.

Lawton, M.P. and E.M. Brody. "Assessment of Older People: Self-Maintaining and Instrumental Activities of Daily Living." *The Gerontologist*, 1969, 9:179–86.

LeClair, M. "The Canadian Health Care System." In *National Health Insurance: Can We Learn from Canada?*, edited by S. Andreopoulos. New York, New York: John Wiley and Sons, 1975, 11–93.

Lee, G.R. "Children and the Elderly." *Research on Aging*, 1979, 1:335–61.

Lee, G.R. and M.L. Lassey. "Rural-urban Differences Among the Elderly: Economic, Social and Subjective Factors." *Journal of Social Issues*, 1980, 36:62–74.

Lee, S.S. "Health Insurance in Canada—an Overview and Commentary." *New England Journal of Medicine*, 1974, 290:713.

Leman, C. "Patterns of Policy Development: Social Security in the United States and Canada." *Public Policy*, 1977, 25:261–91.

Levin, L. and E. Idler. "Self-care in Health." *Annual Review of Public Health*, 1983, 4:181–201.

Liang, J. and K. Bollen. "Dimensions of Social Integration." Paper presented at the annual meeting of the Gerontological Society of America, Toronto, Ontario, 1981.

Liang, J. and T.J. Fairchild. "Relative Deprivation and Perception of Financial Adequacy Among the Aged." *Journal of Gerontology*, 1979, 34:746–59.

Liang, J., L. Dvorkin, E. Kahana and F. Mazian. "Social Integration and Morale: A Re-examination." *Journal of Gerontology*, 1980, 35:746–57.

Lin, N. "Social Resources and Instrumental Action." In *Social Structure and Network Analysis*, edited by P.V. Marsden and N. Lin. Beverly Hills, California: Sage Publications, 1982, 131–45.

Lipman, A. and C.F. Longino. "Mother is Alone Now: Sons and Daughters of Married and Widowed Mothers." Paper presented at the annual meeting of the Gerontological Society of America, San Francisco, California, 1983.

Litwak, E. "Part II—Theoretical Base for Practice." In *Maintenance of Family Ties of Long-term Care Patients: Theory and Guide to Practice*, edited by R. Dobrof and E. Litwak. Rockville, Maryland: U.S. Department of Health and Human Services, National Institute of Mental Health, 1977, 80–116.

Lopata, H.Z. *Widowhood in an American City*. Cambridge, Massachusetts: Schenkman Publishing Company, Inc., 1973.

_____. "Support Systems of Elderly Urbanities: Chicago of the 1970's." *The Gerontologist*, 1975, 15:35-41.

_____. *Women as Widows: Support Systems*. New York, New York: Elsevier North Holland Inc., 1979.

_____. "The Portrayal of Older Women in Gerontological Writings." Guest lecture at the Centre on Aging, University of Manitoba, Winnipeg, Manitoba, 1984.

Lowenthal, M.F. and C. Haven. "Interaction and Adaptation: Intimacy as a Critical Variable." In *Middle Age and Aging*, edited by B. Neugarten. Chicago, Illinois: University of Chicago Press, 1968, 390–400.

Lowenthal, M.F. and B. Robinson. "Social Networks and Isolation." In *Handbook of Aging and the Social Sciences*, edited by R.H. Binstock and E. Shanas. New York, New York: Van Nostrand Reinhold Co., 1976, 432–56.

Lowenthal, M.F., M. Thurnher, D. Chiriboga and associates. *Four Stages of Life: A Comparative Study of Women and Men Facing Transitions*. San Francisco, California: Jossey-Bass Publishers, 1975.

Luciano, K.B. "Components of Planned Family-centered Care." *Nursing Clinics of North America*, 1972, 7:41-52.

Lutz, B. Sub-committee on Retirement Income, Washington, DC, personal communication, September 10, 1984.

Maddox, G.L. and E.B. Douglas. "Self-assessment of Health: A Longitudinal Study of Elderly Subjects." *Journal of Health and Social Behavior*, 1973, 14:87–93.

Maguire, L. *Understanding Social Networks.* Beverly Hills, California: Sage Publications, 1983.

Marcus, A.C. and J.M. Siegel. "Sex Differences in the Use of Physician Services: A Preliminary Test of the Fixed Role Hypothesis." *Journal of Health and Social Behavior*, 1982, 23:186–97.

Marmor, T.R. "Can the U.S. Learn from Canada?" In *National Health Insurance: Can We Learn from Canada*, edited by S. Andreopoulos. New York, New York: John Wiley & Sons, 1975, 231–50.

Marsh, L. *Report on Social Security for Canada.* Toronto, Ontario: University of Toronto Press, 1975.

Marshall, V.W. "Socialization for Impending Death in a Retirement Village." *American Journal of Sociology*, 1975, 80:1124–44.

_____. (ed.) *Aging in Canada: Social Perspectives.* Don Mills, Ontario: Fitzhenry and Whiteside Ltd., 1980a.

_____. "Reflections on the Canadian Research Scene." Paper presented at Towards a Mature Society, Conference on Research in Gerontology in the Social Sciences, Winnipeg, Manitoba, 1980b.

_____. "Generations, Age Groups and Cohorts." *Canadian Journal on Aging*, 1983, 2:51–61.

Marshall, V.W., C.J. Rosenthal and J. Synge. "The Family as a Health Organization for the Elderly." Paper presented at the annual meeting of the Society for the Study of Social Problems, Toronto, Ontario, 1981.

Marshall, V.W. and J.A. Tindale. "Notes for a Radical Gerontology." *International Journal of Aging and Human Development*, 1978–9, 9:163–75.

Martin Matthews, A., K.H. Brown, C.K. Davis and M.A. Denton. "A Crisis Assessment Technique for the Evaluation of Life Events: Transition to Retirement as an Example." *Canadian Journal on Aging*, 1982, 1:28–39.

Matthews, S. "Participation of the Elderly in a Transportation System." *The Gerontologist*, 1982, 22:26–31.

Maxwell, R. *Health Care: The Growing Dilemma.* New York, New York: McKinsey & Co., 1975.

McKeown, T. and C.R. Lowe. *An Introduction to Social Medicine.* Philadelphia, Pennsylvania: F.A. Davis, 1966.

McKinlay, J.B. "Some Approaches and Problems in the Study of the Use of Services — an Overview." *Journal of Health and Social Behavior*, 1972, 13:115–52.

_____. "Social Network Influences on Morbid Episodes and the Career of Help Seeking." In *The Relevance of Social Science for Medicine*, edited by L. Eisenberg and A. Kleinman. D. Reidel Publishing Co., 1980, 77–107.

McLachlin, D. Department of Physiology, University of Toronto, Toronto, Ontario, personal communication, 1983.

McPherson, B. *Aging as a Social Process*. Scarborough, Ontario: Butterworth and Company (Canada) Ltd., 1983.

McPherson, B. and C. Kozlik. "Canadian Leisure Patterns by Age: Disengagement, Continuity or Ageism?" In *Aging in Canada: Social Perspectives*, edited by V.W. Marshall. Don Mills, Ontario: Fitzhenry and Whiteside Ltd., 1980, 113–22.

Mechanic, D. "Correlates of Physician Utilization: Why Do Major Multivariate Studies of Physician Utilization Find Trivial Psychosocial and Organizational Effects?" *Journal of Health and Social Behavior*, 1969, 20:387–96.

Meriam-Webster Dictionary. New York, New York: Pocket Books, 1974.

Meltz, N.M. and D. Stager. *The Occupational Structure of Earnings in Canada, 1931–1975*. Ottawa, Ontario: Minister of Supply and Services, Table A.19, 1979.

Michalos, A. and S. Fortey. "Vignettes of Canada and the United States." In *Perspectives Canada III*, edited by J.H. Adler and D.A. Brusegard. Ottawa, Ontario: Statistics Canada, 1980, 293–306.

Miller, S.J. "The Social Dilemma of the Aging Leisure Participant." In *Older People and Their Social World*, edited by A.M. Rose and W.A. Peterson. Philadelphia, Pennsylvania: F.A. Davis, 1965, 77–92.

Minister of Health and Welfare, Policy and Program Development and Co-ordination Branch. *Social Security in Canada*. Ottawa, Ontario: Information Canada, 1974.

Mishler, E.G. "Social Contexts of Health Care." In *Social Contexts of Health, Illness and Patient Care*, edited by E.G. Mishler, L.R. Amarasingham, S.T. Hauser, S.D. Osherson, N.E. Waxler and R. Liem. Cambridge, Massachusetts: Cambridge University Press, 1981a, 79–103.

_____. "The Health-care System: Social Contexts and Consequences." In *Social Contexts of Health, Illness and Patient Care*, edited by E.G. Mishler, L.R. Amarasingham, S.T. Hauser, S.D. Osherson, N.E. Waxler and R. Liem. Cambridge, Massachusetts: Cambridge University Press, 1981b, 195–217.

_____. "In Conclusion: A New Perspective of Health and Medicine." In *Social Contexts of Health, Illness and Patient Care*, edited by E.G. Mishler, L.R. Amarasingham, S.T. Hauser, S.D. Osherson, N.E. Waxler and R. Liem. Cambridge, Massachusetts: Cambridge University Press, 1981c, 250–53.

Mitchell, J.C. and E.J. Trickett. "Task Force Report: Social Networks as Mediators of Social Support." *Community Mental Health Journal*, 1980, 16:27–44.

Monk, A. and L.W. Kaye. "The Ombudsman Volunteer in the Nursing Home: Differential Role Perceptions of Patient Representatives for the Institutionalized Aged." *The Gerontologist*, 1982, 22:194–9.

Montgomery, R.J.V. "Impact of Institutional Care Policies on Family Integration." *The Gerontologist*, 1982, 22:54–8.

Myers, G.C. "Cross-national Variations in Family Structures Among the Aged." Paper presented at the annual meeting of the Gerontological Society of America, Boston, Massachusetts, 1982.

Myers, G.C. and K.G. Manton. *Some Sociodemographic Observations Relating to Unpaid Productive Roles in Aging Society*. Durham, North Carolina: Center for Demographic Studies, Duke University, 1983.

Myers, G.C. and C.A. Nathanson. "Aging and the Family." *World Health Statistics Quarterly*, 1982, 35:225–38.

Myles, J.F. "Institutionalization and Sick Role Identification Among the Elderly." *American Sociological Review*, 1978, 43:508–21.

———. "The Aged, the State, and the Structure of Inequality." In *Structured Inequality in Canada*, edited by J. Harp and J. Hofley. Toronto, Ontario: Prentice-Hall, 1980.

———. *Old Age in the Welfare State: The Political Economy of Public Pensions*. Toronto, Ontario: Little Brown and Company Ltd., 1984.

National Council on Aging. *Fact Book on Aging: A Profile of America's Older Population*, 1978.

National Health and Welfare. *Report on the Federal-Provincial Working Group on Home Care Programs to the Advisory Committee on Community Health*. Ottawa, Ontario: National Health and Welfare, 1975.

Navarro, V. *Medicine under Capitalism*. New York, New York: Prodest, 1976.

Neuber, K.A., W.T. Atkins, J.A. Jacobson and N.A. Reuterman. *Needs Assessment: A Model for Community Planning*. Beverly Hills, California: Sage Publications, 1980.

Neugarten, B.L. "The Future and the Young Old." *The Gerontologist*, 1975, 15:4–9.

———. "Personality and Aging." In *Handbook of the Psychology of Aging*, edited by J.E. Birren and K.W. Schaie. New York, New York: Van Nostrand Reinhold Co., 1979, 626–49.

———. (ed.) "Older People: A Profile." In *Age or Need? Public Policies for Older People*. Beverly Hills, California: Sage Publications, 1982a, 33–54.

———. (ed.) "Policy for the 1980's: Age or Need Entitlement?" In *Age or Need? Public Policies for Older People*. Beverly Hills, California: Sage Publications, 1982b, 19–32.

———. (ed.) *Age or Need? Public Policies for Older People*. Beverly Hills, California: Sage Publications, 1982c.

Neugarten, B.L., R.J. Havighurst and S.S. Tobin. "The Measurement of Life Satisfaction." *Journal of Gerontology*, 1961, 16:134–43.

New, P. "Traditional and Modern Health Care: An Appraisal of Complementarity." *International Social Science Journal*, 1977, 29:483–95.

Nielson, M., M. Blenkner, M. Bloom, T. Downs and H. Beggs. "Older Persons After Hospitalization: A Controlled Study of Home Aide Service." *American Journal of Public Health*, 1972, 62:1094–101.

Noelker, L.S. and S.W. Poulshock. *The Effects on Families of Caring for Impaired Elderly in Residence*, final report. Washington, DC: U.S. Department of Health and Human Services, Administration on Aging, 1982.

Norris, J.E. "The Social Adjustment of Single and Widowed Older Women." *Essence*, 1980, 4:135–45.

Novak, M. *Successful Aging: The Myths, Realities and Future of Aging in Canada*, Markham, Ontario: Penguin Books, 1985.

NRTA/AARP and Wakefield Washington Associates. "Family Support Systems and the Aging." Policy report submitted to the Select Committee on Aging, House of Representatives, 96th Congress, Washington, D.C., 1980.

O'Brien, J.E. and D.L. Wagner. "Help Seeking by the Frail Elderly: Problems in Network Analysis." *The Gerontologist*, 1980, 20:78–83.

Office of Population Censuses and Surveys, Census 1981, National Report — Great Britain, Table 12: Usually Resident Population Aged 16 and Over: Economic position by age by marital status by sex, 1981a.

_____. Census 1981, Resident population of Great Britain aged 65 and over by country of birth. Table 1500, unpublished, 1981b.

Ohnsorg, D.W. "Burgeoning Day Care Movement Prolongs Independent Living." *Perspective on Aging*, Jan./Feb., 1981, 18–20.

Palmore, E. *The Honorable Elders: A Cross Cultural Analysis of Aging in Japan.* Durham, North Carolina: Duke University Press, 1975.

_____. *Social Patterns in Normal Aging.* Durham, North Carolina: Duke University Press, 1981.

Palmore, E.B., G.G. Fillenbaum and L.K. George. "Consequences of Retirement." *Journal of Gerontology*, 1984, 39:109–16.

Parnes, H.S. "From the Middle to the Later Years: Longitudinal Studies of the Pre- and Postretirement Experiences of Men." *Research on Aging*, 1981, 3:387–402.

Parsons, T. "Age and Sex in the Social Structure of the United States." *American Sociological Review*, 1942, 7:604–20.

_____. "Age and Sex in the Social Structure of the United States." In *Essays in Sociological Theory* (revised edition). Glencoe, Illinois: Free Press, 1954, 89–103.

Patton, M.Q. *Utilization—Focused Evaluation.* Beverly Hills, California: Sage Publications, 1978.

Perkins, F. *The Roosevelt I Knew.* London, England: Hammond, Hammond & Co., 1948.

Peters, G.R. "Friends, Neighbours and Confidants." In *The Development of an Instrument Bank: Assessment of Available Instruments and Measurement Scales for the Study of Aging and the Elderly*, final report, edited by W.A. Peterson, D.J. Mangen and R. Sanders. Kansas: Midwest Council for Social Research in Aging, 1978, 221–35.

Peterson, D.M. "Drug Use Among the Aged." *Addictive Diseases*, 1978, 3:305.

Pihlblad, C. and D.L. Adams. "Widowhood, Social Participation and Life Satisfaction." *Aging and Human Development*, 1972, 3:323–30.

Pilisuk, M., S. Heller, J. Kelly and E. Turner. "The Helping Network Approach: Community Promotion of Mental Health." *Journal of Primary Prevention*, 1982, 3:116–32.

Pitt, B. *Psycho-geriatrics: An Introduction to the Psychiatry of Old Age*, second edition. Edinburgh, Scotland: Church Livingstone, 1982.

Quadagno, J.S. *Aging in Early Industrial Society, Work, Family and Social Policy in Nineteeth Century England.* New York, New York: Academic Press, 1982.

Radloff, L.S. "The CES-D Scale: A Self-report Depression Scale for Research in the General Population." *Applied Psychological Measurement*, 1977, 385–401.

Rakowski, W. and T. Hickey. "Late Life Health Behavior: Integrating Health Beliefs and Temporal Perspectives." *Research on Aging*, 1980, 2:283–308.

Report of the Royal Commission on Health Services. Ottawa, Ontario: Queen's Printer, 1964.

Reynolds, W.J., W.A. Rushing and D.L. Miles. "The Validation of a Function Status Index." *Journal of Health and Social Behavior*, 1974, 15:271–83.

Rhoads, E.C. "Reevaluation of the Aging and Modernization Theory: The Samoan Evidence." *The Gerontologist*, 1984, 24:243–50.

Rice, D.P. and J.J. Feldman. "Living Longer in the United States: Demographic Changes and Health Needs of the Elderly." *Milbank Memorial Fund Quarterly*, 1983, 3:362–96.

Richmond, G.M. "An Analysis of Non-institutional Long-term Care Planning Methods for Care in the Home." *Home Health Care Services Quarterly*, 1980, 1:5–44.

Riley, M.W. "Age Strata in Social Systems." In *Handbook of Aging and the Social Sciences*, edited by R.H. Binstock and E. Shanas. New York, New York: Van Nostrand Reinhold Co., 1976, 189–217.

Riley, M.W. and A. Foner. *Aging and Society. Volume One: An Inventory of Research Findings.* New York, New York: Russell Sage, 1968.

Riley, M.W., M. Johnson and A. Foner (eds.) "The Succession of Cohorts." *Aging and Society. Volume Three: A Sociology of Age Stratification.* New York, New York: Russell Sage Foundation, 1972a, 515–582.

Riley, M.W., M. Johnson and A. Foner in association with E.E. Nelson and B.C. Starr. "Interpretation of Research on Age." In *Aging and Society: A Sociology of Age Stratification*, Vol. 3, edited by M.W. Riley, M. Johnson and A. Foner. New York, New York: Russell Sage Foundation, 1972b, 27–90.

Robertson, D. "Establishing New Services: Canada as a Case Study." In *Establishing a Geriatric Service*, edited by D. Coakley. London, England: Croom Helm Ltd., 1982, 199–216.

Robertson, D., R.A. Griffiths and L.Z. Cosin. "A Community-based Continuing Care Program for the Elderly Disabled — an Evaluation of Planned Intermittent Hospital Re-admission." *Journal of Gerontology*, 1977, 32:334–9.

Robertson, D., K. Rockwood and P. Stolee. "A Short Mental Status Questionnaire." *Canadian Journal on Aging*, 1982, 1:16–20.

Rombout, M.K. *Health Care Institutions and Canada's Elderly: 1971–2031.* Ottawa, Ontario: Health and Welfare Canada, Long Range Planning Branch, 1975.

Rose, A.M. "The Subculture of the Aging: A Topic for Sociological Research." *The Gerontologist*, 1962, 2:123–7.

_____. "The Subculture of the Aging: A Framework for Research in Social Gerontology". In *Aging in America: Readings in Social Gerontology*, edited by C.S. Kart and B.B. Manard. Sherman Oaks, California: Alfred, 1976, 42–60.

Rosenmayr, L. and E. Kockeis. "Propositions for a Sociological Theory of Aging and the Family." *International Social Science Journal*, 1963, 15:410–26.

Rosenstock, J.M. "Why People Use Health Services." *Milbank Memorial Fund Quarterly*, 1966, 44:94–124.

Rosow, I. *Socialization to Old Age*. Berkely, California: University of California Press, 1974.

Rossi, P.H. and S.R. Wright. "Evaluation Research: An Assessment of Theory, Practice and Politics." *Evaluation Quarterly*, 1977, 1:5–52.

Roth, M. "Epidemiological Studies." In *Alzheimer's Disease: Senile Dementia and Related Disorders, (Aging,* Vol. 7), edited by R. Katzman, R.D. Terry and K.L. Bick. New York, New York: Raven Press, 1978, 337–43.

Rubin, A. and G.E. Shuttlesworth. "Engaging Families as Support Resources in Nursing Home Care: Ambiguity in the Subdivision of Tasks." *The Gerontologist*, 1983, 23:633–6.

Rundall, T.G. and C. Evashwick. "Social Networks and Help-seeking Among the Elderly. " Paper presented at the annual meeting of the Gerontological Society of America, San Diego, California, 1980.

Sainsbury, E. "United Kingdom." In *Linking Health Care and Social Services*, edited by M.C. Hokenstad and R.A. Ritvo. Beverly Hills, California: Sage Publications, 1982, 189–206.

Satariano, W.A., M.A. Minkler and C. Langhauser. "Supportive Exchange: A Missing Link in the Study of Social Networks and Health Status in the Elderly." Paper presented at the annual meeting of the Gerontological Society of America, Toronto, Ontario, 1981.

Scharlach, A.E. "Relief of Role Strain Among Women with Aging Mothers." Paper presented at the annual meeting of the Gerontological Society of America, San Francisco, California, 1983.

Schlabach, T.F. *Edwin I. Witte: Cautious Reformer*. Madison, Wisconsin: State Historical Society of Wisconsin, 1969.

Schmidt, M.G. "Personal Networks: Assessment, Care and Repair." *Journal of Gerontological Social Work*, 1981, 3:65–76.

Schuckit, M.A. "Geriatric Alcoholism and Drug Abuse." *The Gerontologist*, 1977, 17:168.

Schulz, J. *The Economics of Aging*. Belmont, California: Wadsworth Publishing Company, 1976.

Schwenger, C.W. and J.M. Gross. "Institutional Care and Institutionalization of the Elderly in Canada." In *Aging in Canada: Social Perspectives*, edited by V.W. Marshall. Don Mills, Ontario: Fitzhenry and Whiteside Ltd., 1980, 248–56.

Scriven, M. "The Methodology of Evaluation." In *Perspectives of Curriculum Evaluation*, edited by W. Tyler, R.M. Gagne and M. Scriven. AERA Monograph Series on Curriculum Evaluation, No. 1. Chicago, Illinois: Rand McNally, 1967, 39–83.

Shanas, E. *The Health of Older People: A Social Survey*. Cambridge, Massachusetts: Harvard University Press, 1962.

_____. "The Family as a Support System in Old Age." *The Gerontologist*, 1979a, 19:169–74.

_____. "Social Myth as Hypothesis: The Case of the Family Retirement of Old People." *The Gerontologist*, 1979b, 19:3–9.

Shanas, E. and G.L. Maddox. "Aging, Health and the Organization of Health Resources." In *Handbook of Aging and the Social Sciences*, edited by R.H. Binstock and E. Shanas. New York, New York: Van Nostrand Reinhold Co., 1976, 592–618.

Shanas, E., P. Townsend, D. Wedderburn, H. Friis, P. Milhoj and J. Stehouwer. *Old People In Three Industrial Societies*. New York, New York: Atherton Press, 1968.

Shapiro, E. and N.P. Roos. "The Geriatric 'Bed Blocker:': A Critique of the Current Formulations of the Problem and the Proposed Solutions." Paper presented at the annual meeting of the Canadian Association on Gerontology, Edmonton, Alberta, 1978.

Sheldon, H.D. "The Changing Demographic Profile." In *Handbook of Social Gerontology*, edited by C. Tibbitts. Chicago, Illinois: University of Chicago Press, 1960, 27–61.

Sherman, S.R. "Mutual Assistance and Support in Retirement Housing." *Journal of Gerontology*, 1975, 30:479–83.

Sherwood, C.C., J.N. Morris and S. Sherwood. "A Multivariate Nonrandomized Matching Technique for Studying the Impact of Social-interventions." In *Handbook of Evaluation Research*, edited by F. I. Struening and M. Guttentag. Beverly Hills, California: Sage Publications, 1975.

Shulman, N. "The Aging of Urban Canada." In *Aging in Canada: Social Perspectives*, edited by V.W. Marshall. Don Mills, Ontario: Fitzhenry and Whiteside Ltd., 1980, 27–34.

Shuttlesworth, G.E., A. Rubin and M. Duffy. "Families versus Institutions: Incongruent Role Expectations in the Nursing Home." *The Gerontologist*, 1982, 22:200–8.

Siegel, J.S. "Demographic Background for International Gerontological Studies." *Journal of Gerontology*, 1981, 36:93–102.

Silverstein, N.M. "Informing the Elderly About Public Services: The Relationship Between Sources of Knowledge and Service Utilization." *The Gerontologist*, 1984, 24:37–40.

Simmons, L.W. *The Role of the Aged in Primitive Society*. New Haven, Connecticut: Yale University Press, 1945.

_____. "Aging in Preindustrial Societies." In *Handbook of Social Gerontology*, edited by C. Tibbitts. Chicago, Illinois: University of Chicago Press, 1960, 62–91.

Simon, A., M.F. Lowenthal and L. Epstein. *Crisis and Intervention: The Fate of the Elderly Mental Patient*. San Francisco, California: Jossey-Bass, 1970.

Sirois, J. *Report of the Royal Commission of Dominion-Provincial Relations*, Vol. 2, 1940.

Skellie, F.A. and R.E. Coan. "Community-based Long-term Care and Mortality: Preliminary Findings of Georgia's Alternative Health Services Project." *The Gerontologist*, 1980, 20:372–9.

Skoglund, J. "Job Deprivation in Retirement: Anticipated and Experienced Feelings." *Research on Aging*, 1979, 1:481–93.

Smith, K.F. and V.L. Bengtson. "Positive Consequences of Institutionalization: Solidarity Between Elderly Parents and their Middle-aged Children." *The Gerontologist*, 1979, 19:438-47.

Snider, E.L. "Factors Influencing Health Service Knowledge Among the Elderly." *Journal of Health and Social Behavior*, 1980, 21:371-7.

_____. "The Role of Kin in Meeting Health Care Needs of the Elderly." *Canadian Journal of Sociology*, 1981, 6:325-36.

Solomon, J.R. and F.D. Hirt. "Beyond Institutionalization: The Development of a Comprehensive Elderly Care System." In *Reaching the Aged: Social Services in Forty-four Countries*, edited by M.I. Teicher, D. Thursz and J.L. Vigilante. Beverly Hills, California: Sage Publications, 1979, 43-52.

Spreitzer, E. and E.E. Snyder. "Correlates of Life Satisfaction Among the Elderly." *Journal of Gerontology*, 1974, 24:454-8.

Stark, A.J., G.M. Gutman and K. Brothers. "Reliability of Level of Care Decisions in a Long-term Care Program." *Journal of Community Health*, 1982, 8:102-9.

Statistics Canada. *1976 Census of Canada*. Ottawa, Ontario: Minister of Supply and Services, 1978.

_____. *Survey of Volunteer Workers*. Ottawa, Ontario: Minister of Supply and Services, 1980, CS71-530.

_____. *1981 Census of Canada*. Ottawa, Ontario: Minister of Supply and Services, 1982.

_____. *Fact Book on Aging in Canada*. Ottawa, Ontario: Minister of Supply and Services, 1983.

_____. *The Elderly in Canada*. Ottawa, Ontario: Minister of Supply and Services, 1984, CS99-932.

Stein, S., M. Lemin and E. Stein. "Self-help Networks and Physical and Psychosocial Functioning." Paper presented at the annual meeting of the Gerontological Society of America, Toronto, Ontario, 1981.

Stewart, A., J.E. Ware and R.H. Brook. "The Meaning of Health: Understanding Functional Limitations." *Medical Care*, 1977, 15:939-52.

Stewart, K.P. and M.R. Ufford. "Patient Education Plays Integral Role in Innovative Acute Care Unit." *Promoting Health*, 1981, 2:4-6.

Stone, L.O. and S. Fletcher. *A Profile of Canada's Older Population*. Montreal, Quebec: The Institute for Research on Public Policy, 1980.

Strain, L.A. and N.L. Chappell. "Confidants — Do They Make a Difference in Quality of Life?" *Research on Aging*, 1982, 4:479-502.

Streib, G.F. and C.J. Schneider. *Retirement in American Society: Impact and Process*. Ithaca, New York: Cornell University Press, 1971.

Sullivan, D.F. *Disability Components for an Index of Health*. Rockville, Maryland: U.S. Department of Health, Education and Welfare, 1971.

Sussman, M.B. (ed.) "Family, Kinship and Bureaucracy." In *Sourcebook in Marriage and the Family*. Boston, Massachusetts: Houghton Mifflin Co., 1974.

_____. "The Family Life of Old People." In *Handbook of Aging and the Social Sciences*, edited by R.H. Binstock and E. Shanas. New York, New York: Van Nostrand Reinhold Co., 1976, 218-43.

Sussman, M.B. and L. Burchinal. "Kin Family Network: Unheralded Structure in Current Conceptualizations of Family Functioning." *Marriage and Family Living*, 1968, 24:321–40.

Swartz, E.I. "The Older Adult: Creative Use of Leisure Time." *The Journal of Geriatric Psychiatry*, 1978, 11:85–7.

Synge, J., C.J. Rosenthal and V.W. Marshall. "Phoning and Writing as Means of Keeping in Touch in the Family of Later Life." Paper presented at the annual meeting of the Canadian Association on Gerontology, Toronto, Ontario, 1981.

Szinovacz, M. (ed.) "Introduction: Research on Women's Retirement." In *Women's Retirement: Policy Implications of Recent Research*. Beverly Hills, California: Sage Publications, 1982, 13–21.

Taietz, P. and S. Milton. "Rural-urban Differences in the Structure of Services for the Elderly in Upstate New York Counties." *Journal of Gerontology*, 1979, 34:429–37.

Task Force on Community Support Systems, President's Commission on Mental Health. *Report of the Task Panel on Community Support Systems*. Washington, DC: U.S. Government Printing Office, 1978.

Tenhoor, W.J. "United States: Health and Personal Social Services." In *Linking Health Care and Social Services*, edited by M.C. Hokenstad and R.A. Ritvo. Beverly Hills, California: Sage Publications, 1982, 25–59.

Tibbitts, C. "Retirement Problems in American Society." *American Journal of Sociology*, 1954, 59:301–8.

Toronto Community Care Services. *A Brief to the Ontario Cabinet*. Toronto, Ontario: Community Care (Metropolitan Toronto), 1978, 18.

Townsend, P. "The Structural Dependency of the Elderly: Creation of Social Policy in the Twentieth Century." *Ageing and Society*, 1981, 1:5–28.

Trager, B. "Home Health Care and National Health Policy." *Home Health Care Services Quarterly*, 1980, 1(2), Special Issue.

Treas, J. "Family Support Systems for the Aged: Some Social and Demographic Considerations." *The Gerontologist*, 1977, 17:486–91.

Trela, J.E. and D.J. Jackson. "Family Life and Community Participation in Old Age." *Research on Aging*, 1979, 1:233-52.

Tsalikis, G. "Canada." In *Linking Health Care and Social Services*, edited by M.C. Hokenstad and R.A. Ritvo. Beverly Hills, California: Sage Publications, 1982, 125–62.

U.N. Demographic Yearbook. New York, New York: United Nations Publication, Department of Internal and Social Affairs, Statistical Office, 1979.

U.N. Demographic Yearbook. New York, New York: United Nations Publication, Department of Internal and Social Affairs, Statistical Office, 1981.

U.S. Bureau of the Census. *Characteristics of the Population, Vol. 1, Part 1*. Washington, DC: U.S. Summary, 1970.

_____. *Statistical Abstract of the United States: 1982-83* (103rd edition), Washington, D.C., 1982.

_____. *America in Transition: An Aging Society*, Current Population Report Series P-23, No. 128. Washington, DC: U.S. Government Printing Office, 1983.

U.S. Department of Commerce, Bureau of the Census. *Social Indicators III.* Washington, DC: U.S. Government Printing Office, December, 1980.

U.S. Department of Health, Education and Welfare. *Health Resources Statistics: Health Manpower and Health Facilities.* Washington, DC: Health Resources Administration, 1975.

U.S. National Center for Health Statistics. "Mortality from Selected Causes by Age, Race and Sex, U.S., 1955," *Vital Statistics Special Reports (National Summary),* 1957, 46:5.

Van den Heuvel, W.J.A. "The Meaning of Dependency." In *Dependency or Interdependency in Old Age,* edited by J.A. Munnichs and W.J.A. Van den Heuvel. The Hague, The Netherlands: Martinus Nijhoff, 1976, 162–73.

Varady, D.P. "Housing Problems and Mobility Plans Among the Elderly." *Journal of the American Planning Association,* 1980, 46:301-14.

Wagner, D.L. "Social Interaction of the Urban Elderly." *Analysis of Survivorship, Decline and Death Among a High Risk Urban Elderly Population.* Report to U.S. Social Security Administration, 1978.

Wagner, D.L. and F. Keast. "Informal Groups and the Elderly: A Preliminary Examination of the Mediation Function." *Research on Aging,* 1981, 3:325-31.

Waldo, D.R. and R.M. Gibson. "National Health Expenditures 1981." *Health Care Financing Review,* 1982, 4:27.

Walley, Sir John. *Social Security: Another British Failure?* London, England: Charles Knight & Co., 1972.

Wan, T.T.H. and B.G. Odell. "Factors Affecting the Use of Social and Health Services Among the Elderly." *Ageing and Society,* 1981, 1:95–115.

Wan, T.T.H. and W.G. Weissert. "Social Support Networks, Patient Status and Institutionalization." *Research on Aging,* 1981, 3:240–56.

Ward, R.A. "Services for Older People: An Integrated Framework for Research." *Journal of Health and Social Behavior,* 1977, 18:61-70.

_____. "The Meaning of Voluntary Association Participation to Older People." *Journal of Gerontology,* 1979, 34:438–45.

Ward, R.A., M. LaGory, S. Sherman and D. Traynor. "Neighbourhood Age Structure and Support Networks." Paper presented at the annual meeting of the Gerontological Society of America, Toronto, Ontario, 1981.

Wasylenki, D. "The Psychogeriatric Problem." *Canada's Mental Health,* 1982, 30:16–9.

Watson, J.A. and V.R. Kivett. "Influences on the Life Satisfaction of Older Fathers." *The Family Co-ordinator,* 1976, 25:482–8.

Weeks, J.R. and J.B. Cuellar. "The Role of Family Members in the Helping Networks of Older People." *The Gerontologist,* 1981, 21:388–94.

Weiler, P.G. and E. Rathbone-McCuan. *Adult Day Care Community Work with the Elderly.* New York, New York: Springer Publishing Co., 1978.

Weiler, P.G., P. Kim and L.S. Pickard. "Health Care for Elderly Americans: Evaluation of an Adult Day Health Care Model." *Medical Care,* 1976, 14:700–8.

Weiner, M.B., A.J. Brok and A.M. Snadowsky. *Working with the Aged.* Englewood Cliffs, New Jersey: Prentice-Hall, 1978.

Weiss, C.H. *Evaluation Research: Methods of Assessing Program Effectiveness.* Englewood Cliffs, New Jersey: Prentice-Hall, 1972.

Weissert, W.G. "Adult Day Care Programs in the United States: Current Research Projects and a Survey of 10 Centers. *Public Health Reports,* 1977, 92:49–56.

Weissert, W.G., T. Wan, B. Livieratos and S. Katz. "Effects and Costs of Day Care Services for the Chronically Ill." *Medical Care,* 1980, 18:567–84.

Weller, G.R. and P. Manga. "The Reprivatisation of Hospital and Medical Care Services: A Comparative Analysis of Canada, Britain and the United States." Revised version of the paper presented at the 10th World Congress of Sociology, Mexico City, Mexico, 1982.

Wellman, B. "Applying Network Analysis to the Study of Support." In *Social Networks and Social Support,* edited by B.H. Gottlieb. Beverly Hills, California: Sage Publications, 1981, 171-200.

Wershow, H.J. (ed.) *Controversial Issues in Gerontology.* New York, New York: Springer Publishing Co., 1981.

Williamson, J.D. and K. Danaher. *Self Care in Health.* London, England: Croom Helm, 1978.

Wilson, L. "Historical Perspectives: Canada." In *Gerontology: A Cross-national Core List of Significant Works* edited by W.M. Edwards and F. Flynn. Ann Arbor, Michigan: The University of Michigan, 1982, 3–18.

Witte, E.E. *The Development of the Social Security Act.* Madison, Wisconsin: University of Wisconsin, 1962.

_____. *The Development of the Social Security Act: A Memorandum on the History of the Committee on Economic Security and Drafting and Legislative History of the Social Security Act.* Madison, Wisconsin: University of Wisconsin, 1963.

Wolinsky, F.D. "Assessing the Effects of the Physical, Psychological and Social Dimensions of Health on the Use of Health Services." *The Sociological Quarterly,* 1982, 23:191–206.

_____. "Health Care Policy and the Elderly: Short Term Cures and Long-term Catastrophies." Paper presented at the annual meeting of the Society for the Study of Social Problems, Detroit, Michigan, 1983.

Wolk, S. and S. Telleen. "Psychological and Social Correlates of Life Satisfaction as a Function of Residential Constraint." *Journal of Gerontology,* 1976, 31:89–98.

Wood, V. and J. Robertson. "Friendship and Kinship Interaction: Differential Effect on the Morale of the Elderly." *Journal of Marriage and the Family,* 1978, 40:367–75.

World Health Organization. *Manual of the International Statistical Classification of Diseases, Injuries and Causes of Death.* Geneva, Switzerland: World Health Organization, 1977.

_____. *World Health Statistics Quarterly,* 1982, 35(3/4).

Yesavage, J.A., T.L. Brink, T.L. Rose, O. Lum, V. Huang, M. Adley and V.O. Leirer. "Development and Validation of a Geriatric Depression Screening Scale: A Preliminary Report." *Journal of Psychiatric Research,* 1983, 37–49.

York, J.L. and R.J. Calsyn. "Family Involvement in Nursing Homes." *The Gerontologist*, 1977, 17:500–5.

Zawadski, R.T. and M. Ansak. "Consolidating Community-based Long-term Care: Early Returns from the On Lok Demonstration." *The Gerontologist*, 1983, 23:364–69.

Zischka, P.C. and I. Jones. "Volunteer Community Representatives as Ombudsmen for the Elderly in Long-term Care Facilities." *The Gerontologist*, 1984, 24:9–12.

Zola, I.K. "Illness Behavior of the Working Class: Implications and Recommendations." In *Blue Collar World*, edited by A.B. Shastak and W. Gomberg. Englewood Cliffs, New Jersey: Prentice-Hall, 1964, 350–61.

_____. "Culture and Symptoms—an Analysis of Patients' Presenting Complaints." *American Sociological Review*, 1966, 31:615–30.

TO THE OWNER OF THIS BOOK:

We are interested in your reaction to **Aging and Health Care.** Through feedback from you, we can improve this book in future editions.

1. What was your reason for using this book?

    _____university course   _____continuing education course

    _____college course   _____personal interest

2. Approximately how much of the book did you use?

    _____ $^1/_4$ _____ $^1/_2$ _____all

3. What is the best aspect of the book?

4. Have you any suggestions for improvement?

5. Is there anything that should be added?

--**Fold here**--------------

43635

POSTAGE - CANADA - POSTES

POSTAGE WILL BE PAID BY

ANTHONY LUENGO
Publisher
College Editorial Department
HOLT, RINEHART AND WINSTON
OF CANADA, LIMITED
55 HORNER AVENUE
TORONTO, ONTARIO
M8Z 9Z9

Tape shut